NORTH AMERICA

A Continental Overview of Environmental Issues

THE WORLD'S ENVIRONMENTS

Kevin Hillstrom and
Laurie Collier Hillstrom, Series Editors

Global warming, rain forest destruction, mass extinction, overpopulation—the environmental problems facing our planet are immense and complex.

ABC-CLIO's series The World's Environments offers students and general readers a handle on the key issues, events, and people.

The six titles in the series examine the unique—and common—problems facing the environments of every continent on Earth and the ingenious ways local people are attempting to address them. Titles in this series:

Africa and the Middle East

Asia

Australia, Oceania, and Antarctica

Europe

Latin America and the Caribbean

North America

NORTH AMERICA

A Continental Overview of Environmental Issues

KEVIN HILLSTROM
LAURIE COLLIER HILLSTROM

ABC CLIO
Santa Barbara, California
Denver, Colorado Oxford, England

Library of Congress Cataloging-in-Publication Data

Hillstrom, Kevin, 1963-
North America : a continental overview of environmental issues / Kevin Hillstrom, Laurie Collier Hillstrom.
p. cm.— (The world's environments)
Includes bibliographical references and index.
ISBN 1-57607-684-9 (alk. paper) — ISBN 1-57607-685-7 (eBook)
1. North America—Environmental conditions. 2. Environmental degradation—North America. 3. Environmental protection—North America. 4. Conservation of natural resources—North America. I. Hillstrom, Laurie Collier, 1965– II. Title. III. Series: Hillstrom, Kevin, 1963–. World's environments

GE160.N7H55 2003
363.7'0097—dc21 2002156276

07 06 05 04 03 10 9 8 7 6 5 4 3 2 1

This book is also available on the World Wide Web as an eBook.
Visit http://www.abc-clio.com for details.

ABC-CLIO, Inc.
130 Cremona Drive, P.O. Box 1911
Santa Barbara, California 93116–1911

This book is printed on acid-free paper ⊗.
Manufactured in the United States of America

Contents

List of Tables and Figures

Tables

Figures

Introduction

The World's Environments

As the nations of the world enter the twenty-first century, they confront a host of environmental issues that demand attention. Some of these issues—pollution of freshwater and marine resources, degradation of wildlife habitat, escalating human population densities that place crushing demands on finite environmental resources—have troubled the world for generations, and they continue to defy easy solutions. Other issues—global climate change, the potential risks and rewards of genetically modified crops and other organisms, unsustainable consumption of freshwater resources—are of more recent vintage. Together, these issues pose a formidable challenge to our hopes of building a prosperous world community in the new millennium, especially since environmental protection remains a low priority in many countries. But despite an abundance of troubling environmental indicators, positive steps are being taken at the local, regional, national, and international levels to implement new models of environmental stewardship that strike an appropriate balance between economic advancement and resource protection. In some places, these efforts have achieved striking success. There is reason to hope that this new vision of environmental sustainability will take root all around the globe in the coming years.

The World's Environments series is a general reference resource that provides a comprehensive assessment of our progress to date in meeting the numerous environmental challenges of the twenty-first century. It offers detailed, current information on vital environmental trends and issues facing nations around the globe. The series consists of six volumes, each of which addresses conservation issues and the state of the environment in a specific region of the world: individual volumes for *Asia, Europe,* and *North America,* published in spring 2003, will be joined by *Africa and the Middle East*; *Australia, Oceania, and Antarctica*; and *Latin America and the Caribbean* in the fall of the same year.

Each volume of The World's Environments includes coverage of issues unique to that region of the world in such realms as habitat destruction, water pollution, depletion of natural resources, energy consumption, and development. In addition, each volume provides an overview of the region's response to environmental matters of worldwide concern, such as global warming. Information on these complex issues is presented in a manner that is informative, interesting, and understandable to a general readership. Moreover, each book in the series has been produced with an emphasis on objectivity and utilization of the latest environmental data from government agencies, nongovernmental organizations (NGOs), and international environmental research agencies, such as the various research branches of the United Nations.

Organization

Each of the six volumes of The World's Environments consists of ten chapters devoted to the following major environmental issues:

Population and Land Use. This chapter includes continental population trends, socioeconomic background of the populace, prevailing consumption patterns, and development and sprawl issues.

Biodiversity. This chapter reports on the status of flora and fauna and the habitat upon which they depend for survival. Areas of coverage include the impact of alien species on native plants and animals, the consequences of deforestation and other forms of habitat degradation, and the effects of the international wildlife trade.

Parks, Preserves, and Protected Areas. This chapter describes the size, status, and biological richness of area park systems, preserves, and wilderness areas and their importance to regional biodiversity.

Forests. Issues covered in this chapter include the extent and status of forest resources, the importance of forestland as habitat, and prevailing forest management practices.

Agriculture. This chapter is devoted to dominant farming practices and their impact on local, regional, and national ecosystems. Subjects of special significance in this chapter include levels of freshwater consumption for irrigation, farming policies, reliance on and attitudes toward genetically modified foods, and ranching.

Freshwater. This chapter provides detailed coverage of the ecological health of rivers, lakes, and groundwater resources, extending special attention to pollution and consumption issues.

Oceans and Coastal Areas. This chapter explores the ecological health of continental marine areas. Principal areas of coverage include the current state of (and projected outlook for) area fisheries, coral reef conservation, coastal habitat loss from development and erosion, and water quality trends in estuaries and other coastal regions.

Energy and Transportation. This chapter assesses historic and emerging trends in regional energy use and transportation, with an emphasis on the environmental and economic benefits and drawbacks associated with energy sources ranging from fossil fuels to nuclear power to renewable technologies.

Air Quality and the Atmosphere. This chapter reports on the current state of and future outlook for air quality in the region under discussion. Areas of discussion include emissions responsible for air pollution problems like acid rain and smog, as well as analysis of regional contributions to global warming and ozone loss.

Environmental Activism. This chapter provides a summary of the history of environmental activism in the region under discussion.

In addition, each volume of The World's Environments contains sidebars that provide readers with information on key individuals, organizations, projects, events, and controversies associated with specific environmental issues. By focusing attention on specific environmental "flashpoints"—the status of a single threatened species, the future of a specific wilderness area targeted for oil exploration, the struggles of a single village to adopt environmentally sustainable farming practices—many of these sidebars also shed light on larger environmental issues. The text of each volume is followed by an appendix of environmental and developmental agencies and organizations on the World Wide Web. Finally, each volume includes a general index containing citations to issues, events, and people discussed in the book, as well as supplemental tables, graphs, charts, maps, and photographs.

Coverage by Geographic Region

Each of the six volumes of The World's Environments focuses on a single region of the world: Africa and the Middle East; Asia; Australia, Oceania, and Antarctica; Europe; Latin America; and North America. In most instances, the arrangement of coverage within these volumes was obvious, in accordance with widely recognized geographic divisions. But placement of a few countries was more problematic. Mexico, for instance, is recognized both as part of North America and as the northernmost state in Latin America. Moreover, some international environmental research agencies (both governmental and nongovernmental) place data on Mexico under the North American umbrella, while others classify it among Central American and Caribbean nations. We ultimately decided to place Mexico in the Latin America volume, which covers Central and South America, in recognition of its significant social, economic, climatic, and environmental commonalities with those regions.

Similarly, environmental data on the vast Russian Federation, which sprawls over northern reaches of both Europe and Asia, is sometimes found in resources on Asia, and at other times in assessments of Europe's environment. Since most of Russia's population is located in the western end of its territory, we decided to cover the country's environmental issues in The World's Environments Europe volume, though occasional references to environmental conditions in the Russian Far East do appear in the Asia volume.

Finally, we decided to expand coverage in the Africa volume to cover environmental issues of the Middle East—also sometimes known as West Asia. This decision was made partly out of a recognition that the nations of Africa and the Middle East share many of the same environmental challenges—extremely limited freshwater supplies, for instance—and partly because of the space required in the Asia volume to fully explicate the multitude of grave environmental problems confronting Asia's central, southern, and eastern reaches. Coverage of other nations that straddle continental boundaries—such as the countries of the Caucasus region—are also concentrated in one volume, though references to some nations may appear elsewhere in the series.

Following is an internal breakdown of the volume-by-volume coverage for The World's Environments. This is followed in turn by two overview maps for the current volume, one showing country locations and key cities and the other indicating physical features.

Africa and the Middle East

Middle East and North Africa:

Algeria
Bahrain
Cyprus
Egypt
Gaza
Iraq
Israel
Jordan
Kuwait
Lebanon
Libya
Morocco
Oman
Qatar
Saudi Arabia
Syrian Arab Republic
Tunisia
Turkey
United Arab Emirates
West Bank
Yemen

Sub-Saharan Africa:

Angola
Benin
Botswana
Burkina Faso
Burundi
Cameroon
Central African Republic
Chad
Congo, Republic of the
Congo, Democratic Republic of (Zaire)
Côte d'Ivoire
Equatorial Guinea
Eritrea
Ethiopia
Gabon
Gambia
Ghana
Guinea
Guinea-Bissau
Kenya
Lesotho
Liberia
Madagascar
Malawi
Mali
Mauritania
Mozambique
Namibia
Niger
Nigeria
Rwanda
Senegal
Sierra Leone
Somalia
South Africa
Sudan
Tanzania
Togo
Uganda
Zambia
Zimbabwe

Asia

Afghanistan
Armenia
Azerbaijan

Bangladesh
Bhutan
Cambodia
China
Georgia
India
Indonesia
Iran
Japan
Kazakhstan
Korea, Democratic People's Republic of (North)
Korea, Republic of (South)
Kyrgyzstan
Lao People's Democratic Republic
Malaysia
Mongolia
Myanmar (Burma)
Nepal
Pakistan
Philippines
Singapore
Sri Lanka
Tajikistan
Thailand
Turkmenistan
Uzbekistan
Vietnam

Australia, Oceania, and Antarctica

Australia
Cook Islands
Fiji
French Polynesia
Guam
Kiribati
Nauru
New Caledonia
Northern Mariana Islands
Marshall Islands
Federated States of Micronesia
New Guinea
New Zealand
Palau
Papua New Guinea
Pitcairn Island
Samoa
Solomon Islands
Tonga
Tuvalu
Vanuatu
Wallis and Futuna
Various territories
(Note: Antarctica is discussed in a stand-alone chapter)

Europe

Albania
Austria
Belarus
Belgium
Bosnia and Herzegovina
Bulgaria
Croatia
Czech Republic
Denmark
Estonia
Finland
France
Germany
Greece
Hungary

Iceland
Ireland
Italy
Latvia
Lithuania
Republic of Macedonia
Moldova
Netherlands
Norway
Poland
Portugal
Romania
Russian Federation
Slovakia
Slovenia
Spain
Sweden
Switzerland
Ukraine
United Kingdom
Yugoslavia

Latin America and the Caribbean

Argentina
Belize
Bolivia
Brazil
Caribbean territories
Chile
Colombia
Costa Rica
Cuba
Dominican Republic
Ecuador
El Salvador
Guatemala
Guyana
Haiti
Honduras
Jamaica
Mexico
Nicaragua
Panama
Paraguay
Peru
Suriname
Trinidad and Tobago
Uruguay
Venezuela

North America

Canada
United States

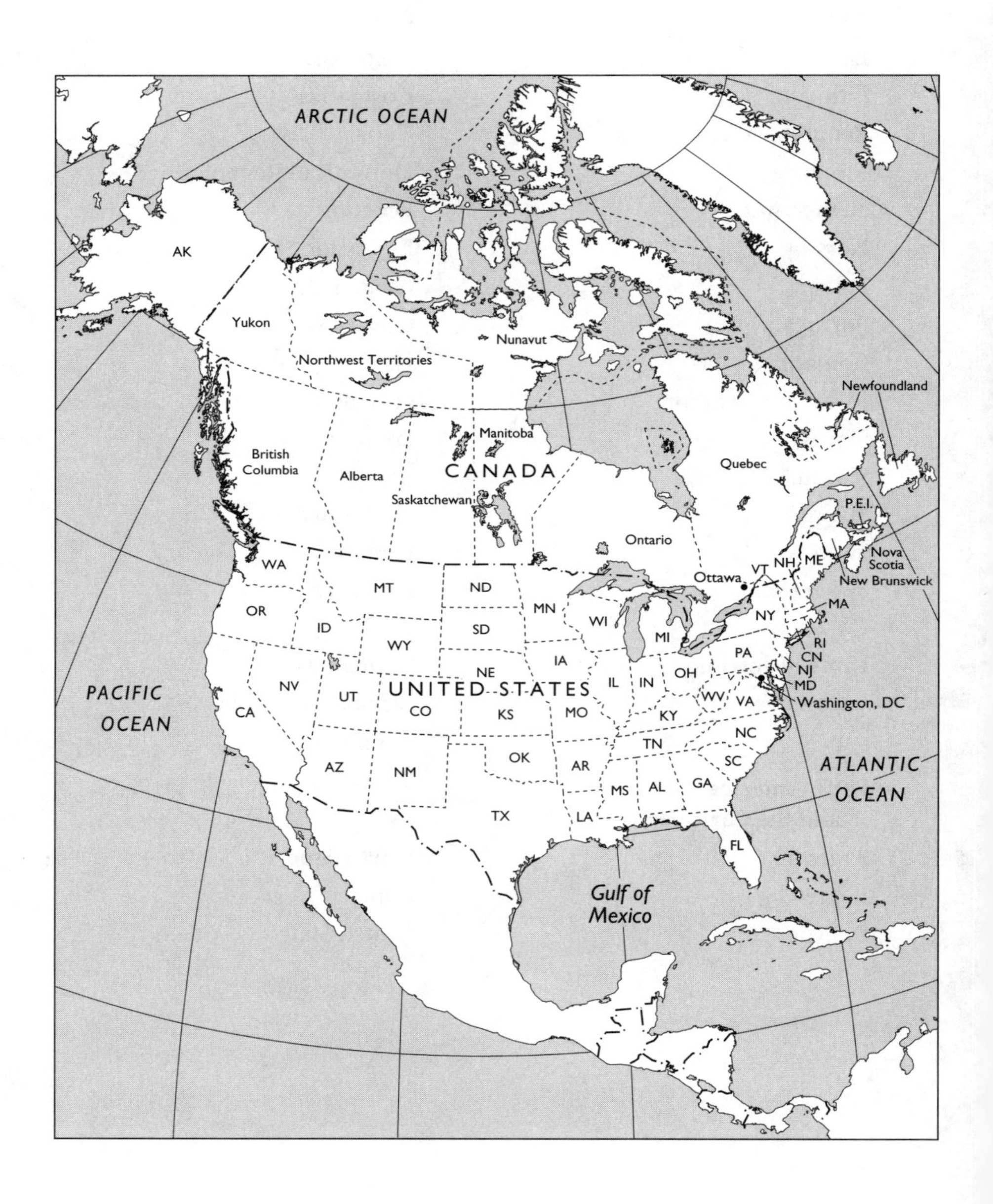

ARCTIC OCEAN
AK
Yukon
Northwest Territories
Nunavut
Newfoundland
British Columbia
Alberta
Manitoba
CANADA
Saskatchewan
Quebec
Ontario
P.E.I.
Nova Scotia
New Brunswick
Ottawa
VT
NH
ME
MA
WA
MT
ND
MN
OR
ID
SD
WI
MI
NY
WY
IA
PA
RI
CN
NJ
MD
Washington, DC
NE
OH
IL
IN
WV
VA
PACIFIC OCEAN
NV
UT
UNITED STATES
CA
CO
KS
MO
KY
NC
TN
OK
AR
SC
AZ
NM
ATLANTIC OCEAN
MS
AL
GA
TX
LA
FL
Gulf of Mexico

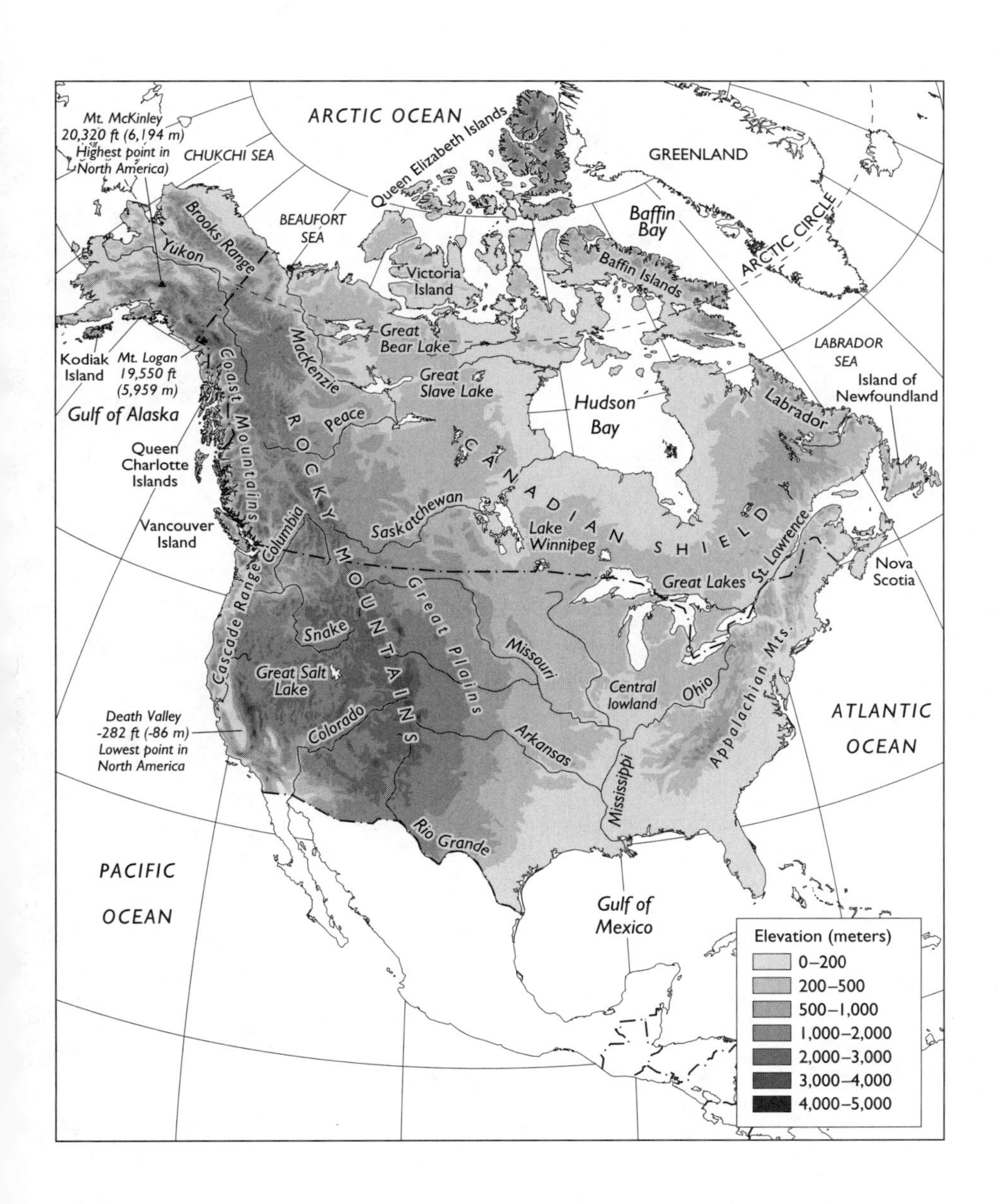
ARCTIC OCEAN
Mt. McKinley 20,320 ft (6,194 m) Highest point in North America)
CHUKCHI SEA
Queen Elizabeth Islands
GREENLAND
BEAUFORT SEA
Baffin Bay
Brooks Range
Yukon
Victoria Island
Baffin Islands
ARCTIC CIRCLE
Great Bear Lake
LABRADOR SEA
Kodiak Island
Mt. Logan 19,550 ft (5,959 m)
MacKenzie
Coast Mountains
Great Slave Lake
Island of Newfoundland
Gulf of Alaska
Hudson Bay
Labrador
Peace
Queen Charlotte Islands
ROCKY MOUNTAINS
CANADIAN SHIELD
Saskatchewan
Lake Winnipeg
Vancouver Island
Columbia
St. Lawrence
Nova Scotia
Great Lakes
Cascade Range
Great Plains
Snake
Missouri
Great Salt Lake
Central lowland
Ohio
Appalachian Mts.
ATLANTIC OCEAN
Death Valley -282 ft (-86 m) Lowest point in North America
Colorado
Arkansas
Mississippi
Rio Grande
PACIFIC OCEAN
Gulf of Mexico
Elevation (meters)
0–200
200–500
500–1,000
1,000–2,000
2,000–3,000
3,000–4,000
4,000–5,000

Acknowledgments

The authors are indebted to many members of the ABC-CLIO family for their fine work on this series. Special thanks are due to Vicky Speck, Martha Whitt, and Kevin Downing. We would also like to extend special thanks to our advisory board members, whose painstaking reviews played a significant role in shaping the final content of each volume, and to the contributors who lent their expertise and talent to this project.

Biographical Notes

Authors

Kevin Hillstrom and **Laurie Hillstrom** have written and edited award-winning reference books on a wide range of subjects, including American history, international environmental issues, environmental activism, outdoor travel, and business and industry. Works produced by the Hillstroms include *Environmental Leaders 1* and *2* (1997 and 2000), the four-volume *American Civil War Reference Library* (2000), the four-volume *Vietnam War Reference Library* (2000), *Paddling Michigan* (2001), *Encyclopedia of Small Business, 2d ed.* (2001), and *The Vietnam Experience: A Concise Encyclopedia of American Literature, Films, and Songs* (1998).

Advisory Board

J. David Allan received his B.Sc. (1966) from the University of British Columbia and his Ph.D. (1971) from the University of Michigan. He served on the Zoology faculty of the University of Maryland until 1990, when he moved to the University of Michigan, where he currently is Professor of Conservation Biology and Ecosystem Management in the School of Natural Resources and Environment. Dr. Allan specializes in the ecology and conservation of rivers. He is the author of *Stream Ecology* (1995) and coauthor (with C. E. Cushing) of *Streams: Their Ecology and Life* (2001). He has published extensively on topics in community ecology and the influence of land use on the ecological integrity of rivers. He serves or has served on committees for the North American Benthological Society, Ecological Society of America, and the American Society of Limnology and Oceanography. He serves or has served on the editorial board of the scientific journals *Freshwater Biology* and *Journal of the North American Benthological Society*, and on scientific advisory committees for the American Rivers and Nature Conservancy organizations.

David Leonard Downie is Director of Education Partnerships for the Earth Institute at Columbia University, where he has conducted research and taught courses on international environmental politics since 1994. Educated at Duke

University and the University of North Carolina, Dr. Downie is author of numerous scholarly publications on the Stockholm Convention, the Montreal Protocol, the United Nations Environment Program, and other topics in global environmental politics. From 1994 to 1999, Dr. Downie served as Director of Environmental Policy Studies at the School of International and Public Affairs at Columbia University.

Seth Dunn is a research associate at the Worldwatch Institute, where he investigates energy and climate policy and strategy. He has contributed to five editions of the institute's annual *State of the World* report, including most recently "Moving the Climate Change Agenda Forward" (2002). He has also authored four WorldWatch papers, including "Micropower: The Next Electrical Era" (2000), "Hydrogen Futures: Toward a Sustainable Energy System" (2001), and "Reading the Weathervane: Climate Policy from Rio to Johannesburg" (2002). His contributions to *World Watch* magazine include "Iceland's Hydrogen Experiment" (2000) and "King Coal's Weakening Grip on Power" (1999). He holds a B.A. in history and studies in the environment from Yale University.

Carmen Revenga is a senior associate with the Information Program at the World Resources Institute. Her current work focuses on water resources, global fisheries, and species conservation. She specializes in environmental indicators that measure the condition of ecosystems at the global and regional level, and is also part of WRI's Global Forest Watch team, coordinating forest monitoring activities with Global Forest Watch partners in Chile. Ms. Revenga is lead author of the WRI report *Pilot Analysis of Global Ecosystems: Freshwater Systems* (2000) and a contributing author to the WRI's *Pilot Analysis of Global Ecosystems: Coastal Ecosystems* (2001). These two reports assess the condition of freshwater and coastal ecosystems as well as their capacity to continue to provide goods and services on which humans depend. Ms. Revenga is also the lead author of *Watersheds of the World: Ecological Value and Vulnerability* (1998), which is the first analysis of a wide range of global data at the watershed level. Before joining WRI in 1997, she worked as an environmental scientist with Science and Policy Associates, Inc., an environmental consulting firm in Washington, D.C. Her work covered topics in sustainable forestry and climate change.

Robin White is a senior associate with the World Resources Institute, an environmental think tank based in Washington, D.C. Her focus at WRI has been on the development of environmental indicators and statistics for use in the *World Resources Report* and in global ecosystems analysis. She was the lead author of the WRI report *Pilot Analysis of Global Ecosystems: Grassland Ecosystems* (2000), which analyzes quantitative information on the condition of the world's grasslands. Her current work focuses on developing an ecosystem goods and services approach to the analysis of the world's drylands. A recent publication regarding this work is WRI's Information Policy Brief, *An Ecosystem Approach to Drylands: Building Support for New Development Policies.* Ms. White completed her Ph.D. in geography at the University of Wisconsin, Madison, with a minor in wildlife ecology. Before joining WRI in 1996, she was a policy analyst with the U.S. Congress, Office of Technology Assessment.

Contributors

ILLISA KELMAN lives and runs in New Haven, Connecticut. A graduate of the Yale School of Forestry and Environmental Studies, she divides her time between freelance writing and the Quinnipiac River Watershed Association, a south-central Connecticut nongovernmental organization. She has completed field science projects for land trusts and research scientists, and writing assignments for National Audubon Society and World Wide Fund for Nature. Illisa and several artists are currently developing The Water Project, a dialogue between scientists and artists focusing on developing enhanced and communicable understandings of interacting human and natural processes.

JODY LARSON is an environmental writer, editor, and communications consultant. She received a master's degree in environmental studies in 1997 from Antioch New England Graduate School in Keene, New Hampshire, where she completed an individualized program in environmental communications and field studies. She has worked for many years as a freelance developmental editor, specializing in college-level textbooks in the life sciences. Her articles have been published in *Whole Terrain Journal* and *Many Hands Magazine.*

KATHRYN MILES received her Ph.D. in literature from the University of Delaware and is currently an assistant professor of English and Environmental Studies at Unity College. She has worked as a freelance environmental writer for several newspapers and magazines, and has published on British modernism in academic journals. She is a member of ASLE (Association for the Study of Literature and the Environment), NAAGE (North American Alliance of Green Education), and the Virginia Woolf Society.

JOHN NAGY is a special projects reporter for Stateline.org, the award-winning online journal of state government published by the Pew Center on the States. Nagy joined Stateline in 2000 as a staff writer and researcher covering land use and environmental policy. He completed his master's degree in American history at the University of Notre Dame in 1999. Prior to graduate study, he taught twentieth-century world history in Dorset, England, worked on an

Irish dairy farm, and published his undergraduate history thesis on baseball and community life while an Echols Scholar at the University of Virginia.

Dan Whipple is a freelance writer whose work has appeared in publications ranging from the *Los Angeles Times* to *Field and Stream*. He has served as a reporter for the *Casper (Wyoming) Star-Tribune* and as editor of *High Country News* and *Northern Lights*. He is a graduate of Georgetown University's School of Foreign Service.

Population and Land Use

—JOHN NAGY

In 1783, during his service as wartime governor of Virginia, Thomas Jefferson prepared a meticulous inventory of his state's resources, in which he unfavorably appraised his neighbors' use of their land: "The indifferent state of [agriculture] among us does not proceed from a want of knowledge merely; it is from our having such quantities of land to waste as we please." The widely read *Notes on the State of Virginia* were published at a time in which citizens of Great Britain's rebellious colonies were fewer than 2 million and their neighbors to the north numbered in the tens of thousands, but Jefferson's observations of his fellow colonists' relationship to the land would apply to their descendants' attitudes at virtually any time and in any place since.

Jefferson's century was a formative one for North America and one in which, as the historian Christopher Lasch observed, "insatiable desire, formerly condemned as a source of frustration, unhappiness, and spiritual instability, came to be seen as a powerful stimulus for economic development" (Lasch, *The True and Only Heaven,* 1991). Although conservationists have worked in recent decades to protect millions of acres of farmland, forests, and wilderness from further degradation, both the United States and Canada have historically exhibited careless land use habits.

Exhausting North America's "Ecological Capital"

The population of North America—defined as Canada and the United States—eclipsed 300 million during the mid-1990s. Slow but steady natural increases in native populations coupled with high immigration rates to introduce 32.7 million new Americans and 2.7 million new Canadians over the course of the decade. In land area, Canada is the second largest country in the world, covering 3,849,670 square miles of land and water; the United States, at 3,618,770 square miles, is fourth.

At first glance, North Americans appear to have a comparative ecological advantage over residents of other continents in efforts to achieve sustainability, for their population density is lower than that of any other continent except Australia. Furthermore, despite being home to two of the wealthiest nations in the industrialized world, North America possesses larger proportions of undeveloped land than Europe, Asia, or Africa (Harrison and Pearce, *AAAS Atlas of Population and Environment,* 2000).

But according to the North American Commission for Environmental Cooperation (CEC), a joint body established by the governments of Canada, Mexico, and the United States under the North American Free Trade Agreement, the continent's ecological advantages are being squandered. "In one area after another, we are not only using up all the ecological interest, we are digging deep into the ecological capital," CEC researchers concluded in 2002. "And while such resources as old-growth forests and water from aquifers are being depleted, human activities are also jeopardizing the functional efficiency of critical ecological processes, such as climate regulation and soil formation" (North American Commission for Environmental Cooperation, *The North American Mosaic,* 2002).

One cause of the waste is a deeply rooted culture of consumption, nourished in both the United States and Canada by patriotic myths of plenty. When measured by per capita consumption, North Americans use more of the world's food, water, energy, and materials than their relatively sparse numbers warrant. Supported by government policies that have long encouraged immigration, widespread settlement, and intensive agriculture and resource extraction, Americans and Canadians have long sought to tame the land upon which they live, often with little regard for the impact of their activities (Outwater, *Water: A Natural History,* 1996).

Population Trends

In 1901, in the middle of an immigration wave that brought 25 million people to North America primarily from Southern and Eastern Europe, the population of Canada stood at about 6 million, while that of the United States was roughly 75 million (Meinig, *The Shaping of America,* 1998). Although the twentieth century would prove no match to the nineteenth in rate of population growth, it would dwarf its predecessor in sheer numbers. Censuses conducted in the United States in 2000 and in Canada in 2001 counted 281 million Americans and 30 million Canadians, for 100-year growth rates of about 275 percent and 400 percent, respectively.

An aerial view of Toronto, Ontario COREL

Changes in immigration policy during the 1960s reopened doors to both countries that had been closed in the middle of the century by war, international economic instability, and political pressures at home. Around the same time, global migration, already lively in 1965, when expatriates numbered roughly 75 million around the world, expanded suddenly and swiftly, adding another 45 million to the total number of those living outside their birth country. Canada and the United States became popular destinations for emigrants primarily from developing nations in Latin America, the Caribbean, Africa, and southern Asia (Harrison and Pearce, *AAAS Atlas of Population and Environment,* 2000). At the turn of the millennium, one in every five Canadians and one in every ten Americans was foreign-born.

Despite their tremendous population growth over the past 100 years, Canada (with 8.1 people per square mile) and the United States (77.8 people per square mile) are still among the planet's least crowded nations. But North Americans are participating in their own version of a global trend toward urbanization, often seeking a balance between city and country life in large, rapidly growing metropolitan areas. Urban population eclipsed rural population in the United States around 1920, a milestone that Canada soon duplicated.

Today, roughly three-quarters of Canadians and Americans live in or near cities (Statistics Canada, *Human Activity and the Environment 2000,* 2000). Toronto, Canada's largest metropolitan area, had a population of 4.8 million in 2000, but it is smaller than any of the nine largest metropolitan areas in the

United States. The New York and Los Angeles metropolitan areas, taken together, are home to more people than live in all of Canada. Meanwhile, despite an overall revival of rural growth trends in the United States, large swaths of both countries continue to depopulate, most notably in poorer rural areas such as the Atlantic Maritime provinces, Appalachia, and the states of the Great Plains.

Canada—The Other "Melting Pot"

At midcentury, conventional wisdom in sparsely populated Canada—the name is derived from an Iroquois word meaning "village" or "community"—held that the nation's population would reach somewhere between 15 and 20 million by the year 2000 (Vincent, "How We Lived," 2001). That projection dramatically underestimated the nation's population growth for two primary reasons. First, it did not fully appreciate the scale of the post–World War II "baby boom," which had already peaked in 1947 but would last another decade or so. Second, it did not anticipate the change in immigration policy that would rank Canada among the world's most popular permanent destinations for immigrants (Statistics Canada, *Annual Demographic Statistics,* 2001). By 2002, despite precipitous long-term drops in birth and fertility rates, Canada's population was edging past 30 million.

Indeed, net migration overtook natural increase as the primary driver of population growth for the first time in Canadian history in the early 1990s. According to Statistics Canada, the rate of natural increase actually halved during the 1990s. Moreover, Canadian officials expect national population growth to continue the long-term deceleration that began in the mid-1950s. Federal statisticians have predicted that by the year 2020, Canada's natural increase will approach zero (Statistics Canada, *Human Activity and the Environment 2000,* 2000).

During the 1990s, however, migration added an average of eight new Canadians for every 1,000 existing Canadians each year. Newcomers from China, India, the Philippines, and Vietnam are the most numerous, but what makes Canadian immigration truly remarkable is "how closely it matches the global distribution of the human population. Canada, more than anywhere else, is truly becoming the world in one country" (Dyer, "Visible Majorities," 2001).

Regardless of their birthplace, most Canadians are congregating in the nation's largest cities, primarily in the provinces of Quebec and Ontario in the east and Alberta and British Columbia in the west. In 2000, one out of every three Canadians lived in the country's three largest metropolitan areas—Toronto (4.8 million), Montreal (3.5 million), and Vancouver (2.0 million)

(Statistics Canada, *A Profile of the Canadian Population,* 2002). The majority of foreign-born Canadians settle in Ontario.

Interprovincial migration, meanwhile, continues long-term trends: Alberta's service- and petroleum-based boom economy attracted the highest growth rates during the 1990s with Ontario and British Columbia not far behind. Indeed, Ontario's provincial government is bracing itself for the arrival of as many as 3 million new residents by 2015, most of them relocating from other, less economically vibrant provinces. In fact, several provinces actually experienced net population losses for part or all of the 1990s, including New Brunswick, Newfoundland, Nova Scotia, Prince Edward Island, and Saskatchewan (ibid.). Population declines in the Maritime Provinces have been attributed in large part to the region's devastated commercial fisheries, which are now paying the price for years of unsustainable harvesting.

In regional terms, most of Canada's growth took place in three "ecozones" as identified by the Canadian government: the "Mixed Wood Plains" that stretch across the northern shores of Lake Erie and Lake Ontario and up the St. Lawrence River to Quebec; the "Pacific Maritime" around Vancouver and Victoria; and the "Prairie," which includes Calgary, Edmonton, and the booming agriculture- and extraction-based towns along the Highway 2 corridor.

In some cases, Canadian municipalities—and the regional ecosystems upon which they are built—are struggling to keep up with the steady influx of new arrivals. In July 2001, at a time of worsening drought, the *Calgary Herald* reported that the city's homeless shelters were being "flooded with young people lured here by the city's booming economy." By March of the following year, Alberta environment minister Lorne Taylor worried publicly that "there may not be enough water for future economic and population growth" in the province.

United States Sees Dramatic Population Shift to the West and South

The United States is the third most populous country in the world and is expected to hold that position through most of the twenty-first century. By 2025, credible estimates suggest, the nation may add another 65 million people for a fifty-year growth rate of 23 percent (Population Reference Bureau, "World Population Data Sheet," 2001).

The U.S. population grew 13.2 percent during the 1990s, climbing 32.7 million from the 1990 count of 248.7 million people. The decade saw the largest ten-year population increase in U.S. history, according to the U.S. Census Bureau, far surpassing the previous record of 28 million set during the baby-boom 1950s. Americans also reversed a thirty-year trend of shrinking growth rates during the 1990s. Although natural increase still accounted for the bulk of the population growth, Americans were getting married later and having fewer children than their parents had. The birth rate dropped from 16.7 births per 1,000 people in 1990 to 14.5 in 1999, while the fertility rate—the number of births the average woman will experience during her lifetime—hovered between 2.0 and 2.1, just above the replacement rate. Meanwhile, the percentage of foreign-born Americans climbed from 8.0 to 9.5 over the same period. Illegal immigrants, entering primarily across the U.S.–Mexico border, numbered roughly 7 million in 2000 (Cohn, "Illegal Immigrant Total Is Raised," 2001).

Much of the new growth took place in the South and West, home to the ten fastest-growing states: Nevada, Arizona, Colorado, Idaho, Utah, Georgia, Florida, Texas, North Carolina, and Washington. Growth rates in these two regions more than doubled those of the Northeast and Midwest. Although every state in the country grew, rates of increase varied widely, from 66.3 percent in Nevada to 0.5 percent in North Dakota. Nevada retained its distinction as the fastest growing state for the fourth decade in a row, as persistent interest in Las Vegas as a residential hub sustained century-old efforts to irrigate the desert. Regional growth trends reflect long-term changes in economic vitality and a slow shift of political power historically concentrated in New England, the Mid-Atlantic, and the Great Lakes regions. But these areas still boast six of the ten most populous states in the nation—New York, Illinois, Pennsylvania, Ohio, Michigan, and New Jersey—according to the 2000 census.

Metropolitan areas (up 13.9 percent) drove the growth. More than four out of every five Americans live in or near cities with total metropolitan populations of at least 250,000 people. Metro areas such as Dallas–Forth Worth, Texas, and Phoenix-Mesa, Arizona, with between 2 and 5 million residents, experienced the largest increase (about 20 percent). Small town and rural populations continued to grow overall, but at a slower rate (10.2 percent) than cities and suburbs.

Census 2000 data reveals another striking suburban trend: increasing ethnic, economic, and lifestyle diversity. A study of the 2000 census by the Brookings Institution found minority groups, particularly Hispanics, fueling much of the new suburban growth during the 1990s (Lucy and Phillips, "Suburbs and the Census," 2001). Another analysis of census data found that the suburbs were no longer dominated by two-parent families and were instead increasingly typified by a variety of lifestyles, including a swiftly rising contingent of young singles. Although not strictly an indicator of suburban lifestyles, one federal analysis of census estimates performed shortly before the 2000 headcount calculated that slightly more than one in four Americans lived alone in 2000, up from 17 percent in 1990 (Fields, "America's Families and Living Arrangements," 2000). The jump upward in solo living was among the prominent factors behind the inefficient land use patterns that marked the decade.

Socioeconomic Factors and Consumption

If the swift growth of the populations of Canada and the United States germinated in promises of plenty, reality for many has fallen short. The history of North America is a story of prosperity achieved at the expense of various groups, most notably Native Americans, African Americans, and Hispanics. Considerable economic, legal, political, and social progress was made in the last half of the twentieth century toward racial equality and respect for cultural differences. Yet poverty persists in both countries, and while it cuts across racial lines to some extent, minorities remain more likely to live in poverty than their white countrymen and women.

The percentage of people considered by their governments to be living in poverty at the turn of the millennium hovered around 16 percent in Canada and 11 percent in the United States, meaning that roughly 36 million North American men, women, and children lived without the resources necessary for a healthy life. Millions more qualified for some level of public assistance in the midst of one of the most robust periods of economic growth in world history. Trends between the two countries were not uniform. The number of Canadians living in poverty actually grew during the 1990s, especially in rural areas. Americans of every ethnic background in 2000 found their poverty rates at all-time lows, although African American and Hispanic communities still wrestled with poverty levels nearly twice as high as the national average.

Nevertheless, the standard of living in Canada and the United States is among the highest in the world. Affluence, not austerity, is the salient characteristic of North American society. It has been praised as an engine of global economic and technological development, lamented as the driver of a cultural juggernaut that threatens to crush non-Western customs, and condemned as an exploitative siphon that taps into foreign labor and resources while giving few direct benefits in return.

Spurred in large part by U.S.-led investment in Europe, Japan, and emerging democracies after World War II, global trade mushroomed during the latter half of the twentieth century, jumping from the hundreds of billions of dollars to just below U.S.$7 trillion by the late 1990s (Brown and Flavin, "A New Economy for a New Century," 1999). The contributions of the United States and Canada account for more than U.S.$1 trillion of that total each year, according to the World Trade Organization (WTO). The United States is the world's leading importer and exporter of both merchandise and commercial services; Canada stood in the top ten in each category except for commercial service exports.

From the standpoint of nutrition and environmental health, such affluence has its downside. "We live today in a nutritionally divided world, one where some people eat too much and others too little. Both are forms of malnutrition," writes Lester R. Brown, president of the Worldwatch Institute (ibid.). Indeed, most North Americans consume more than 3,000 calories a day, and more than a third of this intake comes from meat, cheese, and eggs, a far higher proportion of animal products than in most other cultures around the globe (Harrison and Pearce, *AAAS Atlas of Population and Environment,* 2000). As a result, obesity constitutes a serious public health threat in North America. In the United States, more than one in three people are overweight, including a majority of those over twenty years of age, while Statistics Canada reports that 46 percent of Canadian adults are overweight.

Diet is not the only factor, however. A 2002 study by the U.S. Centers for Disease Control (CDC) directly implicated predominant trends in neighborhood design and automobile dependence in Americans' struggle with weight and poor health. Homebuilders criticized the report, citing an earlier CDC study that highlighted the breadth and depth of opportunities for exercise that most suburbs have to offer. But while the jogger is among the most familiar of suburban icons, it is clear that many suburbanites decline—or do not have the time—to make that kind of extra effort. One reason may be the five or so car trips made by the typical North American family in the course of a day. An increasingly familiar suburban icon is the three-car garage: nearly one in five new houses built during the latter part of the 1990s were so equipped (Mitchell, "Urban Sprawl," 2001). "People assume the suburban lifestyle is inherently more healthy, largely because of access to nature. But the suburbs aren't like that anymore. People have small yards, and they are surrounded by traffic," remarked California land use expert William Fulton (Halper, "CDC Study on Suburban Life Hits a Nerve," 2002).

Heavy television use is another hallmark of the affluent, sedentary lifestyle. According to the annual General Social Survey conducted by the National Opinion Research Center at the University of Chicago, most Americans report watching between one and four hours of television every day. More Americans watch five hours per day than watch no television at all. Canadians display similar habits, watching an average of twenty-three hours of television each week (Taras, "Swimming against the Current," 2000).

North America's Outsized "Ecological Footprint"

Social scientists coined the term "ecological footprint" during the 1990s to describe the amount of land and water "required to support indefinitely the material standard of living of a given human population, using prevailing technology." In 1997, with an estimated 1.7 hectares available for every person in the world, Americans left the largest footprint, at 10.3 hectares (26 acres). Canadians ranked third (after Australians) with 7.7 hectares (19 acres) per person. Americans and Canadians differ chiefly in that Americans dramatically exceed their locally available ecological capacity, while Canadians live more within their means. Yet, assuming that the ecological footprint is a reasonable gauge of nation-by-nation consumption, both countries are heavily taxing global productivity. Americans consume six times more than their share in food, energy, and materials and Canadians consume more than four times their share of these resources (Wackernagel, "Ranking the Ecological Impact of Nations," 1997). The message is clear for observers of global environmental trends. "It is not the number of people that make a difference to the environment: it is our total burden of resource use and waste output" (Harrison and Pearce, *AAAS Atlas of Population and Environment,* 2000).

Consumption in Canada

North American affluence is rooted in the continent's abundant natural resources. Canada no longer derives its wealth chiefly from logging, fishing, and fur trapping, but the Canadian economy is still heavily reliant upon its land and water resources. Despite a long-term shift from resource-based industries such as agriculture, forest products, and mining toward social services, the retail service sector, and other areas, Canada claims that one-third of all jobs in the country are still related to the environment. In recent years, the biggest sector jumps in contribution to Canada's gross domestic product occurred in real estate and personal services, reflecting a new relationship to the land based less upon production and more upon consumption. Short-term trends during the 1990s, however, indicated a modest turnaround for some resource-based industries such as the production of timber, pulp, and paper, and the manufacture of transportation equipment (Statistics Canada, *Human Activity and the Environment 2000,* 2000).

Canada is a major global supplier of food and raw materials. Despite the decline of the agriculture sector, the conversion of some of the most fertile land to residential and commercial uses, and other adverse conditions, Canada still stands among the world's leading producers of grain and meat, ranking sixth and eleventh, respectively, on international lists managed by the

Food and Agriculture Organization of the United Nations (FAO). Conversely, Canadians register far lower as per capita food consumers, standing out mainly as meat-eaters (thirteenth in the world) by consuming about 207 pounds per person each year. Similar declines in forestry and mining as engines of the Canadian economy have not knocked the nation out of the international top ten. Canada ranks fourth in the production of paper products and sixth in plywood, while Canadians rank seventh in the use of these products. Canada is also a major source of gold, copper, zinc, nickel, and iron ore. Loosely regulated at best, Canadian mining has left 10,000 abandoned and polluted sites that will be able to be cleaned only at enormous taxpayer expense (North American Commission for Environmental Cooperation, *The North American Mosaic*, 2002).

For thirty-five years Canada has produced more energy than it has consumed, a fact all the more striking when compared with the appetites of its energy-gulping southern neighbor. But here, too, Canadians consume more than their global share. Constituting roughly 0.5 percent of the world's population, Canadians use about 2.6 percent of available energy. Some observers attribute this level of consumption to the country's relatively cold climate, which boosts its dependence on energy for home heating (Boychuk, "World Class Energy Gobblers," 2001). Fossil fuel use is responsible for the bulk of Canadian carbon dioxide emissions, another area in which Canada is a world leader. As of 1995 the Canadian economy generated 14.8 metric tons of carbon dioxide per person. Finally, Canada has the dubious distinction of generating a higher proportion of nuclear waste for amount of energy produced than any other nation in the world (Harrison and Pearce, *AAAS Atlas of Population and Environment*, 2000).

Consumer trends in housing, transportation, and recreation display similar inefficiency. As is the case in most developed nations, the average Canadian household is home to three people, reflecting dominant trends in marriage, fertility, and divorce. Smaller households are typically less efficient in their use of water and energy, may produce more waste per person, and significantly increase demand for household goods and appliances, luxury items, and automobiles. Furthermore, Canadians are heavily reliant on automobiles, with about 560 vehicles on the road for every 1,000 people, and the percentage of Canadians regularly utilizing public transportation has dropped steadily in recent years (Statistics Canada, *Human Activity and the Environment 2000*, 2000). Three out of every four Canadian workers drive to work, often covering distances shorter than 10 kilometers (6 miles). And although the bulk of Canadian shipping currently takes place via water or rail, trucking is a growth industry providing more jobs to Canadian men than any other single occupation and reflecting the overwhelming demand for direct commercial deliveries rather than delivery to central shipping facilities. Meanwhile, consumer spending trends show fewer dollars spent on essentials such as food and nonalcoholic beverages over the last forty years, while spending on such things as travel, entertainment, books, outdoor recreation, dining out, and financial and legal advice has nearly filled the gap.

Consumption in the United States

Americans' appetites overwhelmingly exceed their collective ecological grasp. Early in the twenty-first century, the nation bears little resemblance to the idyllic Revolution-era vision of a small agrarian republic. Over the course of its history, it has developed into a land in which both breathtaking innovation and unrestrained consumerism abound. It is also a land of convenience and disposability, and symbols embodying all of these qualities abound; the aluminum soda can, the direct mail advertising campaign, Hollywood and the film industry, the department store, the fast-food chain, the assembly line, the Astroturf stadium, the plastic sandwich bag, and the suburban single-family dwelling stand among the most universally recognized contributions to world culture of the United States. Today, U.S. men, women, and children lead the world in waste production, throwing away about 1,600 pounds of trash each year on an individual basis. Nearly 60 percent of this refuse is packed into massive landfills, according to the Organisation for Economic Co-operation and Development. Yet, far from having cornered the market on disposability, Americans recognized its economic potential early on and exported it as quickly as politics and logistics allowed.

Disposability has long defined industrial use of natural resources in the United States. A major exporter of timber and easily the world's most productive source of plywood and paper products, the United States is also the world's leading importer of such goods, most of which come from Canadian forests, FAO data shows. Americans used more than 80 million metric tons of paper products in 1998, more than double the amount used by second-place China. Regarding water, the United States and the nations of Central Asia use more per capita than other nations of the world (Harrison and Pearce, *AAAS Atlas of Population and Environment,* 2000). Nearly two-thirds of that water goes to industrial and energy production. U.S. agricultural practices, some of which are abusive of water and land alike, rank a distant second.

U.S. agriculture's historically wasteful use of freshwater resources is attributable to the loss of some of the nation's best farmland to urbanization and subsequent efforts to find suitable replacement land for farming. The latter effort produced a variety of twentieth-century policies intended to turn arid

Western lands into a new, agriculturally productive "American Eden." These efforts relied in large measure on irrigation schemes. The primary benefit of irrigation is increased production, which in turn sustains larger populations and helps keep products affordable. Drawbacks include soil erosion and salinization and the degradation of water quality in a watershed.

The U.S. tendency toward consumer excess may nowhere be more evident than in the realms of energy and transportation. The world's largest energy producer, consumer, and net importer, the United States accounts for about one-quarter of global energy consumption. Canada generates most of its electricity through hydro- and nuclear power, but the United States relies on its plentiful coal resources for the majority of its production, despite the lower efficiency of coal-fired plants and well-documented environmental concerns associated with coal extraction and consumption.

Urbanization in North America

Human activity affects the environment in countless ways, but few activities have as intense an impact on the environment or human health as commercial and residential development. North Americans overwhelmingly and enthusiastically choose roomy suburban lifestyles and transportation independence, but they also recognize that these preferences have created problems. A survey conducted by the Pew Center for Civic Journalism in October 1999 offered respondents in four major metropolitan areas and around the United States as a whole an open-ended opportunity to name the most important problem facing their communities. Urban sprawl and traffic congestion was the leading answer for every group except Philadelphians, more of whom cited crime as their number one concern. In Denver, one of the fastest-growing cities in the United States, 60 percent of those questioned named sprawl and traffic as top priorities. Meanwhile, environmental issues did not top the list for more than 4 percent of respondents in any group.

Sprawling urban development is by no means a North American invention. The world's largest cities passed the 1 million resident milestone roughly a century before the construction of the first genuine skyscrapers. By the end of the nineteenth century, the development of efficient modes of public transportation in Europe and North America made living farther away from one's work possible for a growing class of professionals. The "streetcar suburb" was born in the 1890s and took strikingly similar forms around London, Paris, Boston, New York, and Chicago. Tree-covered and parklike, they were pitched as refuges from the stresses of the dehumanizing city for those who could afford them.

Urbanization in the United States

By most accounts, however, it was not until after World War II, when the United States passed two landmark pieces of federal legislation, that the suburbs pressed farther away from urban centers and took on lives of their own. The first legislation provided military veterans low-cost loans toward the purchase of single-family homes and offered them college tuition. The second established the interstate highway system. Both innovations made the suburbs accessible to tens of millions of people who otherwise might never have been able to afford them (Jackson, *Crabgrass Frontier: The Suburbanization of the United States,* 1985).

As these enticements lured U.S. consumer tastes out of the city, other factors conspired to give them a push. Social and economic shifts driving African Americans out of the South and into Northern cities combined with racial tension, violence, rising crime, and a sense of social dislocation during the 1950s and 1960s to generate a pattern in the United States known as "white flight" (Sugrue, *Origins of the Urban Crisis,* 1996). Suburban life gave the evacuees a chance to stretch out.

Between 1950 and 2000, low-density suburban development ate up land at more than twice the rate of population growth—the simplest definition of the term "sprawl" (U.S. Environmental Protection Agency, "Our Built and Natural Environments," 2001).

Some observers, however, are dubious that sprawl is such a great threat. After all, Canada and the United States are enormous countries where development takes up only tiny fractions of the land. "Urban built-up areas" covered about 0.2 percent of Canada in 1992; 5.2 percent of the United States was "developed" in 1997, according to government definitions (Statistics Canada, *Human Activity and the Environment 2000,* 2000; U.S. Department of Agriculture, "Natural Resources Inventory," 2001). Grazing pastures still cover more ground in both countries than do pavement and rooftops. But in those areas where humans choose to live and work, land is frequently consumed at rates that far exceed the rate of population growth (Fulton, "Who Sprawls Most?" 2001). Between 1992 and 1997, new development ate up more than 11 million acres in the United States alone, an area almost the size of New Hampshire and Vermont combined.

For those whose concerns delve beyond important quality of human life issues such as suburban aesthetics and the time lost while sitting in traffic, the mere loss of acreage is less troublesome than the quality of the land that most frequently attracts intense development: fertile agricultural areas, wetlands,

Figure 1.1 Spreading Ourselves Thin: Percent Change in Population and Land Use in Some Major Urban Areas, 1970–1990

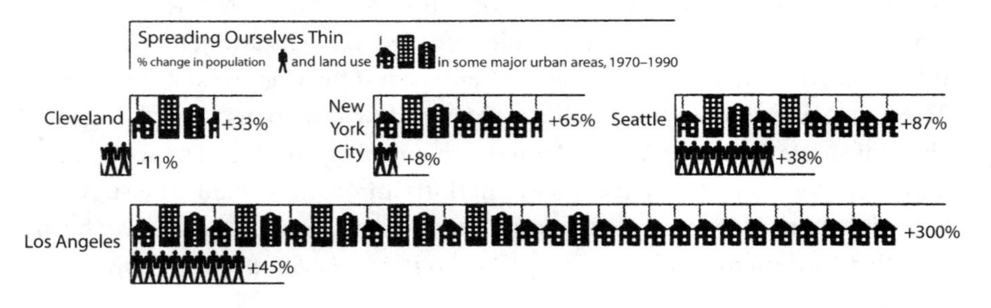

SOURCE: Henry Diamon and Patrick Noonan, *Land Use in America*, Island Press.

riparian plains, and coastlines. Dominant urban land use patterns typically have a significant negative impact upon natural cycles and wildlife habitat regardless of whether they radiate in concentric circles from a city center or thread out along major transportation corridors. Low-density development increases vehicle volume and traffic congestion, extending the amount of time during which idling automobile engines pollute the air. Other impacts include increased soil erosion, greenhouse gas emissions, artificially raised temperatures, and water pollution as well as the long-term effects of pouring tar or concrete over ground that once delivered water on its natural return to the biosphere or the aquifers below.

Sprawl in Canada

Although the political, social, and cultural factors driving Canadian urbanization throughout the twentieth century were radically different than those that shaped the cities of the United States, by 2000 the major difference in outcome seemed to be mainly one of scale. "Canadians have long prided themselves on the fact that their cities have never suffered as much as American cities," the Canadian Urban Institute observed in a March 2001 report. "Yes, we have traffic congestion and many people endure long commutes every day, but we never abandoned transit as an alternative. Yes, we are paving over farmland at a greater rate, but with our smaller population, we don't put quite as much pressure on the environment. At the same time, many Canadians feel that our cities could and should function better and that Canadian complacency is misplaced." Indeed, Canadian metropolitan areas such as Saskatoon and Regina are increasingly exhibiting patterns of "donut growth" (in which the urban core is vacated by residents and businesses in favor of the suburban perimeter) very much like those found in older U.S. cities.

Canadian surveys of land use and soil erosion trends from 1992 recorded nearly one-third of Canadian land cover as barren land, perennial ice and snow, or tundra, much of which compose the Arctic regions of the territories. Forests cover more than one-half of the country and represent 15 percent of the earth's natural forest ecosystems, according to Environment Canada. The country also claims to support one-quarter of the earth's wetlands, despite the loss of more than 65 percent of its natural wetlands in populated areas to settlement. Farms and grazing lands cover less than 7 percent, and the total amount of land in agriculture has receded marginally since 1940 with the decline of family operations and the growth in average farm size. Macro-level land use trends in recent years remain unclear, but local data fill in a picture of dynamic change, particularly around and between Canadian cities (Statistics Canada, *Human Activity and the Environment 2000*, 2000).

Although Alberta's economy attracted the fastest growth during the 1990s, the largest number of people continued to settle around the western shores of Lake Ontario in an area known as the Golden Horseshoe, home to one out of every five Canadians and six of Canada's twenty-five fastest growing municipalities. The northern rim of the horseshoe coincides with the Oak Ridges Moraine, a sensitive and valuable aquifer. In 2001, developers proposed to build as many as 10,000 new houses on the moraine and along the rivers that feed the lake, continuing a pattern of intense development that has prompted concern among community groups and government officials for the health of the region's ecosystems and the supply of fresh water. "People want to live on the Oak Ridges Moraine because it offers a combination of rolling hills, bucolic splendour and ready access to Toronto. Residents of its many subdivisions can flush their toilets and drain their washing machines knowing that the effluent will end up 50 kilometers away at the mouth of an enormous southward flowing sewer pipe. Plans are also under way to construct another gigantic sewer main flowing into Lake Ontario, allowing for even more construction on the moraine" (McDougall, "Watershed Down," 2001).

These and other proposed developments also constitute a potential threat to the region's flora and fauna. Stretched along a segment of the Windsor–Quebec City corridor, the moraine supports one of the most species-rich ecosystems in the country. It is home to many of the 1,600 species of plants and animals that live in southern Ontario. Although Canada does not have an equivalent to the Endangered Species Act, Canadian scientists have identified more than 200 "at risk" species throughout the country for which habitat destruction is the greatest threat.

Demographers expect as many as 2 million new residents of Greater Toronto by 2030. City planners are working to promote infill development, often on abandoned industrial sites called brownfields, and integrate it with an upgraded public transit system in hopes of limiting the impact of escalating levels of automobile use. Other fast-growing Canadian cities, such as Calgary, face similar transportation issues.

Where new development occurs on open space, that open space is often farmland. Southern Ontario, for example, has lost more than half of its prime farmland since 1967. Losses were smaller in rapidly growing Alberta (6 percent) and in Saskatchewan (less than 1 percent) in 1996 (Statistics Canada, *Human Activity and the Environment 2000*, 2000). But the losses in Ontario are all the more acute because the province holds the majority of Canada's most fertile soil.

Sprawl in the United States

The pace and scale of urban growth in the United States has intensified its impact upon the environment, particularly in natural and seminatural areas that have been targeted for development. In fact, population growth in the 1990s was faster in unincorporated areas and in new suburbs (22 percent) than in existing suburbs (14 percent), according to the Brookings Institute. Some regions of the country have been particularly affected by the sprawl phenomenon. New development in Pittsburgh, Pennsylvania, for instance, outpaced population growth nearly twenty-two to one between 1950 and 1990. It consumed more than 313 square miles of land around Washington, D.C., during

An aerial view of suburban Las Vegas, Nevada in 2000 LESTER LEFKOWITZ/CORBIS

the 1980s alone (U.S. Environmental Protection Agency, "Our Built and Natural Environments," 2001).

Canadian sprawl typically involves the loss of good farmland, but U.S. sprawl is not as discriminating. According to the Natural Resources Inventory (NRI), a five-year survey of nonfederal land uses commissioned by the U.S. Department of Agriculture, nearly half of all new development (4.8 million acres) in 1997 stood on land that had been forest just five years earlier. Croplands were another major source, contributing another 2.9 million acres over the same period. Wetlands, which serve a variety of environmental functions from habitat support to flood mitigation to soil restoration to pollution reduction, were highly vulnerable to new development. The Interior Department estimates that an average of 60,000 acres of wetlands disappear each year, mostly the result of the construction of new roads, houses, offices, and shopping malls.

Numbers aside, farmland loss receives the most attention from antisprawl groups (Staley, "The 'Vanishing Farmland' Myth and the Smart-Growth Agenda," 2000). One reason that soil scientists offer for the high-profile concern, apart from the quiet trend toward reforestation, is the quality of the farmland that is lost. Nearly 90 percent of urban land in the United States stands on soil with moderate, moderately high, or high productivity. As in Canada, highly productive soil is rare, accounting for no more than 3 percent of all land in the country. But homebuilders and other developers are attracted to this type of land as well, for it typically features good drainage and nearly level ground (Nizeyimana et al., "Tracking Farmland Loss," 2002).

One school of thought on sprawl argues that farmland conversions may actually relieve pressure that might otherwise be placed on biodiversity because agriculture is already inhospitable to some forms of wildlife. Furthermore, it is argued, the suburbs are not inherently hostile to plants and animals. Free-market environmentalist Jane Shaw points to the large deer populations that still inhabit dozens of U.S. suburbs as evidence of "an apparent compatibility—albeit perhaps an uneasy one—of animals and humans in growing metropolitan areas." Others say that the perseverance of resilient "weedy" species such as deer, squirrels, and raccoons in the new, simplified suburban ecosystems merely masks the problem. The acceleration of species loss, including 3 percent of U.S. bird species, closely coincides with the postwar sprawl period and the attendant loss and fragmentation of wildlife habitats. "The numbers of wildlife do not necessarily decline; the overall biomass may stay the same or even increase. But the numbers of species plummet," writes Kathrin Day Lassila, editor of the Natural Resources Defense Council's *OnEarth* magazine (Dudley, *The Environment,* 2001).

Inefficient community design is one cause of habitat fragmentation. Another is the haphazardly built system of secondary highways and roads that is both a cause and result of sprawl. Construction crews using federal dollars built on average more than 16,000 miles of new roads each year during the 1990s. The EPA estimated that by 1997 the United States had paved a total of 11.1 million acres of land for vehicle traffic nationwide. The associated impacts of this activity on wildlife and air and water purity are enormous. Roadkill is only the most obvious evidence of the incompatibility of high-volume car travel and a thriving natural ecosystem. Road-building destroys plant life in the path of the roadbed, often involves the burial of streams or wetlands, and disrupts animal feeding, breeding, and migratory behavior. Automobile travel also threatens atmospheric quality: transportation activities were responsible for one-third of U.S. carbon dioxide emissions in the 1990s and are projected to grow nearly 50 percent by 2020. Cars emit high levels of carbon monoxide, nitrogen oxides, volatile organic compounds, sulfur dioxide, and particulate matter; they kick up more than 14 million short tons of road dust annually; and they are responsible for more than half the amount of toxic benzene released into the air. Meanwhile, roads and parking lots produce sixteen times the storm-water runoff volume of undeveloped land and send loose soil, engine fluids, oil, and road treatment residues standing on the road surface into nearby waterways. This runoff has significantly damaged the ecological health of countless U.S. rivers and lakes. In fact, more than a third of the nation's estuaries were considered too impaired for fishing or swimming in 1996, largely because of runoff from development (U.S. Environmental Protection Agency, *Our Built and Natural Environments,* 2001).

Addressing the Problem of Urban Sprawl

Efforts to mitigate sprawl's impact in both countries are widespread. But while Canada has made greater inroads in addressing the problem at the federal level, it has not yet attained the coherence necessary to achieve noticeable results. Organizations such as the Smart Growth Network contend that reining in sprawl will be possible only if North American communities begin giving greater priority to mixed commercial and residential zoning, compact building design, the provision of a range of housing choices, and establishment of conservation areas. Some local governments, such as Boulder, Colorado, have followed the lead set by Oregon, which in 1972 imposed strict limitations on growth. But in the case of Boulder, a relatively isolated community, the new regulations adversely impacted housing values and contributed to sprawl development in neighboring communities.

In the mid-1990s, provincial, state, and local governments began to take advantage of an extended economic recovery and healthy tax revenues and passed a range of measures designed to address sprawl. But the policy process has often amounted to a tug-of-war. In Ontario, the provincial government tightened planning policy only to see the provisions rolled back beyond their starting point by the new government a few years later (Tomalty and Paul, *Human Settlements,* 1999). In the United States, eleven states updated their growth management laws to promote regional cooperation among local governments, loosen zoning restrictions, and require long-term land use planning (Nagy, "Land Use and Environment," 2001).

Other initiatives have tackled the sprawl issue from less obvious angles. In the United States, forty-seven states and the federal government passed laws encouraging brownfield cleanups, intrigued by estimates that projects in major industrial cities could absorb anywhere between one and five years of housing needs and hundreds of years' worth of demand for new office space (U.S. Environmental Protection Agency, *Our Built and Natural Environments,* 2001). In addition, dozens of states and the federal government have enacted or authorized income and property tax incentives for historic preservation in an effort that one Maryland official termed "the most important smart growth initiative bar none" (Nagy, "Preservation Tax Credits Working . . . Too Well?" 2002). Finally, voters in states and communities across the United States have approved billions of dollars' worth of conservation funds and other incentives to save valuable open space.

Sources:

Boychuk, Rick. 2001. "World Class Energy Gluttons." *Canadian Geographic* 121 (May–June).

Brown, Lester. 1999. "Feeding Nine Billion." In Lester Brown, Christopher Flavin, and Hilary French, eds., *State of the World 1999.* New York: W. W. Norton.

Brown, Lester, and Christopher Flavin. 1999. "A New Economy for a New Century." *State of the World 1999.* New York: W. W. Norton.

Cohn, D'Vera. 2001. "Illegal Immigrant Total Is Raised." *Washington Post,* October 25.

———. 2001. "1990s Further Reshape Suburbs." *Washington Post,* June 25.

———. 2002. "Cities and Suburbs Are Trading Places." *Washington Post,* February 2.

Dudley, William, ed. 2001. *The Environment.* San Diego: Greenhaven.

Dyer, Gwynne. 2001. "Visible Majorities." *Canadian Geographic* 121 (January–February).

Fields, Jason. 2000. *America's Families and Living Arrangements.* Washington, DC: U.S. Census Bureau.

Food and Agriculture Organization of the United Nations. 2002. FAOSTAT (FAO Statistical Databases). March. http://apps.fao.org/ (accessed March 16, 2002).

Fulton, William, et al. 2001. *Who Sprawls Most? How Growth Patterns Differ across the U.S.* Washington, DC: Brookings Institution.

Halper, Evan. 2002. "CDC Study on Suburban Life Hits a Nerve." *Los Angeles Times*, January 7.

Harrison, Paul, and Fred Pearce. 2000. *AAAS Atlas of Population and Environment*. Berkeley: University of California Press.

Immen, Wallace. 2001. "Urban Sprawl Threatens Prime Farmland." *Toronto Globe and Mail*, June 11.

Jackson, Kenneth T. 1985. *Crabgrass Frontier: The Suburbanization of the United States*. New York: Oxford University Press.

Jefferson, Thomas. 1982. *Notes on the State of Virginia*. Edited by William Peden. Chapel Hill: University of North Carolina Press.

Kriz, Margie. 2002. "Working the Land." *National Journal*, February 23.

Lasch, Christopher. 1991. *The True and Only Heaven: Progress and Its Critics*. New York: W. W. Norton.

Lucy, William H., and David L. Phillips. 2001. *Suburbs and the Census: Patterns of Growth and Decline*. Washington, DC: Brookings Institution.

Marchand, Roland. 1985. *Advertising the American Dream: Making Way for Modernity 1920–1940*. Berkeley: University of California Press.

McDougall, Bruce. 2001. "Watershed Down." *Canadian Geographic* 121 (November–December).

Meinig, D. W. 1986–1998. *The Shaping of America: A Geographical Perspective on 500 Years of History*. 3 vols. New Haven: Yale University Press.

Mitchell, John G. 2001. "Urban Sprawl." *National Geographic* 200 (July).

Nagy, John. 2001. "Land Use and Environment." *State of the States 2000*. Washington, DC: Pew Center on the States.

———. 2002. "Preservation Tax Credits Working . . . Too Well?" *Stateline.org*. March 22. http://www1.stateline.org/story.do?storyId=229232 (accessed March 23, 2002).

Nizeyimana, Egide L., Gary W. Peterson, and Eric D. Warner. 2002. "Tracking Farmland Loss." *GeoTimes* (January).

North American Commission for Environmental Cooperation. 2002. *The North American Mosaic: A State of the Environment Report*. Montreal: CEC.

Outwater, Alice. 1996. *Water: A Natural History*. New York: Basic.

Pew Center for Civic Journalism. 2000. *Straight Talk from Americans—2000*. Washington, DC: Pew Center for Civic Journalism.

Population Reference Bureau. 2001. "World Population Data Sheet 2001." May.

Staley, Samuel. 2000. *The 'Vanishing Farmland' Myth and the Smart-Growth Agenda*. Los Angeles: Reason Public Policy Institute.

Statistics Canada. 2000. *Human Activity and the Environment 2000*. Ottawa: Statistics Canada.

———. 2001. *Annual Demographic Statistics (March 2001)*. Ottawa: Statistics Canada.

———. 2002. *A Profile of the Canadian Population: Where We Live*. Ottawa: Statistics Canada.

Stockle, Claudio O. 2001. *Environmental Impact of Irrigation: A Review*. Pullman: State of Washington Water Research Center, Washington State University.

Sugrue, Thomas J. 1996. *The Origins of the Urban Crisis: Race and Inequality in Postwar Detroit*. Princeton: Princeton University Press.

Taras, David. 2000. "Swimming against the Current: American Mass Entertainment and Canadian Identity." *Canada and the United States: Differences That Count*. Edited by David M. Thomas. 2d ed. Peterborough, ON: Broadview.

Tomalty, Ray, and Francis Paul. 1999. *Human Settlements: Sustainable Land Use and Transportation*. Toronto: Canadian Institute for Environmental Law and Policy.

Trust for Public Land and the Land Trust Alliance. 2002. *Land Vote 2001: Americans Invest in Parks & Open Space*. Boston: Trust for Public Land and the Land Trust Alliance.

U.S. Census Bureau. 2001. *Population Change and Distribution 1990 to 2000*. Washington, DC: U.S. Census Bureau.

U.S. Department of Agriculture (USDA), Natural Resources Conservation Service. 2001. *Natural Resources Inventory*. Revised data. Washington, DC: USDA.

U.S. Department of Energy, Energy Information Administration (EIA). 2001. "United States of America." October. http://www.eia.doe.gov/emeu/cabs/usa.html (accessed April 8, 2002).

U.S. Environmental Protection Agency. 2001. *Our Built and Natural Environments: A Technical Review of the Interactions between Land Use, Transportation, and Environmental Quality*. Washington, DC: EPA.

Vincent, Mary. 2001. "How We Lived: Canada's Century of Change." *Canadian Geographic* 121 (January–February).

Wackernagel, Mathis, et al. 1997. "Ranking the Ecological Impact of Nations." Earth Council, November 20.

Wilkins, Van. 2001. "Lessons from Calgary." *Mass Transit* 27 (September 1).

2

Biodiversity

The sprawling North American landscape contains myriad terrestrial ecosystems, from short-grass prairie lands to coastal rain forests to marshlands to mountain ranges. Many of these regions support a rich tapestry of flora and fauna, making the continent one of the globe's primary centers of biodiversity. But experts agree that North American biodiversity—generally defined as the variety of life forms found in a given region (whether an ecosystem, nation, or continent)—is at risk from a host of human-induced factors, including habitat loss and degradation, invasive species, and pollution. Indeed, by the close of the twentieth century, nearly 1,600 North American species of plants, birds, mammals, reptiles, amphibians, and fish had been classified by U.S. and Canadian agencies as vulnerable or endangered (Committee on the Status of Endangered Wildlife in Canada, *Canadian Species at Risk,* 2000; Department of the Interior, *Federal List of Endangered and Threatened Wildlife and Plants,* 2001).

Researchers warn that unless the United States and Canada can halt their inexorable conversion of wildlife habitat for farming, ranching, resource extraction, transportation, and settlement, many of these species will eventually be snuffed out, joining the great auk, the passenger pigeon, the Labrador duck, and dozens of other species that have vanished from the North American landscape over the past few centuries. Moreover, unchecked conversion and disturbance of habitat will ultimately impact many currently stable species, pushing them down the path toward extinction as well. "In a scientific and intuitive sense, 'endangered species' and 'endangered habitats' are practically synonymous. . . . Habitats and the ecosystems from which they are derived are the life-sustaining systems for wild species. When the country's wildlife habitats undergo degradation, significant alterations, or finally disappear, the effects are mimicked in species" (Gauthier and Wiken, "Avoiding the Endangerment of Species," in Beazley and Boardman, *Politics of the Wild,* 2001).

Fortunately, broad public support for the protection of wildlife and wilderness exists in both the United States and Canada, giving scientists and conservationists hope that the continent may yet embrace biodiversity-friendly land-use philosophies. "Attitudes have changed profoundly in North America regarding both spaces and species and these changes have taken place over the course of only several decades, a comparatively short period of time for a change in value perspective so broad and deep" (Paehlke, "Biodiversity: The Policy Challenge," in Bocking, *Biodiversity in Canada,* 2000).

Habitat Loss Crowding Some Species to the Brink of Extinction

A recent study carried out by the Association for Biodiversity Information (ABI) and the Nature Conservancy confirmed the crucial role that intact habitats play in preserving biodiversity in the North American wild. Their analysis found that habitat destruction was implicated in the decline of fully 85 percent of endangered plants and animals in the United States. The next greatest threat—invasive species—was judged a factor in 49 percent of the declines. Other significant factors included pollution (25 percent, though much higher among aquatic species), overhunting and other forms of overexploitation (17 percent), and disease (3 percent) (Stein et al., *Precious Heritage,* 2000).

Human alteration of landscapes impacts biodiversity in numerous ways. It diminishes the size and quality of natural habitat; fragments important breeding, feeding, and migratory routes; and changes the natural pattern of environmental variation, including natural disturbance patterns. The sheer number of animals and plants do not necessarily decline when humans encroach on habitat, but the variety of species often declines, as hardier, more adaptable species—native or exotic—take over (Mac et al., *Status and Trends,* 1998).

No major type of ecosystem present in North America has escaped some degree of habitat alteration, though large wilderness areas remain in both the United States and Canada. Canada's vast forests, for example, still support a wonderful variety of flora and fauna. But studies carried out in the late 1990s found that more than 60 percent of the nation's total forest area was already tenured (licensed to timber companies for eventual logging) or within close proximity (10 kilometers) of a road, village, town, dam, mine, oil drilling facility, or other development activity. This percentage will likely grow in future years, for energy and timber companies are increasingly looking to the Yukon, the Northwest Territories, and northern reaches of provinces that have thus far remained relatively free of activity. Indeed, logging, mining, and other activities have already been proposed for about 20 percent of Canada's

Table 2.1 Percentages of Endangered Species in the United States

Cause	*Overall* (n = *1,207*)	*Vertebrates* (n = *329*)	*Invertebrates* (n = *155*)	*Plants* (n = *723*)	*Mammals* (n = *67*)	*Birds* (n = *91*)	*Reptiles* (n = *39*)	*Amphibians* (n = *16*)	*Fish* (n = *116*)	*Insects* (n = *39*)	*Arachnids* (n = *4*)	*Crustaceans* (n = *20*)	*Mollusks* (n = *23*)	*Mussels* (n = *69*)
Agriculture	38	40	57	33	25	42	33	63	45	56	75	55	35	64
Land conversion for commercial development	35	30	42	36	31	33	56	44	16	67	75	65	13	29
Water development	30	47	66	15	10	22	28	63	91	21	0	70	48	99
Outdoor recreation (including ORVs)	27	16	19	33	18	15	31	25	9	41	0	30	26	4
Livestock grazing	22	17	10	33	19	20	8	19	16	15	0	30	9	1
Pollutants	20	27	66	7	5	10	21	25	55	26	75	55	48	97
Infrastructure development (including roads)	17	16	12	20	9	8	28	38	17	23	25	10	9	6
Disruption of fire regimes	14	5	6	20	7	8	5	6	0	18	25	0	4	0
Logging	12	16	25	7	12	18	13	19	19	5	25	5	13	46
Mining, oil and gas, geothermal	11	12	31	11	2	3	13	13	23	10	0	0	17	58
Military activities	4	2	1	5	2	3	5	0	0	0	0	5	4	0

NOTE: The data above shows the percentages of federal endangered, threatened, and proposed species in the United States harmed by various types of habitat destruction and degradation.

remaining wilderness forests (Global Forest Watch, *Canada's Forests at a Crossroads,* 2000; Bryant et al., *The Last Frontier Forests,* 1997).

Many scientists and conservation groups see roads—whether four-lane freeways or logging roads—as the single greatest cause of habitat fragmentation. Roads are usually a precursor to increased human activity in a region, and many of these activities—development, logging, drilling, poaching—can erode the quality of a habitat for its species. In addition, "roads isolate some species that depend on interior habitat and/or are unwilling to cross open areas [and] create artificial edges that encourage invasion by weeds and opportunists such as the brown-headed cowbird [which parasitizes songbird nests] and serve as direct sources of mortality to many animals" (Noss, "Protecting Natural Areas," 1987). In fact, conservation organizations report that collisions with motor vehicles are the chief cause of mortality among Florida panthers, a critically endangered species that is now confined to remote corners of Florida's Everglades and Big Cypress Swamp.

Agricultural operations are another key factor in the loss of biodiversity. Farming provides the people of North America with dietary staples, and it is an important part of the economy in both the United States and Canada. But as the Department of Interior's National Biological Service acknowledged, "[T]he effects of modern agriculture on wildlife are indisputable, ranging from habitat elimination to long-term effects of agrochemicals on water quality and reproductive success of ground-nesting birds. . . . In many regions, wetland drainage, consolidation of fields and farms, and elimination of fencerows and idle areas have reduced habitat diversity even further, thereby diminishing the ability of agricultural ecosystems to sustain viable populations of wildlife" (U.S. Department of the Interior, *Our Living Resources,* 1995).

For example, tall-grass prairies that once extended from southern Manitoba to southern Texas have been almost entirely depleted to make way for corn and soybean fields (Samson, *Prairie Conservation,* 1996). Short-grass and mixed grass prairies in the continent's midsection have also been degraded, although not to the same extent. Fortunately, the continued existence of some major tracts of mixed and short-grass prairies, combined with healthy species numbers in adjacent regions, has enabled most prairie-dependent species to avoid outright extermination thus far. "Given all that has happened to the central grasslands, it seems nothing less than miraculous that relatively few grassland animals have become extinct. Some—the whooping crane and black-footed ferret being obvious examples—teeter on the brink, while others, such as the mountain plover and lesser prairie-chicken, are marching steadily toward that precipice. But the fact remains that the tall-grass, mixed-grass, and short-grass prairies combined have nowhere near as many critically

A black-footed ferret, one of North America's many endangered species. D. ROBERT & LORRI FRANZ/CORBIS

endangered species as some other ecosystems. . . . There is still time to save virtually all of the prairie animals" (Wilcove, *Condor's Shadow,* 1999).

But preservation of these and other habitats will depend on the institution of fundamental changes in farming practices. "In agricultural and urbanizing regions drainage and pollution of wetlands and waterways continues and farmers are being allowed by governments to continue the use of fertilizers and new kinds of pesticides that affect biodiversity in soils, rivers, and lakes. Large regions of northern Alberta are being 'opened up' for agriculture with ongoing annihilation of entire ecosystems. On the plus side for biodiversity, some parts of southern Ontario, Quebec, and the Maritimes continue to be abandoned by farmers (for economic reasons) and here normal biodiversity is slowly returning" (Mosquin, "Status of and Trends in Canadian Biodiversity," in Bocking, *Biodiversity in Canada,* 2000).

In recognition of the importance of preserving fragile wildlife habitat, both the United States and Canada have steadily boosted the number and extent of their protected areas. Approximately 2.5 million square kilometers of North American land, freshwater, and coastal areas (about 9 percent of the continent's total land area) receive some measure of protection from development or extraction activities, and efforts to protect important wildlife habitat are ongoing in both countries (Commission for Environmental Cooperation, *On Track?* 1999). But proponents of increased habitat conservation claim that much of the land currently under protection was set aside because of its scenic or historic value rather than its importance in ecosystem preservation, and they contend that ecosystem preservation needs to be given greater weight in selecting such areas. "The national parks have been highly successful in achieving their earliest goals: to preserve the parks from commercial exploitation and to make easily accessible the most scenic portions of the United States. [But] it is becoming evident that we should have paid more attention to the 'ordinary' landscapes such as prairies, coastal lagoons, marshlands, and hardwood forests, which might be ecologically more important than spectacular landscapes like mountains" (O'Brien, *Our National Parks,* 1999).

Yet arranging meaningful protection for endangered habitats is a difficult, often politically charged, process. Development pressure remains strong in both countries, fed by continued economic prosperity and demographic trends. As a result, the task of stopping or modifying even those projects that are obviously detrimental to regional flora and fauna is often a daunting one.

North America Bedeviled by Alien Species

Another frequently cited threat to North America's biodiversity is the introduction of alien species into ecosystems. Alien species—also referred to as invasive, nonindigenous, or exotic species—are flora and fauna that have been introduced to areas beyond their native range by human activity. These animals and plants often create havoc in regional ecosystems, which, because of their complex and interdependent structure, are intensely vulnerable to outside disturbances. They can, and often do, disrupt and alter ecosystems into which they are introduced in a variety of ways, including replacing native species, introducing new diseases, diluting genetic purity through breeding, and altering links in the food chain upon which all of the region's creatures depend. Indeed, the introduction of alien species into a region—whether done intentionally or not—can have significant ripple effects throughout entire ecosystems. "Invasive exotics can do a great deal more than simply displace native species," stated one analyst. "Take, for example, the case of the tiny opossum shrimp in Montana's Flathead River system. Wildlife officials introduced the shrimp around 1970 to increase the forage base for the kokanee salmon, another introduced species. But salmon tend to feed near the surface and the shrimp only rose to the surface at night, when the salmon could not see them. So the salmon could not eat the shrimp, but the shrimp ate all the plankton that the salmon fry depended on. The salmon population crashed, then the bears, birds of prey, and other creatures that had come to depend on the salmon disappeared. A tiny shrimp had starved eagles out of the sky" (Bright, *Life out of Bounds,* 1999).

Alien species first came to the attention of the United States and Canada when an assortment of invasive species—primarily insects and weedy plants—damaged valuable farm crops. But awareness of the problem has risen in recent decades, in part because of increased recognition of the environmental toll that some alien species can take, and in part because the problem has been exacerbated by the "global economy" phenomenon, which has greatly increased levels of trade and travel. By the mid-1990s, studies indicated that 4,500 to 6,500 nonindigenous animals, plants, and microbes had established self-sustaining populations in the United States. In 1998, Michigan's Office of the Great Lakes estimated that at least 139 nonindigenous aquatic species had infiltrated the Great Lakes ecosystem alone, with the number likely to rise in the future from ballast water of oceangoing vessels, aquaculture operations, and other sources. San Francisco Bay and its associated delta, meanwhile, has been invaded by at least 234 non-native species of plants, animals, and micro-organisms (Cohen and Carlton, "Accelerating Invasion Rate in a Highly Invaded Estuary," 1998). "The San Francisco Estuary . . . has the dubious distinction of being perhaps the most extensively invaded estuary in the world, with a higher proportion of its habitats dominated by non-native species than is the case in any other comparable aquatic ecosystem. In some parts of the estuary it is difficult to find any native species in abundance. Entire food webs have been disrupted and reconfigured by alien species. Fish from the eastern United States and clams and mussels from Asia and the Mediterranean now dominate many portions of the estuary" (Wilcove, *Condor's Shadow,* 1999).

Some species introductions have been benign. For instance, ring-necked pheasants, mute swans, and other birdlife introduced to North America in past centuries have been popular additions to the continent's fabric of wildlife. Other exotic species have provided significant economic returns while contributing to healthy, albeit altered, ecosystems. For example, many state and federal wildlife management agencies have successfully introduced nonindigenous species of trout and salmon to rivers and lakes throughout North America, both to boost sport-fishing opportunities and address imbalances in the marine food chain. Some—though by no means all—of these projects have met with significant success.

But many introductions of alien species, whether intentional or unintentional, have had disastrous consequences for native species. The brown tree snake, introduced to the island of Guam in the 1950s, has decimated the island's native forest-dwelling bird community. In Louisiana, officials are engaged in a grim struggle to fend off Formosan termites that are destroying groves of trees and historic buildings in New Orleans's famed French Quarter.

In the intermountain West, explosions of leafy splurge have ruined valuable grazing land. And in Canada, the European corn borer continues to threaten valuable corn crops (the pest destroyed roughly 30 percent of the 1995 corn harvest in some regions of the nation).

Zebra mussels provide a particularly notorious example of the negative impact that alien species can have on an ecosystem. These small freshwater mollusks, introduced from Russia in the 1980s through the ballast water of oceangoing ships, has transformed inland waters throughout the United States and Canada. Within a few years of its introduction, the zebra mussel—which filters out the plankton that serves as the base of marine food chains—was being blamed for plummeting fish populations throughout the Great Lakes and elsewhere. It remains a scourge in as many as two-thirds of America's waterways, damaging marine ecosystems wherever it goes. Moreover, it has triggered economic hardships in numerous communities that rely on dollars from sport or commercial fishing activities. In addition, the zebra mussel causes economic damage in a host of other ways, from clogging water intakes to encrusting the hulls of vessels. Indeed, the United States spent an estimated $3.1 billion over ten years to combat the zebra mussel's relentless infiltration of the country's waterways (Pimental, "Environmental and Economic Costs," 1999).

Most analysts agree that the heightened interest in invasive species can be directly attributed to a growing appreciation of the economic toll that they can take. One 1999 study estimated that invasive species cost the United States a total of $123 billion each year in treatment, control, and eradication efforts. Noteworthy pests discussed in the report include the fire ant ($2 billion annually), the Asian clam ($1 billion annually), the sea lamprey ($10 to $15 million annually, just to fund control programs), and the Formosan termite ($1 billion annually) (ibid.).

Both the United States and Canada have adopted a variety of measures to increase their defenses against alien species. But analysts note that programs to root out destructive exotic species that have already become entrenched in North American soil and water will be time consuming and expensive (and in many instances impossible). Moreover, experts agree that laws such as the Nonindigenous Aquatic Species Act of 1990, which requires ships entering the Great Lakes with ballast water to exchange it on the high seas, can help staunch the flood of alien flora and fauna. But they admit that erecting airtight defenses against future contamination is a practical impossibility.

In December 1997, for instance, the U.S. Fish and Wildlife Service (USFWS) announced that it had discovered four new species of zooplankton in Alaska's Prince William Sound, delivered via tanker ballast. Researchers believe that this seemingly innocuous discovery is actually freighted with a host of disquieting implications. "Scientists are concerned that the invaders may develop a taste for the same foods that are needed by the Dungeness crab, an important fishery species. As more and more Alaskan oil is pumped, some scientists fear that ballast releases like these could become a general threat to the state's fisheries. The biotic spills, in other words, could become a far greater danger to Alaskan coasts than . . . oil spills [like the 1989 *Exxon Valdez* accident]. After all, oil spills may be a grave environmental insult, but they eventually go away. Biotic spills do not" (Bright, *Life out of Bounds,* 1999).

Protecting At-Risk Species in the United States

At 3.5 million square miles, the United States possesses the fourth-largest land area of any nation in the world, behind only Canada, Russia, and China. This land area stretches from north of the Arctic Circle to south of the Tropic of Cancer, and it spans almost one-third of the globe from east to west. The United States features a wide variety of ecosystems across this expanse. In fact, all but two of the world's fourteen major ecological zones are represented in the United States.

As of 1999, the United States holds approximately one-tenth of all scientifically documented species on earth, although scientists acknowledge that U.S. species tend to be documented more extensively than those in many other countries. By one estimate, the total number of native species includes 15,320 flowering plants, 768 species of birds, 416 mammals, and 799 freshwater fishes (Stein et al., *Precious Heritage,* 2000). Another report offered roughly similar results, detailing the existence of 19,473 higher plants, 650 bird species, 432 mammals, and 822 species of fish (World Conservation Monitoring Centre Species Database, December 1999). The United States is also the world leader in species diversity for several groups of organisms, particularly those that depend on freshwater habitat. For example, the nation is home to 61 percent of the world's known species of freshwater crayfishes, 40 percent of the world's salamanders, 29 percent of freshwater mussels, 22 percent of freshwater turtles, and 17 percent of freshwater snails (Stein et al., *Precious Heritage,* 2000).

The biodiversity of U.S. states varies in accordance with climate, topography, and level of habitat disturbance. Those areas with the greatest diversity are located in the West and Southwest. California has the largest number of endemic species (species confined to a particular area) in the nation, with almost 1,500 known plants and animals, while Hawaii has the largest percentage of endemic species because of its isolation. But Hawaii and California also have the highest proportion of species at risk. Other areas of the country with high concentrations of imperiled species can be found in the Southeast, specifically Florida and the southern Appalachians. The upper Midwest,

Figure 2.1 Distribution of Imperiled Species by Ecoregion in the United States

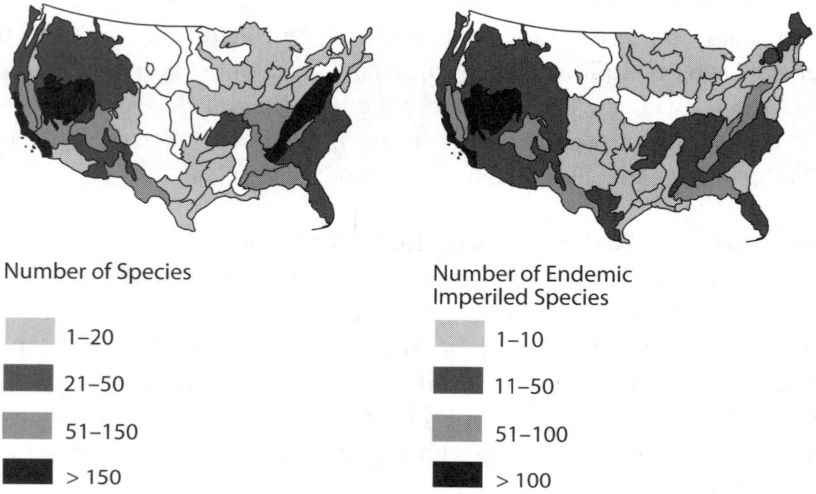

Number of Species

1–20
21–50
51–150
> 150

Number of Endemic Imperiled Species

1–10
11–50
51–100
> 100

SOURCE: Stein, et al. 2000. *Precious Heritage*. New York: Oxford University Press, 2000.

characterized primarily by species with wide ranges, has the lowest proportion of at-risk species.

Those regions with large numbers of at-risk species are also, historically, the ones that have already seen a high number of extinctions. For instance, the isolated islands of Hawaii, a largely predator-free incubator for the creation and nourishment of numerous distinctive species, has lost an estimated 250 species, mostly because of human activity. In the continental United States, Alabama and California rank second and third in number of species lost, in large measure because so many of the waterways in those states have been dramatically altered for human use (Stein et al., *Precious Heritage*, 2000).

Some of America's multitude of creatures have maintained stable populations or even increased in numbers in recent decades, even as the country's overall consumption of energy, food, and other resources continues to grow. A number of species have been bolstered by habitat conservation measures (both voluntary and mandated by state and federal laws), while others have benefited from reduced exposure to air- and waterborne pollutants. Species as diverse as pronghorn antelopes, peregrine falcons, greenback cutthroat trout, and black-footed ferrets have all been brought back from the brink of extirpation (both the greenback cutthroat trout and black-footed ferret were believed extinct at one time), nurtured by the efforts of wildlife biologists, environmentalists, and sportsmen. Still other species adept at feeding on the refuse of human settlements have actually experienced tremendous growth as a direct result of encroaching human activity. "What is habitat destruction for one species often turns out to be habitat enhancement for another," observed one researcher. "The past half century has seen an extraordinary rise in the numbers of gulls, raccoons, foxes, rats, and other animals that thrive in close association with humans" (Wilcove, *The Condor's Shadow,* 1999).

Overall, however, the biodiversity outlook in the United States is trending downward. The Association for Biodiversity Information, for example, assessed the status of more than 30,000 species of plants and animals in America, weighing criteria such as total population, number of distinct populations, viability of populations, and short- and long-term trends. The organization reported that about one-third of the nation's flora and fauna are at risk, with 16 percent vulnerable, 8 percent imperiled, 7 percent critically imperiled, and 1 percent missing or extinct. As a group, flowering plants were found to be in greatest danger, with 5,090 of 15,300 species—about one-third of the total examined—at risk. Other sectors at particularly high risk included freshwater mussels (70 percent), crayfish (51 percent), and freshwater fish (37 percent). These findings corroborate other studies that indicate that North America's freshwater species are being depleted at a much more rapid rate than land animals (Stein et al., *Precious Heritage,* 2000; Ricciardi and Rasmussen, "Extinction Rates for North American Freshwater Animals," 1999).

American wildlife conservation agencies also report only spotty success in returning formally designated endangered species to healthy numbers. Only 10 percent of plants and animals receiving protection under the Endangered Species Act (ESA), the principal biodiversity protection law in the land, have seen improvements in their populations since being listed. Another 25 to 30 percent of ESA-listed flora and fauna have remained stable, but the populations of 30 to 40 percent have continued to decline. The fate of the remaining animals and plants is unknown, but it is believed that at least 2 percent of listed species (e.g., the blue pike and the dusky seaside sparrow) have permanently vanished from the land (U.S. Fish and Wildlife Service, *Report to Congress on the Recovery Program for Threatened and Endangered Species,* 1996; Department of the Interior, *Federal List of Endangered and Threatened Wildlife and Plants,* 2001). These figures show that despite several notable successes, the future is decidedly uncertain for much of America's threatened wildlife.

Of course, some groups are faring better than others. According to the Department of the Interior, the number of U.S. bird species in decline is roughly equal to that of the number that have experienced growth in their populations. Species showing troubling downturns include those reliant on grassland habitats, many of which have been converted to agricultural use in recent decades. Many duck populations have also declined, buffeted by significant losses of breeding and wintering habitats. Loss of critical breeding and feeding areas has also harmed a number of shorebird species along the Atlantic and Pacific seaboards. Indeed, urban expansion and loss of avian habitat have marked declines in many bird populations. A 2002 study released by the National Audubon Society estimated that fully 25 percent of North America's bird species are threatened, endangered, or in decline. But researchers have been heartened by rebounding raptor populations in many areas of the country. During the 1960s and 1970s, many of these birds were decimated by DDT and other insecticides, as well as the destruction of vital habitat. But the 1972 nationwide ban on DDT, coupled with careful reintroductions of selected species in hospitable habitats, has produced gratifying increases in the number of ospreys, bald eagles, and peregrine falcons. Moreover, populations of most owls, hawks, and other raptors are believed to be stable, although the northern spotted owl and the California condor are well publicized exceptions (U.S. Department of the Interior, *Our Living Resources*, 1995).

Researchers admit that information on the status and health of U.S. populations of amphibians and reptiles is incomplete because of the lack of a national monitoring program. But studies of individual species indicate that habitat degradation and loss have severely affected many amphibian and reptile populations. "The drainage and loss of small aquatic habitats and their associated wetlands have had a major adverse effect on many amphibian species and some reptiles," observed the Department of the Interior. "Many other factors in the decline of reptiles and amphibians have been implicated; most, perhaps all, are human-caused. For example, non-native species of game-fish introduced for sport have been implicated in the decline of frog populations in mountainous areas of some western states" (ibid.).

The decline in U.S. freshwater fisheries has drawn special attention because of the recreational and economic value of sport-fish to area communities. According to the DOI, reductions in the populations and diversity of freshwater fish have been particularly extensive in the country's arid western regions

> We have massively modified fish habitat through the very water demands that define our society (domestic, agricultural, and industrial water supplies; waste disposal; power generation; transportation; and flood protection). . . .Physical and chemical changes in their habitats are not the only stresses that fishes have encountered over time.

> Through fish management programs, the aquarium trade, and accidental releases, many aquatic species have been introduced to new areas far beyond their native ranges. Although these introductions were often done with the best of intentions, they have sometimes subjected native fish species to new competitors, predators, and disease agents that they were ill-equipped to withstand. (ibid.)

Scientists are also concerned about the future prospects of a number of marine mammals. Eleven of thirty-six marine mammals in Pacific waters have been placed under the protection of the Endangered Species Act, while seven of thirty-five marine mammals found along the shores of the Atlantic and Gulf of Mexico have been listed as endangered (Department of the Interior, *Federal List of Endangered and Threatened Wildlife and Plants,* 2001), including all five species of sea turtle—Kemp's ridley, hawksbill, loggerhead, green, and leatherback—that breed on the Atlantic seaboard. The decline in these species is partially the result of extensive development of nesting habitat. "Sea turtles demonstrate remarkable intergenerational fidelity to their nesting beaches. After spending 10 to 50 years at sea, most females return to the place where they were born to lay their own eggs. How many of these ancient nesting sites now lie buried under asphalt or overbuilt with summer houses is anyone's guess. Still more sites literally washed away when overzealous engineers installed seawalls, riprap, and jetties to protect beachfront property" (Wilcove, *The Condor's Shadow,* 1999). Even beaches that are not developed are increasingly illuminated by artificial light. This causes problems for the turtles because they nest at night and avoid brightly lit areas. But fishing industry resistance to protection measures has also been a factor in the decline of these creatures. In the early 1980s, a few years after the last of these five sea turtle species was given ESA protection, researchers developed turtle excluder devices (TEDs) for use by shrimp trawlers, believed responsible for the drowning deaths of up to 40,000 sea turtles annually. Tests showed that the TEDs would not significantly diminish shrimp catches, but shrimpers and their political allies nonetheless fought regulations that would have required the use of the devices in waters traversed by turtles. As a result, the first regulations mandating use of TEDs were not implemented until 1989, and compulsory year-round use of the devices in sea turtle habitat did not become a reality until 1994, more than fifteen years after all five species had been placed under ESA protection (Ross et al., *The Status of Kemp's Ridley,* 1989; U.S. Department of the Interior, *Our Living Resources,* 1995; Wilcove, *The Condor's Shadow,* 1999).

Proposed Grizzly Reintroduction in Idaho and Montana

Grizzly bear sow and cubs in Yellowstone National Park NATIONAL PARK SERVICE

North America's most awesome predator, the grizzly bear, has been listed as a threatened species in the Lower Forty-eight since 1975 (Alaska and Canada both have stable grizzly populations). Once numbering around 50,000, grizzlies have declined to about 1,000 individuals south of the Canadian border since the mid-nineteenth century, mostly the result of hunting and habitat loss. Dependent on large, intact wilderness areas for feeding and mating, the grizzly has been eliminated from all but 2 percent of its original range. The primary remaining populations of grizzlies in the Lower Forty-eight are found in and around Yellowstone National Park in Wyoming and Glacier National Park in Montana.

Although the Yellowstone and Glacier populations have remained stable or grown in recent years, these bears are becoming increasingly isolated as human activity encroaches on their habitat. As a result, the genetic variability within the populations has begun to decline, prompting some biologists to worry about the species' long-term survival. To address this concern, they have proposed reintroducing grizzlies to nearby areas and then establishing corridors of protected land to encourage migration and genetic interchange between the discrete populations.

One of the most publicized grizzly reintroduction proposals centers around the Greater Salmon-Selway-

(continues)

Bitterroot ecosystem of western Montana and central Idaho. This 15-million-acre area represents one of the largest remaining tracts of wild mountain habitat in the Lower Forty-eight. Grizzlies roamed the region for thousands of years before they disappeared in the 1930s or 1940s.

The U.S. Fish and Wildlife Service released an environmental impact statement regarding grizzly reintroduction in the Bitterroot ecosystem in 1997. Its "preferred alternative" proposed releasing a minimum of 25 bears over 5 years, with the ultimate goal of establishing a population of 280 bears in the region over the next 50 to 100 years. If successful, this reintroduction program would eventually increase the number of grizzlies in the Lower Forty-eight by one-third.

The plan recommended by the USFWS represented a cooperative effort between several environmental groups and timber-industry officials. Under this alternative, the reintroduced grizzlies would be considered a "nonessential, experimental population" under the Endangered Species Act, a designation that provides limited protection for animals that wander outside of the recovery area. The reintroduction project would be managed by a committee of scientists and citizens appointed by the governors of Montana and Idaho, the U.S. secretary of the interior, and the Nez Perce tribe.

Several aspects of the proposed plan came under intense criticism from other environmental groups. They argued that the "experimental" designation—which had allowed earlier wolf reintroduction projects to proceed successfully—was not suitable for grizzlies, which breed so slowly that the loss of even a few animals could doom the entire project to failure. They also worried that the citizen-oversight committee would be loaded with political appointees that favored logging and ranching interests.

The controversy led several environmental groups to release their own plan for grizzly reintroduction in the Bitterroots, called the Conservation Biology Plan. This alternative provided bears with full legal protection under the Endangered Species Act, expanded the recovery area from 5,785 to 21,645 square miles, created corridors of protected land for grizzly migration, prohibited logging and road-building within the grizzly habitat, and replaced the citizen-oversight committee with a panel of scientists. Although this plan provided greater protection for the bears and their habitat, backers of the USFWS "preferred alternative" said that it had no chance of implementation because it lacked critical industry support (Rembert and Motavalli, "Troubled Homecoming," 1998).

The debate between environmental groups over grizzly reintroduction scenarios became moot in 2001, when Secretary of the Interior Gale Norton set aside the plan. Norton was responding, in part, to a lawsuit filed by Idaho governor Dirk Kempthorne, who said that "massive,

(continues)

flesh-eating carnivores" had no place in his state (Devlin, "Norton Snubs Grizzlies," 2001).

Norton claimed that grizzly reintroduction was unpopular in the Bitterroot region and lacked the support of state leaders. She cited local concerns about public safety, loss of livestock to grizzly predation, and reduced tourism as factors in her decision. Although Norton planned to seek additional public comment before making a final decision, supporters feared that the proposal was dead. Environmental groups and their allies in the scientific community called Norton's actions a significant setback for grizzly recovery as well as for the cooperative approach to endangered-species management.

Sources:

Devlin, Sherry. 2001. "Norton Snubs Grizzlies." *High Country News,* July 30.

Mattson, David J., et al. 1996. "Designing and Managing Protected Areas for Grizzlies: How Much Is Enough?" In R. Gerald Wright, ed., *National Parks and Protected Areas: Their Role in Environmental Protection.* Cambridge, MA: Blackwell.

Peacock, Doug. 1997. "Making the West Safe for Grizzlies." *Audubon* 99 (November–December).

Rembert, Tracey C., and Jim Motavalli. 1998. "Troubled Homecoming: Through Reintroduction Programs, Predators Are Returning to the Wild, Challenging Our Expectations and Fears." *E: The Environmental Magazine* 9 (March–April).

U.S. Fish and Wildlife Service. 1997. *Grizzly Bear Recovery Plan.* Missoula, MT: USFS.

The Endangered Species Act

In the United States, the principal law utilized to protect threatened species is the Endangered Species Act. Enacted in 1973, this law remains one of the most vital pieces of conservation legislation in place around the world. It extends protection not only to endangered and threatened species but also to their habitats ("endangered" species are those in imminent danger of extinction throughout all or a significant portion of their range, while "threatened" species are those judged likely to become endangered), with the ultimate hope of nourishing the species to the point at which they no longer require federal protection.

Since its enactment, the ESA has also become one of the nation's most controversial laws. Environmental groups, scientists, and other proconservation constituencies praise the Endangered Species Act as a "formal testament to U.S. society's concern for its living inheritance" (Stein, "A Fragile

Cornucopia," 2001), and it is regarded in many circles as the country's best and last line of defense in ensuring the preservation of America's rich heritage of biological diversity. But as one observer noted, "When it became clear how broad were the ramifications of the listing of a species—residential, commercial, and agricultural development could be stymied, forests could not be cleared, roads and dams could not be built—there was great reluctance by various vested interests to include new species" (Middleton and Liittschwager, *Witness,* 1994).

Indeed, the Endangered Species Act is strongly opposed by the timber industry and other extractive industries, which object to restrictions on activities on public land where endangered or threatened species reside. Many Americans also see the act as an unreasonable infringement on private property rights. The law prevents private landowners from carrying out any actions that would result in the death of listed fauna (endangered plant species enjoy no such protection on private land). "The ESA epitomizes the classic quandary of diffuse social benefits and concentrated private costs," observed one analysis.

> About half of the listed endangered species have 80 percent of their habitat on private land, and many landowners complain that the costs of complying with the ESA are too great. . . .Some landowners argue that if society asks landowners to supply a public good on private land, society should fairly compensate those affected. They contend the ESA has and will unfairly constrain their freedom to protect or enhance their investment. They are upset because no compensation has been forthcoming for what they perceive as a "taking" of their land, that is, the incurred impact from managing private land in ways compatible with the ESA. (Smith, "Protecting Species on Private Land," in Shogren and Tschirhart, *Protecting Endangered Species in the United States,* 2001)

Unhappiness with various aspects of the act has prompted repeated attempts to modify the law. Some constituencies simply want to suspend the law entirely, or weaken it so that it no longer poses a significant hurdle for industries operating on public land or private landowners wishing to develop their holdings. Other people believe that the law reflects a worthwhile goal but is too restrictive to business and private landowners as currently constituted. And still other parties believe that the ESA could be modified to address perceived shortcomings in implementation, but that the end result of such modifications should be *increased* protection for imperiled species and their habitats. Indeed, America's environmental community insists that modifications to the ESA should be made only after extensive study of the potential consequences for America's wildlife. "The tricky part about modifying the ESA is that its uncompromising qualities are precisely what made it a catalyst for change. There are no compromises about extinction itself. It is a one-way passage into nothingness. Once gone, a particular organism, with its unique chemistry and code of genetic instructions for how to live on the planet, whatever splendor of form and behavior it might have offered, will be gone forever" (Chadwick and Sartore, *The Company We Keep*, 1996). These differing perspectives have created a political deadlock over the act. Since 1992 the Endangered Species Act has been temporarily funded on an annual basis because neither opponents nor supporters of the law have been able to generate enough political momentum to either gut it or further strengthen it.

In the whirlwind of debate surrounding the merits of the ESA, much has been made of the law's track record over the past three decades. When the act first took effect in 1973, 109 species were on the original list. By the end of 2000, the number of protected species had grown to 1,244. Many of the species listings—including high-profile species such as the spotted owl and the grizzly bear of the Greater Yellowstone region—have been the result of citizen lawsuits (see sidebar on page 36). In 2001 the Bush administration tried to halt such maneuvers, calling for a suspension of funding for Fish and Wildlife Service programs protecting endangered species and associated habitats if their listing came about because of citizen lawsuits (the USFWS is the agency responsible for nurturing endangered species back to healthy population levels). But that effort, which environmental groups claimed would hinder the public's ability to hold the government responsible for enforcing the ESA, died in Congress.

Some critics of the ESA program contend that the expanding size of the endangered list indicates that use of the law has spiraled out of control. Another common complaint is that environmental organizations focus on gaining ESA protection for species with extensive ranges or habitat requirements as a way of keeping large tracts of land free of logging, energy exploration, and other development activities. The ESA has also been criticized for failing at its most basic goal: the recovery of species to the point that ESA protection is no longer necessary. Indeed, only eleven species had been delisted because of recovery as of May 2001, whereas seven species had actually become extinct since being added to the endangered species list. Statistics compiled by the USFWS indicate that only about 10 percent of endangered or threatened species receiving formal ESA protection have seen significant improvement in their status.

Defenders of the Endangered Species Act, however, argue that a more accurate assessment of the act's value can be gained if one examines the number of species that have seen their population levels hold steady or improve after listing (approximately 40 percent, according to the USFWS). Indeed, advocates state that numerous species would have vanished entirely from the U.S. landscape without ESA protection. Moreover, population trends for species that have been listed under the ESA for longer periods of time indicate greater levels of success. Of the 108 U.S. species listed between 1968 and 1973, 58 percent were stable or improving by 1996 (U.S. Fish and Wildlife Service, *Report to Congress,* 1996; Beissinger and Perrine, "Extinction, Recovery, and the Endangered Species Act," in Shogren and Tschirhart, *Protecting Endangered Species in the United States,* 2001).

Some observers also cite environmental groups as a factor in the low number of delistings. They charge that some organizations are so committed to permanent protection of imperiled species—and all individuals therein—that they force the DOI to carry recovered species on the list or risk expensive litigation. Indeed, many scientists and environmentalists are openly skeptical that states or federal agencies such as the U.S. Forest Service are able or willing to adequately safeguard recovered species and their habitat if they lose formal ESA protection. But former interior secretary Bruce Babbit contends that keeping recovered species listed is a counterproductive strategy that strains the limited resources of the DOI and its member agencies and strays from the act's basic mandate: "Perpetual protection is not the goal; seeing species reach the point that they can survive in the wild, on their own, is" (Williams, "Living with Wolves," 2000).

Other factors that have hindered efforts to restore endangered species to healthy population levels include spotty monitoring of wildlife population trends and inadequate funding of recovery initiatives, especially for little-known species. In 1995, fifty-three species on the ESA list received less than $1,000 each for research and recovery activities, while ten species received more than half of the total allocation of ESA funds (Baker, "Spending on the ESA," 1999). Continued hostility from private landowners is also a serious issue. "Many landowners . . . are capable of aiding in the recovery of endangered species by creating or restoring habitats on their land, but are unwilling to do so. Their unwillingness stems from a fear that if they take actions that attract endangered species to their property or increase the populations of endangered species that are already there, their 'reward' for doing so will be more regulatory restrictions on the use of that property. In its most extreme manifestations, this fear has prompted some landowners to destroy unoccupied habitat before the endangered animals could find it" (Wilcove, *The Condor's Shadow,* 1999).

In recent years, several efforts have been initiated to address this problem. In 1998, for example, the Department of the Interior introduced a "No Surprises" policy, in which private landowners who agree to restore or enhance the habitats of endangered species on their property are assured that there will be no further costs or restrictions on the use of the property to benefit the endangered species, except by mutual consent. This policy has proven popular in states where it has been offered, but it has been criticized by conservationists for providing inadequate safeguards in the event of changing habitat conditions. Other voluntary agreements available to private landowners include "Safe Harbor" agreements and Candidate Conservation Agreements, both of which provide incentives for landholders to conserve critical habitat.

Finally, advocates of the ESA are convinced that the act would be better able to restore depleted species if endangered species did not have to negotiate so many obstacles prior to listing.

> Once a candidate [species] has been proposed for listing, the process of evaluation, overseen by the USFWS, is very methodical and is based on such criteria as the magnitude of the threat and the species' taxonomic distinctness. Nevertheless, to become a candidate for listing a species must often have the focused attention of a group of dedicated biologists willing to complete reams of forms full of meticulously gathered scientific data. And, once listed, if a species is to receive sufficient funding for its habitat to be adequately preserved, it must have a certain amount of political clout, and it helps a lot to have some popular appeal. . . .Only when a species is facing extinction does it come within the auspices of the act, and by then it is already late, in some cases too late. Some species go extinct even before they are listed. (Middleton and Liittschwager, *Witness,* 1994)

Habitat Loss Blamed for Canada's Growing Number of Imperiled Species

The second-largest country in the world, Canada contains a wealth of diverse habitats that support a tremendous array of flora and fauna. For instance, the country is home to about 20 percent of the world's Arctic land areas and 10 percent of the globe's total forest area, including 35 percent of the world's boreal forest and 20 percent of its temperate rain forest. It also houses one-fourth of the world's wetlands, and more than 7 percent of its total surface area is covered by rivers and lakes burgeoning with aquatic species. All told,

Canada's vast landscape includes more than 20 major habitat/ecosystem types and over 300 regional habitats/ecosystems, with most of the land-based habitats in temperate forested areas or Arctic regions (Environment Canada, *The State of Canada's Environment 1996*; Gauthier and Wiken, "Avoiding the Endangerment of Species," in Beazley and Boardman, *Politics of the Wild*, 2001). But while many of these regions remain largely unmarked by human activity, numerous other critical habitats, feeding grounds, and migratory routes have been altered by logging, energy exploration, agriculture, urbanization, and air and water pollution.

Pollution is a particularly insidious form of habitat degradation, fundamentally impacting fragile ecosystems in myriad ways, some of which are invisible to the naked eye. The damage wreaked on Canada's forests by acid rain, for example, may be plain to see, but other species—such as freshwater fish and other aquatic species—have been buffeted by less visible forms of pollution. "Crustaceans, molluscs, frogs, salamanders, and fish in our increasingly acidified, over-fertilized, and pesticide-laden ditches, creeks, lakes, and rivers are disappearing (and sometimes developing gross deformities) over large sections of southern Canada. The federal government approved farm pesticides that cause debilitating deformities in frogs" (Mosquin, "Status of and Trends in Canadian Biodiversity," in Bocking, *Biodiversity in Canada*, 2000).

Some of Canada's flora and fauna have been able to adapt to these changes, maintaining stable populations despite increased fragmentation and modification of wilderness areas. A smaller number have actually thrived in their altered environments, taking advantage of beneficial side-effects of development activity (such as ready availability of refuse to supplement their diets). Many other species, however, are laboring to maintain viable populations as essential habitat is infiltrated to accommodate new roads, subdivisions, mining and drilling operations, and other manifestations of Canada's steadily expanding population and economy. For example, wetlands have been reduced by as much as 90 percent in some settled areas of Canada, primarily the result of draining for agricultural use (Environment Canada, *The State of Canada's Environment 1996*), and in 1996, World Wildlife Fund Canada estimated that the country was losing wilderness to development at a rate of more than one acre every fifteen seconds. "In Canada, as elsewhere, the finite land base and the surrounding sea are increasingly subject to competing forces. Land is continually and incrementally being converted from natural ecosystems and habitats to areas dominated by human activities such as agriculture, urbanization, and various forms of industrialization. Forests are being harvested at unprecedented and often unsustainable rates, and increasingly remote areas are being subject to mineral and energy exploration and development. Rising human populations and expectations exacerbate this

Table 2.2 Canadian Forest-Dwelling Species at Risk, 1999

Categories	*Mammals*	*Birds*	*Plants*	*Reptiles*	*Total*
Endangered	3	4	14	1	22
Threatened	2	4	11	3	20
Vulnerable	13	9	14	6	42
Total	*18*	*17*	*39*	*10*	*84*

SOURCE: Canadian Forest Service. 1999. *The State of Canada's Forests: 1998–1999 Innovation.* Ottawa: Natural Resources Canada.

situation. These multiple pressures on habitats are having direct and significant effects on species" (Beazley and Boardman, *Politics of the Wild,* 2001).

Large carnivores are particularly affected by habitat fragmentation, because they require large expanses of territory to survive. "Across Canada and especially in the south, large carnivores are disappearing or are absent, spinning natural predator-prey relationships and cycles out of control. Even though large carnivores are protected within national parks, these predators are threatened by stresses such as human use and development inside parks, as well as hunting, land development, and other pressures that occur outside park boundaries. From Ontario eastward, wolves are gone from all national parks except Pukaskwa and La Mauricie. In the west, wolves have been extirpated from Elk Island and Grasslands national parks. In several national parks—including Riding Mountain, La Mauricie, Banff, and Waterton—wolf populations are low and struggling" (Panel on the Ecological Integrity of Canada's National Parks, *Unimpaired for Future Generations?* 2000).

The task of finding an appropriate balance between economic growth and habitat conservation confronts all major regions of Canada, but the challenge is particularly acute in the nation's more heavily populated south. As one analysis observed, "[T]he more imminent threats to endangered species are somewhat limited to smaller and southern portions of Canada, such as the Prairie and Mixed-wood ecozones. While restricted in size, these areas stand out as serious triggers or signals and, strikingly, impinge on some of the more productive and diverse habitats in the country. Thus, the problem of endangered species and degraded habitats has wide implications for all of Canada" (Gauthier and Wiken, "Avoiding the Endangerment of Species," in Beazley and Boardman, *Politics of the Wild,* 2001).

By the close of the twentieth century, Canada had already lost a number of creatures to extinction, including the great auk, the Dawson caribou, and the blue pike. These and other animals now vanished from the Canadian landscape fell victim to the same combination of factors—habitat loss and alteration, overhunting, invasive species, pollution—that threaten today's imperiled species. According to a 2000 study by the Committee on the Status of Endangered Wildlife in Canada (COSEWIC), 353 species of flora and fauna in Canada have been classified as extinct (12 species), extirpated (15), endangered (102), threatened (71), or vulnerable (153). The COSEWIC imperiled species list includes vascular plants (33 percent), fish (21 percent), mammals (16 percent), birds (15 percent), reptiles (6 percent), amphibians (4 percent), and invertebrates (4 percent), though the study acknowledges that vertebrate animals are over-represented because they are monitored most closely (Committee on the Status of Endangered Wildlife in Canada, *Canadian Species at Risk,* 2000).

The study also confirmed earlier governmental and nongovernmental organization reports indicating that the highest frequency of species at risk are in southern Ontario and Quebec, where most wooded plains and other natural areas have been converted to agricultural fields, commercial and residential development, and other land uses. In fact, this region is home to about 30 percent of the species on the COSEWIC list, even though it constitutes only 2 percent of Canada's total land area (ibid.).

The task of protecting Canada's endangered animals and plants is a daunting one, given the array of economic and philosophic forces calling for continued incursions into vital habitat areas. But Canada has taken a number of steps in recent years to safeguard at-risk ecosystems. The number and size of protected wilderness areas in Canada has roughly doubled since the 1970s, with about 8 percent of the nation's land mass—800,000 square kilometers—under some measure of protection (only half of this area is not subject to resource extraction activities). Even southern Canada—much of which has been covered with a quilt of metropolitan areas, towns, and agricultural operations, all connected by networks of roads, highways, and railroads—has made strides in setting aside natural areas in recent years. This has been accomplished in part because federal and provincial authorities have made habitat preservation more attractive to private landowners, who have extensive holdings in southern Canada. Since the mid-1990s, for example, private landholders—both individuals and corporations—have received tax breaks in exchange for their donation of conservation easements to participating environmental organizations.

Canada's large national park system has also been a potent weapon in protecting at-risk species. Many of the parks serve as vital wildlife sanctuaries, and some have even been utilized to reintroduce species to ranges they once inhabited. In addition, officials are increasingly taking the needs of endangered species into account when establishing the parameters of new protected areas. For example, the boundaries of a proposed new national park in the Torngat Mountains of northern Labrador were altered to protect the breeding ranges of the Harlequin duck, peregrine falcon, and other species at risk. But in some instances, such considerations remain secondary. A new park established in the Interlake region of Manitoba, for instance, excludes the region's most important woodland caribou habitat because of its potential development value (Dearden, "Endangered Species and Terrestrial Protected Areas," in Beazley and Boardman, *Politics of the Wild,* 2001).

Most provinces have also passed laws to protect wildlife (endangered or otherwise), and the federal government, though it has limited jurisdiction over endangered species, has made important contributions as well. The Canadian Wildlife Service, for instance, manages migratory waterfowl and other species that cross international boundaries. Canada has also taken a visible role in the international arena, participating in CITES (the Convention on International Trade in Endangered Species), the UN Convention on Biological Diversity (Canada was the first industrialized nation to ratify the agreement), and other global initiatives concerned with endangered species.

Nonetheless, conservation organizations, scientists, and other constituencies concerned about the state of biodiversity in Canada continue to urge passage of a federal endangered species act similar to the one in place in the United States. They contend that existing legislation in place at the provincial and federal levels is insufficient to halt the slow but steady decline in Canada's animal and plant populations. For example, since 1988 the Canadian Wildlife Service's RENEW (Recovery of Nationally Endangered Wildlife) program, which is responsible for preparing recovery plans for Canada's endangered species, has approved recovery plans for only nineteen species, about 5 percent of the total species on the COSEWIC list (Mosquin, "Status of and Trends in Canadian Biodiversity," in Bocking, *Biodiversity in Canada,* 2000).

As of 2001, however, attempts to pass national endangered species legislation have fallen short. In 1996 the Canadian Endangered Species Protection Act (CESPA—Bill C-65) was introduced, but it foundered under criticism from environmentalists who wanted greater protection for species and their habitats, private landowners and industries who feared greater regulation of their activities, and provinces and First Nations groups who disliked the bill's increased allocation of power to the federal government. Four years later the Species at Risk Act (SARA—Bill C-33) was introduced, but it was abandoned when elections were called for October 2000 (Beazley and Boardman, *Politics of the Wild,* 2001).

Sources:

Abramovitz, Janet N. 1996. *Imperiled Waters, Impoverished Future: The Decline of Freshwater Ecosystems.* Washington, DC: WorldWatch Institute.

Baker, Beth. 1999. "Spending on the ESA—Too Much or Not Enough?" *Bioscience* 49.

Barker, Rocky. 1993. *Saving All the Parts: Reconciling Economics and the Endangered Species Act.* Washington, DC: Island.

Beazley, Karen, and Robert Boardman, eds. 2001. *Politics of the Wild: Canada and Endangered Species.* Don Mills, Oxford University Press.

Bocking, Stephen, ed. 2000. *Biodiversity in Canada: Ecology, Ideas, and Action.* Peterborough, ON: Broadview.

Bright, Chris. 1999. *Life out of Bounds: Bio-Invasions in a Borderless World.* London: Earthscan.

Bryant, Dirk, D. Nielson, and L. Tangley. 1997. *The Last Frontier Forests: Ecosystems and Economies on the Edge.* Washington, DC: World Resources Institute.

Campbell, Faith Thompson, and Scott E. Schlarbaum. 1994. *Fading Forests: North American Trees and the Threat of Exotic Pests.* New York: Natural Resources Defense Council.

Canadian Wildlife Service. 1997. *Endangered Species in Canada.* Ottawa: Environment Canada.

Chadwick, Douglas H., and Joel Sartore. 1996. *The Company We Keep: America's Endangered Species.* Washington, DC: National Geographic Society.

Christen, Kris. 2001. "Why Biodiversity Matters." *OECD Observer* (summer).

Cohen, A. N., and J. T. Carlton. 1998. "Accelerating Invasion Rate in a Highly Invaded Estuary." *Science* 279.

Commission for Environmental Cooperation (CEC). 1999. *On Track? Sustainability and the State of the North American Environment.* Montreal: CEC.

Committee on the Status of Endangered Wildlife in Canada (COSEWIC). 2000. *Canadian Species at Risk.* Ottawa: COSEWIC.

Department of the Interior, National Biological Service. 2001. *Federal List of Endangered and Threatened Wildlife and Plants.* Washington, DC: DOI.

DiSilvestro, Roger L. 1993. *Reclaiming the Last Wild Places: A New Agenda for Biodiversity.* New York: John Wiley.

Environment Canada. 1996. *The State of Canada's Environment 1996.* Ottawa: Environment Canada.

———. 1998. *Conserving Wildlife Diversity: Implementing the Canadian Biodiversity Strategy.* Ottawa: Environment Canada.

Global Forest Watch. 2000. *Canada's Forests at a Crossroads: An Assessment in the Year 2000.* Washington, DC: World Resources Institute.

Mac, M. J., et al. 1998. *Status and Trends of the Nation's Biological Resources.* 2 vols. Reston, VA: U.S. Geological Survey.

Matthiessen, Peter. 1987. *Wildlife in America.* New York: Viking Penguin, Elisabeth Sifton Books.

Middleton, Susan, and David Liittschwager. 1994. *Witness: Endangered Species of North America.* San Francisco: Chronicle.

Mosquin, Ted, Peter G. Whiting, and Don E. McAllister. 1995. *Canada's Biodiversity: The Variety of Life, Its Status, Economic Benefits, Conservation Costs, and Unmet Needs.* Ottawa: Canadian Museum of Nature.

Noss, Reed. 1987. "Protecting Natural Areas in Fragmented Landscapes." *Natural Areas Journal* 7, no. 2.

O'Brien, Bob R. 1999. *Our National Parks and the Search for Sustainability.* Austin: University of Texas Press.

Panel on the Ecological Integrity of Canada's National Parks. 2000. *"Unimpaired for Future Generations?" Conserving Ecological Integrity with Canada's National Parks.* 2 vols. Ottawa: Minister of Public Works and Government Services.

Pimental, David, et al. 1999. "Environmental and Economic Costs Associated with Non-indigenous Species in the United States." Paper presented at the American Association for the Advancement of Science, Anaheim, California, January.

Reid, Walter V. 2001. "Biodiversity, Ecosystem Change, and International Development." *Environment* 43 (April).

Ricciardi, Anthony, and Joseph Rasmussen. 1999. "Extinction Rates for North American Freshwater Animals." *Conservation Biology* (October).

Ross, J. P., et al. 1989. *The Status of Kemp's Ridley.* Washington, DC: Center for Marine Conservation.

Samson, F. B., ed. 1996. *Prairie Conservation: Preserving North America's Most Endangered Ecosystem.* Washington, DC: Island.

Shogren, Jason F., and John Tschirhart, eds. 2001. *Protecting Endangered Species in the United States: Biological Needs, Political Realities, Economic Choices.* Cambridge: Cambridge University Press.

Smith, Robert J., and M. Danielle Smith. 1997. "Endangered Species Protection: Lessons Canada Should Learn from the U.S. Endangered Species Act." *Property Rights Journal* 1, no. 1.

Stein, Bruce A. 2001. "A Fragile Cornucopia." *Environment* 43 (September).

Stein, Bruce A., Lynn S. Kutner, and Jonathan S. Adams, eds. 2000. *Precious Heritage: The Status of Biodiversity in the United States.* New York: Oxford University Press.

Stolzenburg, William. 2000. "America the Bountiful." *Nature Conservancy* 50 (May–June).

UN Environment Programme. 1999. *Global Environmental Outlook 2000.* London: Earthscan.

U.S. Congress, Office of Technology Assessment. 1993. *Harmful Nonindigenous Species in the United States.* Washington, DC: OTA.

U.S. Department of the Interior. 1995. *Our Living Resources: A Report to the Nation on the Distribution, Abundance, and Health of U.S. Plants, Animals, and Ecosystems.* Washington, DC: Department of the Interior, National Biological Service.

U.S. Fish and Wildlife Service. 1996. *Report to Congress on the Recovery Program for Threatened and Endangered Species.* Washington, DC: USFWS.

Wilcove, David S. 1999. *The Condor's Shadow: The Loss and Recovery of Wildlife in America.* New York: W. H. Freeman.

Williams, Ted. 1998. "Back from the Brink." *Audubon* 100 (November–December).

———. 2000. "Living with Wolves." *Audubon* 102 (November–December).

World Conservation Monitoring Centre (WCMC) Species Database. 1999. Cambridge, UK: WCMC, December.

Parks, Preserves, and Protected Areas

The North American continent has perhaps the greatest system of protected areas on the planet, as measured in terms of size, scenic splendor, and ecological wealth. Both the United States and Canada have set aside vast areas of wilderness and other biologically rich landscapes for protection over the years, including world-famous national parks such as Wyoming's Yellowstone National Park, Arizona's Grand Canyon National Park, and the four linked national parks that straddle Alberta and British Columbia in Canada's Rocky Mountain range (Yoho, Jasper, Banff, and Kootenay national parks). These national parks, wilderness areas, and other protected lands are now recognized as critical components in the long-term protection of endangered species and other flora and fauna.

But the park systems of both nations—as well as many other public lands in Canada and the United States that are supposed to be managed in a manner that preserves their ecological integrity—are under significant stress from an array of internal and external forces, from levels of visitation that overwhelm park resources to destructive land use practices immediately outside the boundaries of protected areas. In 2000 the Panel on the Ecological Integrity of Canada's National Parks reported findings about the state of Canada's park system that are applicable to the U.S. system as well: "To many Canadians, national parks contain seemingly endless forests, expanses of tundra, great rivers and lakes, and protected lands that reach beyond the horizon. This bountiful majesty is often misleading, disguising serious problems beneath a beautiful facade of soaring mountains, shimmering lakes, sparkling glaciers, and roaring surf" (Panel on the Ecological Integrity of Canada's National Parks, *Unimpaired for Future Generations?* 2000).

Table 3.1 North America's Protected Areas by IUCN Category

Country	*Total Land Area (Sq.km)*	*Ia/Ib Parks*			*II Parks*			*III Parks*			*IV Parks*			*V Parks*			*VI Parks*			*Total Parks*		
		No.	*Area (Sq. km)*	*% of Land Area*	*No.*	*Area (Sq. km)*	*% of Land Area*	*No.*	*Area (Sq. km)*	*% of Land Area*	*No.*	*Area (Sq. km)*	*% of Land Area*	*No.*	*Area (Sq. km)*	*% Land Area*	*No.*	*Area (Sq. km)*	*% of Land Area*	*No.*	*Area (Sq. km)*	*% of Land Area*
Canada	9,922,385	630	32,964	0.33	1,046	400,233	4.03	70	217	0.00	563	398,592	4.02	772	93,056	0.94	143	28,041	0.28	3,224	953,103	9.61
United States	9,372,614	644	391,043	4.17	205	253,754	2.71	265	58,069	0.62	650	402,930	4.30	1,294	122,322	1.31	275	760,336	8.11	3,333	1,988,444	21.22

SOURCE: Michael J. B. Greene and James Paine. 1997. State of the World's Protected Areas. Cambridge, UK: World Conservation Monitoring Centre.

Protected Areas in the United States

The U.S. federal government owns 655 million acres of the nearly 2.3 billion acres of land in the United States, about 29 percent of the country's total land mass. Four federal agencies administer 628 million acres—96 percent—of this public land: the U.S. Forest Service (USFS) in the Department of Agriculture; and the National Park Service (NPS), Bureau of Land Management (BLM), and U.S. Fish and Wildlife Service (USFWS), all of which are agencies of the Department of the Interior. Of these four agencies, the BLM is responsible for the greatest amount of land, though the total amount of land it manages has declined significantly since the mid-1960s (when it managed 465 million acres) as a result of transfers of federal land to the state of Alaska and Alaska's Native American tribes. The agency now manages a total of 264 million acres across the country, most of it under a multiple-use mandate that provides for energy development, timber harvesting, grazing, and motorized and nonmotorized recreational activities, in addition to nature conservation. The Forest Service administers approximately 192 million acres of forests and grasslands from Alaska to Florida. The USFWS manages 94 million acres of wildlife refuges and other lands across the country, and while oil and natural gas drilling and other development activities occur in some of these areas, the USFWS mandate is primarily concerned with habitat and species conservation. The National Park Service is responsible for the smallest amount of acreage of the four agencies—78 million acres of federal land and 6 million acres of nonfederal land—but it is the most visible of the four agencies because it is responsible for America's hugely popular national park system. This system—which includes not only national parks but also designated historic areas, monuments, battlefields, parkways, seashores, lakeshores, recreation areas, and wild and scenic rivers—consists of 379 units scattered across forty-nine states (Alaska alone contains 58 percent of the total acreage of the National Park System), four territories, and the District of Columbia (Congressional Research Service, *Federal Land Management Agencies*, 2001). Individual states also maintain state park systems and state forests of varying sizes, usually under a multiple-use mandate.

The "crown jewels" of the protected area system administered by the National Park Service are America's fifty-four national parks. Most of these parks are managed to conserve and study natural resources while simultaneously making them available for public use, with activities that harvest or remove resources generally prohibited. But the NPS also administers fifteen national park/preserves that allow sport hunting and other activities, provided that they do not jeopardize the NPS's conservation mandate. Of those preserves, ten are located in Alaska, where parkland encompasses the traditional hunting grounds of Native Americans. Notable examples include Gates of the Arctic National Park and Preserve, which sprawls across northern Alaska's Brooks Range; Wrangell–St. Elias National Preserve in Alaska, which is larger than any park in the lower forty-eight yet is itself but a part of a much larger national park; and California's Mojave National Preserve, which was designated as a preserve instead of a park in order to accommodate hunters who had objected to hunting prohibitions that would have been incorporated into a park designation.

Nearly half of all units in the National Park System are historic parks that commemorate important events and people in U.S. history. But these parks account for less than 1 percent of the total acreage under NPS care (National Park Service, *The National Parks: Index 1995*). The National Park Service is also responsible for administering a variety of national recreation areas, including national parkways such as the Blue Ridge Parkway of Virginia and North Carolina, reservoirs such as Glen Canyon National Recreation Area, national seashores such as Cape Hatteras, national lakeshores such as Michigan's Sleeping Bear Dunes, and a smattering of urban parks such as California's Golden Gate Recreation Area.

All of the above-mentioned units in the National Park System can only be established through an act of the Congress. But the other major component of the system—national monuments—can be established by presidential proclamation via the Antiquities Act of 1906. Historically, presidents have exercised this discretionary power to protect some of the most spectacular and unspoiled wilderness areas in the United States. Indeed, the monument designation has often served as a sort of incubator for national parks; Olympic, Acadia, Zion, and Grand Canyon national parks all were once national monuments.

In recent years, however, the designation of national monuments has come under renewed scrutiny. During his two terms, President Bill Clinton used his authority twenty-two times to proclaim nineteen new monuments and to expand the size of three others. With only one exception, all of these monuments were designated during his last year in office. Environmentalists and allied scientists hailed the creation of these new monuments, touting various ecological benefits associated with the preservation of the designated lands. But some opponents have characterized the large number of designations as an abuse of presidential authority and a federal "land grab" that provided little or no opportunity for public input. State and local officials and communities have charged that monument designation can limit or prohibit mineral exploration, timber development, and other development activities on federal lands, and they contend that local communities are hurt by the loss of jobs and tax revenues that accrue with these activities. The potential effect of monument designation on energy development has drawn particularly strong fire from proponents of increased domestic oil and gas production (Congressional Research Service, *National Monument Issues*, 2001).

The National Park Service, the Forest Service, the Bureau of Land Management, and the Fish and Wildlife Service are also responsible for managing lands within their purview that have been formally designated for inclusion in one of three special management categories. Examples of all three of these special categories—National Trails, National Wild and Scenic Rivers, and National Wilderness Areas—can be found in lands administered by all four agencies. The National Trails System contains four classes of trails managed to provide access to historic landmarks and natural sites. The National Wild and Scenic Rivers System contains nearly 11,300 miles of designated wild, scenic, and recreational rivers across the country. Both of these systems are notable, but the National Wilderness Preservation System is the most important of the special management categories in terms of preserving natural habitat and protecting flora and fauna.

The first units in the National Wilderness Preservation System, which was signed into law in 1964, were limited to wilderness tracts contained within national forests. Over time, however, the system was expanded to include other roadless areas over 5,000 acres in size in national parks, national wildlife refuges, and other areas of the public domain. These federally designated wilderness areas, which can be created only by an act of Congress, enjoy significant protections from development activities of any kind. No permanent facilities or new roads may be built in designated wilderness, and motorized vehicles are permitted only for search and rescue missions or other special circumstances. Scientific research is permitted in these areas, however, and some outdoor activities—including hunting, fishing, paddling, backpacking, cross-country skiing, and camping—are permitted in certain areas, albeit with certain restrictions that aim to preserve the essential wilderness character of the units. At the start of the twenty-first century, the U.S. National Wilderness Preservation System consisted of 104 million acres of protected wilderness areas.

Protected Areas in Canada

Canada had 3,083 protected areas in 1999, covering 9.1 percent of its total land area. These included 102 protected areas of at least 100,000 hectares and 20 protected areas of over 1 million hectares (Protected Areas Database, World Conservation Monitoring Centre, 1999). Nongovernmental conservation groups are a key factor in land protection efforts across much of the country, with dozens of organizations managing protected areas of significant size and ecological note. Ducks Unlimited, the Nature Conservancy of Canada, and Wildlife Habitat Canada are the leading protected area landowners of this type (World Conservation Union, *1992 Protected Areas of the World,* 1991).

Canada's individual provinces also offer protected area programs, and during the 1990s a number of them—British Columbia, Ontario, Manitoba, and Nova Scotia in particular—significantly expanded the size of their protected areas. But the philosophy of stewardship concerning protected areas varies considerably from province to province. For example, some provincial governments permit logging, trapping, hunting, and other resource extraction within provincial parks and other sites. Ontario's hugely popular Algonquin Provincial Park, for instance, accommodates commercial logging operations as well as canoeists, hikers, and campers.

This dual use philosophy reflects the fact that, historically, few of the parks and reserves that have been established and maintained by Canada's provinces were created with ecosystem preservation as their primary concern, "so the protection afforded endangered species can be quite uneven. Nonetheless, provincial parks can be large and afford valuable protection to some endangered species," observed one analysis. "Most provinces also have other forms of protective legislation that might include ecological reserves, wildlife management areas, and similar designations. Typically, such areas are small but have strong protective powers, and their location and boundaries have often been designed with ecological criteria as a main concern and endangered species an important factor. The Vancouver Island marmot, for example, is Canada's only endemic endangered mammal species, and one of the remaining colonies is protected by a provincially designated ecological reserve" (Dearden, "Endangered Species and Terrestrial Protected Areas," in Beazley and Boardman, *Politics of the Wild,* 2001).

Canada's provinces are also active participants in the Canadian Heritage Rivers program. This joint federal-provincial program was established in the 1970s in recognition of the vital role that rivers played in Canada's frontier history and their enduring importance in maintaining healthy ecosystems. It thus is primarily concerned with maintaining the natural, recreational, and cultural integrity of each river included in the program.

The two agencies primarily responsible for managing federally protected areas in Canada are Parks Canada, which is part of the Department of Canadian Heritage, and the Canadian Wildlife Service (CWS) of Environment

Canada. The latter agency establishes and manages the country's national wildlife areas and its migratory bird sanctuaries. There are more than 150 national wildlife areas scattered across Canada; regulations for these protected areas provide for year-round habitat protection and regulation of activities. Migratory bird sanctuaries, however, do not provide habitat protection, controlling activities within sanctuary boundaries only when migratory birds are actually present. Together, Canada's national wildlife areas and migratory bird sanctuaries cover nearly 12 million hectares. In addition to its administration of these protected areas, the CWS also is responsible for managing Canada's participation in the North American Waterfowl Management Plan, leasing and purchasing habitat upon which migratory waterfowl depend. Finally, the CWS buys and manages protected areas in cooperation with provinces.

Parks Canada, meanwhile, manages the country's thirty-nine national parks. As in the United States, these parks are the most beloved and important components of Canada's network of protected areas. They cover only 2.6 percent of the Canadian land mass, but contain more than 70 percent of the native terrestrial and freshwater vascular plant species and approximatley 81 percent of the vertebrate species. "This high degree of coverage is a result of the explicit systems plan of Parks Canada to establish parks in the 39 representative natural regions of the country. Almost 50 percent of the endangered vertebrate species can be found in parks, as are 57 percent of vascular plant species. The national parks have also played a critical and increasingly important role as sites for the reintroduction of species." (ibid.).

Canada's national parks currently represent twenty-five of the country's thirty-nine terrestrial natural regions, and include several of Canada's twelve World Heritage Sites, including Wood Buffalo National Park, Gros Morne National Park, and the four national parks located in the Canadian Rockies. The first of these parks—Rocky Mountain National Park, now Banff National Park—was established in 1885, but the majority (twenty) of Canada's national parks have actually been created since 1970, with others on the way. Most of these recent additions to the national park system were established as a result of land claims agreements with First Nations.

In contrast to the steady growth in the size of its national park system, the extent of Canada's marine protected areas (MPAs) remains modest. Only three National Marine Conservation Areas (Gwaii Haanas National Marine Conservation Area Reserve off British Columbia's Queen Charlotte Islands; Fathom Five National Marine Park in Georgian Bay, Ontario; and Saguenay-St. Lawrence Marine Park in Quebec) are currently in existence. But Canada's Oceans Act, which became law in 1997, contains strong provisions for the establishment of marine protected areas, and the Fisheries Act contains provisions for habitat protection that have been used to establish de facto MPAs by excluding fishing from specified areas for long periods of time.

During the 1990s, Canada embarked on a concerted effort to further develop and enhance its existing network of terrestrial protected areas. This plan originated in 1989, when the World Wildlife Fund and the Canadian Parks and Wilderness Society announced a national Endangered Spaces Campaign that aimed to chart a protected areas system that would include representatives of 486 distinct ecoregions within the country. Federal, provincial, and territorial governments all agreed to the overarching goals of the campaign, and in 1992 the Endangered Spaces goal became public policy when the Statement of Commitment to Complete Canada's Network of Protected Areas was signed by the Tri-Council of Environment, Parks, and Wildlife Ministers, the federal, provincial, and territorial ministers responsible for environment, wildlife, and parks in Canada. This statement committed Canada to complete the terrestrial protected areas network by 2000.

Subsequent efforts in this area "doubled the amount of protected land in Canada in the 1990s. Canada still ranked only thirty-sixth in the world in terms of area legally protected from industrial development, behind countries such as New Zealand, Venezuela, Guatemala, and Chile." (Panel on the Ecological Integrity of Canada's National Parks, *Unimpaired for Future Generations?* 2000). Indeed, according to World Wildlife Fund Canada, although the initiative helped create 1,000 new protected areas, only 27 percent of Canada's 486 terrestrial ecoregions identified by the organization had representative protected areas by the close of the ten-year campaign. The remaining ecoregions either had levels of protection that did not meet basic criteria for representation of habitat (30 percent) or remained without protection (43 percent).

Protecting Parks from External Threats

Heavy levels of visitation, destructive industrial and recreational activities within park boundaries, and growing maintenance backlogs constitute significant threats to the continued health and vitality of many of North America's protected areas. But in addition to these internal management issues, the ecological integrity of numerous parks and preserves are at risk from a host of external threats, including logging, drilling, mining, farming, and residential and commercial development. North America's protected areas do not exist in isolation from the larger world around them. Activities outside park boundaries can—and do—have a significant impact on the flora and fauna contained within parks and refuges. "External threats are now recognized as the most serious causes of loss of ecological integrity in most protected areas," according to one analysis.

> The proximity to the protected area, the nature of the threat, and its intensity vary widely. At the local scale, for example, land-use practices just outside the boundary can have a negative impact on species inside the protected area. The ability of park management authorities to influence such impacts varies. In 1996, for example, concern over declining wolf populations led to a request by Riding Mountain National Park to Manitoba's Department of Natural Resources to remove wolves from the list of species that could be hunted around the park. As a result, wolf hunting was dropped from 10 to 3 months of the year, with also a reduction in wolf trapping. Other impacts are much less amenable to change at the local level. The pollutants that threaten the health of the endangered beluga whales at Saguenay National Park in Quebec originate in industrial areas many kilometers away. (Dearden, "Endangered Species and Terrestrial Protected Areas," in Beazley and Boardman, *Politics of the Wild,* 2001)

Indeed, agencies responsible for maintaining protected areas generally have little power to stem the infiltration of air and water pollution generated outside park boundaries. As a result, air pollution originating miles from protected area boundaries has compromised the beauty and health of numerous parks and refuges in both countries. Scenic vistas in parks such as Grand Canyon National Park and Great Smoky Mountains National Park have become clouded by smog generated hundreds of miles away, while acid rain has caused extensive damage in Ontario's Killarney Provincial Park and other protected areas in the east. Some protected areas are even bedeviled by multiple types of airborne pollution. Acadia National Park in Maine, for instance, is grappling not only with the effects of acid rain on its forests but also with high levels of smog, which have forced park officials to issue health advisories warning park visitors to avoid bicycling, hiking, and other strenuous activities (Natural Resources Defense Council and National Trust for Historic Preservation, *Reclaiming Our Heritage,* 1997).

Some parks and refuges have also had the quality of their waterways compromised by pollution generated outside protected area boundaries. Rivers, lakes, wetlands, and coastal waters contained within protected areas all can be damaged by water pollution generated upstream by agricultural operations, industrial activities, and population centers. Parks and preserves located in

Figure 3.1 Yellowstone to Yukon: Protected Areas

**The Yellowstone-to-Yukon Initiative:
A Bold Plan for Landscape-Based Conservation**

Traditional approaches to preserving North American biodiversity have centered around protecting individual species or parcels of wilderness habitat. In recent years, however, a growing number of biologists have recognized the need to expand the focus of such efforts to include entire bioregions or landscapes. These biologists have noted that the current system of parks and preserves in the United States and Canada—in which protected wilderness areas are often surrounded by areas of rapidly increasing human activity—is insufficient to accommodate the habitat needs of wildlife, particularly large, wide-ranging mammals such as bears, wolves, and caribou. They stress that human activities also must be minimized in surrounding areas in order to conserve biodiversity.

"Parks are viewed as being embedded within the greater ecosystem and the regional landscape; so much so, that it is now increasingly accepted among ecologists that keeping the wild alive depends more on human activities in the surrounding matrix than in the parks and protected areas themselves," Rick Searle wrote in *Phantom Parks: The Struggle to Save Canada's National Parks*. "As a consequence, fostering compatible land uses adjacent to and between protected areas is viewed as critical to their success."

Known as landscape-based conservation, this new way of thinking is based in part upon Harvard University scientist and author E. O. Wilson's research on island biogeography. In studies of tropical islands, Wilson found that the smaller and more isolated an island, the fewer individual members of various species it would support. Furthermore, he found that these individuals tended to be more susceptible to disease, natural disturbances, and human influence than members of larger, genetically diverse populations.

Proponents of landscape-based conservation compare North America's parks and preserves to Wilson's tropical islands, claiming that the small size and relative isolation of most protected areas serve to limit biodiversity. This situation poses a significant risk for large carnivores, which generally require extensive ranges for feeding and mating. "Most bear biologists agree that the continued existence of grizzlies on these islands of habitat is precarious at best," Jeff Gailus wrote in *Alternatives Journal* (fall 2001). "Continued development inside protected areas and industrial-scale activities—including urban sprawl, road-building, off-highway vehicle use, and unsustainable methods of timber harvesting, farming, ranching, and mining—on their borders [prevent] individuals from dispersing, [limit] the diversity in the gene pool, and [kill]

(continues)

enough animals every year to make population stability impossible." Landscape-based conservation attempts to address this problem by linking protected areas with "wildlife corridors" in order to maintain biological connectivity throughout an entire region.

Perhaps the most prominent landscape-based conservation proposal in North America is the Yellowstone-to-Yukon Conservation Initiative (Y2Y). Founded in 1997 by environmental lawyer Harvey Locke, Y2Y proposes to create a single vast wildlife corridor in the West by connecting a chain of protected areas that begins with Yellowstone National Park in Wyoming and runs 3,200 kilometers northward along the Rocky Mountains into the Mackenzie Mountains in Canada's Yukon territory. The 1.2 million-square-kilometer area targeted by the Y2Y initiative stretches across two Canadian territories, two Canadian provinces, five U.S. states, and the lands of thirty-one indigenous peoples. The area provides habitat for 118 species of fish and breeding grounds for 275 species of birds. Far from unspoiled, however, it is also home to 2 million people, 420,000 miles of road, and 51,000 oil and gas wells (Finkel, "From Yellowstone to Yukon," 1999).

Although Y2Y was still in its planning stages as of 2002, the initiative had gained a broad base of support from scientists, environmental groups, and some outdoor recreation enthusiasts. In fact, Y2Y boasts more than 200 supporting organizations and a million-dollar budget. Supporters recognize that economic and political realities make it impossible to create wildlife corridors simply by establishing new protected areas or expanding existing ones. Instead, the initiative proposes to find a way to manage the entire landscape so that humans and nature can coexist. Some of the potential means toward that end include creating conservation easements on private property and revising management plans for multiuse public lands. The ultimate goal is to create ecologically intact corridors to facilitate migration and genetic interchange between isolated populations of animals. A related goal is to surround the corridors and the existing protected areas with "buffer zones" in which human activities are limited to uses compatible with the habitat needs of animals.

Y2Y also faces opposition, however, particularly among industries and communities that depend on resource extraction for their economic livelihood. For example, the Forest Alliance of British Columbia published a report claiming that Y2Y, if successfully implemented, would cause the loss of 80,000 jobs in British Columbia alone. The conservative magazine *British Columbia Report* called Y2Y "a bid to eradicate humanity from much of BC" (ibid.).

(continues)

Y2Y supporters admit that the initiative would require scaling back human activity in many places, and even eliminating human presence from a few areas in order to restore critical habitat. But they claim that protecting biodiversity entails economic benefits as well as costs, and they express a desire to involve representatives of competing interests in the process. "We have maintained all along that we are very aware, and very concerned, about the needs of the people that reside in the region," Y2Y executive director Jim Pissot told Gailus. "But history has shown us over and over again that the boom-and-bust nature of resource-based economies is not always the best way to meet the needs of natural or human communities. We're simply inviting people to join us to find a better way" (Gailus, "Yellowstone to Yukon," 2001).

Landscape-based conservation requires people to think about their relationship with nature in new and different terms. Calling Y2Y "a great societal challenge," Locke admitted that one of the greatest obstacles facing the initiative is the traditional conservation mind set, which has focused on protecting individual species within the artificial boundaries of national parks. "One of the difficulties we face in articulating this program is that we're thinking in much longer terms than people are used to," World Wildlife Fund Canada biologist Paul Paquet told Finkel. "We're speaking of 500-year protection plans, 1,000-year plans. People have trouble conceiving of those terms, especially politicians" (Finkel, "From Yellowstone to Yukon," 1999).

Sources:

Berger, Carol. 1997. "Fur May Fly over Plan to Give Big Mammals Room to Roam." *Christian Science Monitor,* October 7.

Finkel, Michael. 1999. "From Yellowstone to Yukon." *Audubon* 101 (July).

Foreman, Dave, ed. 1992. "The Wildlands Project: Plotting a North American Wilderness Recovery Strategy. *Wild Earth.*

Gailus, Jeff. 2001. "Yellowstone to Yukon." *Alternatives Journal* 27 (fall).

Harris, Larry D., et al. 1996. "The Role of Networks and Corridors in Enhancing the Value and Protection of Parks and Equivalent Areas." In R. Gerald Wright, ed., *National Parks and Protected Areas: Their Role in Environmental Protection.* Cambridge, MA: Blackwell.

Hudson, W., ed. 1991. *Landscape Linkages and Biodiversity.* Washington, DC: Island.

Schneider, Howard. 1997. "Conservationists Take Stock of the Land: Group Envisions Protected Area from Yellowstone to Yukon." *Washington Post,* October 27.

Searle, Rick. 2000. *Phantom Parks: The Struggle to Save Canada's National Parks.* Toronto: Key Porter.

mountainous areas are above most pollution sources and usually escape severe water contamination, thus sparing many headwaters areas. Protected areas located downstream of pollution sources, however, are much more vulnerable. For example, the ecological integrity of Everglades National Park in southern Florida has been heavily compromised by waste generated by upstream communities, fertilizers, and other pollutants issuing from sugar plantations and agricultural operations, as well as an assortment of industrial activities that deposit chemicals in the ecosystem. Widespread artificial manipulation of hydrological resources that have long been the lifeblood of the Everglades further adds to the plight of the so-called River of Grass.

But while air- and waterborne pollutants can have severe consequences for affected protected areas, some conservationists and scientists contend that the greatest external threat facing North America's parks and refuges are destructive or incompatible land use practices in areas immediately adjacent to or between protected areas. "The notion that natural areas can be protected simply by putting a fence around them is giving way to the realization that natural areas can be protected only in the context of a protected landscape. That is, the core natural area must be surrounded by landscape units that have minimal use and buffer the natural area from damage due to inappropriate or illegal uses" (Halvorson, "Changes in Landscape Values and Expectations," in Wright, ed., *National Parks and Protected Areas,* 1996).

Certainly, the challenge of protecting parks, refuges, and preserves from environmentally destructive land uses in adjacent areas is a daunting one. In 1997, Parks Canada reported that at least half of the country's thirty-nine national parks were experiencing significant ecological stress because of changes stemming from timber harvesting, residential development, farming, sport hunting, and energy exploration outside park boundaries. Mining alone was implicated in the decline of ecological integrity in fifteen national parks, including Banff, Cape Breton Highlands, Gros Morne, Nahanni, and Kluane (Parks Canada, *State of the Parks 1997,* 1997). The net effect of this conversion of adjacent lands "has been to reduce the national parks to islands of wildness in a vast landscape of domestication. However, they are too small, too few, too isolated and too fragmented to adequately protect the ecosystems and species found within their boundaries" (Searle, *Phantom Parks,* 2000).

Numerous examples of incompatible land uses adjacent to and between protected areas can be found in both the United States and Canada. Montana's Glacier National Park, which sits on the border of Canada, is threatened by Canadian coal mines and timber harvesting to the north and construction of roads and residential subdivisions on U.S. soil. Clear-cutting has also taken place right up to the boundary lines of other famous U.S. national parks, including Olympic and Redwood (Sellars, *Preserving Nature in the National Parks,* 1997). Farther north, Manitoba's Riding Mountain National Park "clings to a tentative existence in a region that has undergone, and is still undergoing, dramatic change. Over the past few decades, farming, timber harvesting and recreational subdivisions have carved away the surrounding native ecosystems, leaving virtually every metre of the park's boundary sharply defined" (Searle, *Phantom Parks,* 2000). Even Yellowstone—America's first and arguably greatest national park—is struggling to blunt the impact of logging, mining, commercial development, and an array of other activities immediately outside its boundaries while simultaneously adhering to a model of stewardship that lets park ecosystems evolve naturally (see sidebar on page 59).

> In the case of Yellowstone, intensive development activities on adjacent lands are fragmenting critical wildlife habitats and cumulatively threatening the environmental and aesthetic integrity of the park's ecosystems, putting vital resources like the grizzly bear at risk. At the same time, Yellowstone's commitment to allowing natural processes to function unabated poses risks for its neighbors. Wandering bison threaten to transmit disease, transplanted wolves will occasionally depredate livestock, and wildfires can jump the boundary and destroy nearby homes and timber. (Keiter, "Ecosystem Management: Exploring the Legal-Political Framework," in Wright, ed., *National Parks and Protected Areas,* 1996)

In a few instances, concerns about incompatible land use have prompted federal authorities to purchase private property adjacent to protected areas. In the late 1990s the U.S. government paid $65 million to a Canadian company to prevent gold mining just outside Yellowstone National Park. In Colorado, the U.S. Forest Service purchased an inholding within a Rocky Mountain wilderness area when a developer threatened to build houses on the land. These and other purchases have sparked concerns that speculators are buying land adjacent to parks and protected areas, then threatening to defile it unless the government purchases it for an exorbitant price. This practice—dubbed "environmental extortion" by the environmental community—forces the government to divert limited land acquisition funds that could otherwise be used to buy other ecologically vulnerable lands, including inholdings and other private parcels in existing protected areas. (In the mid-1990s, the National Park Service estimated that it needed $1.5 billion just to acquire private holdings within established park boundaries to complete existing parks in the lower forty-eight states.)

Yellowstone Falls, Wyoming PHOTODISC, INC.

Public land located adjacent to protected areas does not always provide an adequate buffer against potentially damaging activities, either. Many public lands are managed under a multiple-use mandate that provides for coal mining, oil and gas drilling, logging, off-road vehicle (ORV) use, hunting, and other activities. Political factors influence the administration of public lands as well. In the United States, for example, the Bush administration has shown greater support for logging, mining, oil and natural gas drilling, and other extractive activities on BLM and Forest Service land than did its predecessor, the Clinton administration. In October 2001, for instance, the BLM relaxed temporary management rules in fourteen national monuments to allow increased mining and off-road vehicle use.

Opponents of mining, drilling, and logging on public lands believe that these activities usually prove harmful to natural resources in nearby parks or refuges. They contend that habitat fragmentation, air and water pollution, sedimentation of rivers and streams, and destruction of migratory corridors are almost inevitable by-products of these activities. Defenders of extraction and recreational activities on lands administered by the BLM and Forest Service, however, contend that the environmental community has exaggerated the ecological impact of these commercially significant activities on public lands and nearby parks, especially with the advent of new exploration and extraction technologies.

Shielding Protected Areas from Incompatible Land Uses

In recent years, North American scientists, administrators of protected areas, and environmental groups have all examined ways to foster compatible land uses adjacent to and between protected areas. Many analysts have concluded that progress in this endeavor will require increased cooperation and interaction with communities and landowners outside park boundaries. "Management of landscapes that will provide for the long-term well-being of both natural populations and human populations requires the cooperative efforts of all who live in and manage that landscape" (Halvorson, "Changes in Landscape Values and Expectations," in Wright, ed., *National Parks and Protected Areas,* 1996).

Nurturing an environment of cooperation between public and private landowners will be challenging, however, especially in areas of the U.S. and Canadian West where property rights are an especially emotional issue. Some private landowners, including those holding lands of significant ecological value, are actively hostile to the concept of federal land ownership and resistant to any overtures that place limitations on the use of their property (Hage,

Storm over Rangelands, 1990). In addition, some environmentalists and scientists have expressed profound doubts about the negotiations inherent in such partnerships, citing concerns about the level of compromise necessary to obtain regional land-use agreements with surrounding communities.

But proponents of this pathway contend that enlisting the participation of nearby communities and other neighbors is essential, especially when creating new protected areas. "Establishing protected areas in isolation from regional planning and decision-making processes is not an effective way to ensure the maintenance of their long-term ecological integrity. Past experience has shown that surrounding communities, landowners, and commercial developers systematically encircle and encroach on protected areas. The result is often the loss of protected area values and demands for inappropriate uses of these resources" (Canadian Environmental Advisory Council, *A Protected Areas Vision for Canada,* 1991).

Some researchers believe that effectively disseminating information to local communities about the environmental—and perhaps more important, economic—benefits of maintaining the ecological integrity of protected areas can blunt much of this development pressure. In Canada's Yukon and Northwest Territories, for example, steady growth in tourism

> has had a progressive effect on perceptions of and interest in protected areas. Through the 1980s, the potential economic benefits of major protected areas from Kluane to Auyuittuq became clearer to local and territorial interests. New protected areas often become more acceptable and the territorial governments become much more interested in establishing their own, often tourism- and recreation-oriented, protected areas. Access and development of facilities have remained issues in many parks, for example Kluane, but the growth of backcountry use and spending associated with it is even leading to greater acceptance of wilderness parks and reducing demands for large-scale infrastructural development. (Wright, *National Parks and Protected Areas,* 1996)

Observers also believe that federal agencies can do a better job of cooperating with one another to meet their common goal of habitat and species protection.

> Notwithstanding their divergent statutory mandates, the federal land management agencies [in the United States] have each promulgated ecosystem management policies that are remarkably similar, reflecting a core concern for maintaining the integrity of ecological processes. While this common federal commitment to an ecosystem

> management regime should enable park managers to address resource problems more effectively, adjacent land managers are still confronted with powerful contrary political pressures, which could upset tenuous cooperative relationships. Ecosystem management, in other words, is not yet fully institutionalized on the public domain. (Wright, *National Parks and Protected Areas,* 1996)

Conservationists and scientists have also touted linked networks of protected areas as a way of preserving habitat and wildlife, especially for wide-roaming species such as cougars, wolves, and grizzly bears. In 2000, for example, a Canadian panel of scientists issued a widely publicized report proclaiming that "establishing a comprehensive and linked network of protected areas with the involvement of all jurisdictions, of which national parks are a key part, is the best way to conserve ecological integrity within greater ecosystems and the Canadian landscape as a whole" (Panel on the Ecological Integrity of Canada's National Parks, *Unimpaired for Future Generations?* 2000).

Under this network arrangement, national and state/provincial parks, wildlife refuges, and other protected areas would all be linked by undeveloped or semideveloped corridors. These wildlife corridors, stitched together using a combination of undeveloped public land and conservation easements on private land, would provide otherwise isolated populations of animals with the means to migrate and breed with distant populations, thus strengthening the entire ecosystem's biodiversity. The best known of these proposed networks is the Yellowstone-to-Yukon initiative, which seeks to establish a continuous wilderness corridor spanning the Rocky Mountains from Yellowstone National Park to the Yukon Territory's Mackenzie Mountains. But other, smaller-scale proposals are also being explored by U.S. and Canadian conservationists and scientists.

North America's Protected Areas: Overused and Underfunded?

North America's protected areas also face a multitude of problems within their boundaries, most of them linked to heavy levels of use and associated funding issues. These administrative challenges are particularly acute in the national park systems of Canada and the United States, which are enormously popular with Canadians, U.S. citizens, and tourists from all over the globe. The steadily growing popularity of the parks has dramatically increased development pressure in some units during the past two decades, a period in which funding has remained stagnant or fallen. In the United States, the national park system received 40 million more visitors in 1996 than in 1978. During

A traffic jam at Arches National Park NIK KLEINBERG/CORBIS

this same period, more than eighty park units were added to the system, significantly increasing the National Park Service's administrative and maintenance duties. But annual funding for the park system dropped by $635 million in constant dollars during that time (Natural Resources Defense Council and National Trust for Historic Preservation, *Reclaiming Our Heritage,* 1997).

In fact, from 1977 to 2002, the National Park Service budget has dropped by nearly 20 percent (adjusting for inflation). In Canada, meanwhile, a 1997 *State of the Parks* report indicated that utility and transportation corridors were a source of significant ecological impact in twenty-five national parks, while tourism and visitor service development inside and outside park boundaries was implicated in the decline of ecological integrity in twenty-six parks. But the Parks Canada budget experienced a series of cuts during the 1980s and 1990s, culminating with a 24 percent reduction in funding to be spread over five years beginning in 1995.

The increasing pressure to provide and maintain roadways and facilities (lodging, concession shops, parking, information centers, etc.) to accommodate large numbers of visitors has diminished the resource protection efforts of Parks Canada and the National Park Service in two ways. First, it has encouraged infrastructure development on a scale that has sometimes proven harmful to park flora and fauna. "Although its mandate makes the protection of park resources the highest priority, park managers and administrators have been caught in the unfortunate rhetorical position of saying that the parks have two equal and conflicting goals: protection of park resources and provision of human use and enjoyment. This argument has led to overcrowding, the building of facilities in locations and ways that harm important park resources and natural systems, and the use of park resources in ways that result in their degradation," claimed one report on the U.S. park system (ibid.). Second, development activities have forced many park administrators to allocate the bulk of their limited financial resources toward facility construction and maintenance, leaving little money for research studies and other programs that help preserve ecosystem health.

Of course, not all parks are subject to the same degree of tourism pressure. Whereas the Grand Canyon, Yosemite, Great Smoky Mountains, and some other parks receive a great deal of attention from tourists, parks such as Michigan's Isle Royale National Park (an island located in northern Lake Superior) and Alaska's Lake Clark National Park and Kobuk Valley National Park receive relatively few visitors. In fact, only ten of the national parks in the United States accounted for 43 percent of the total number of visitor days in the entire park system in the mid-1990s (National Park Service, *Statistical Abstract 1996*, 1996). Canada's national parks are used unevenly as well, with parks located in the provinces under much greater pressure than those in the Arctic. For instance, Banff National Park in Alberta, which is intersected by both the Trans-Canada Highway and the Canadian Pacific Railway, receives about 5 million visitors a year and has experienced an explosion of commercial development in its central Bow Valley. This intensive development has shaken the park's ecosystem to its core and prompted concerns that the park's fundamental wilderness character is in serious jeopardy (Banff-Bow Valley Study, *Banff-Bow Valley*, 1996).

Indeed, overuse and excess development loom as critical issues in the majority of U.S. and Canadian parks. Analysts warn that prevailing trends of development, if left unchecked, could eventually cause catastrophic damage to the ecological integrity of numerous national parks in both countries. "The changes occurring within the national parks are not yet obvious to most people, and so there is a very real danger that they may continue to the point where wild species and ecosystems become a thing of the past. Taken together, the changes amount to the domestication of the wild. In a world where nothing is quite what it seems to be, we are increasingly creating a legacy of phantom parks: places that still look beautiful, but where the essential quality of wildness is largely absent" (Searle, *Phantom Parks*, 2000).

Protected Areas Starved for Operating Funds

Many state and federal land management agencies in the United States have difficulty ensuring the continued ecological health of protected habitats, flora, and fauna under current levels of funding, especially given public and legislative expectations that they provide visitors with an assortment of facilities and programs for their comfort and enjoyment. "The [National] Park Service has been defined largely by the demands of recreational tourism management and

The Land and Water Conservation Fund

The Land and Water Conservation Fund (LWCF) is a federal trust that was established in 1965 for the express purpose of buying and maintaining land for parks and recreation. Created to take in as much as $900 million annually, LWCF income is primarily collected from leases on offshore oil and gas wells in federal waters (oil and gas leases generate a total of about $3 billion a year for the federal treasury).

Since its inception, the LWCF has been a significant factor in the expansion of the U.S. network of protected areas. By the late 1990s, the trust had provided nearly $5.5 billion to the National Park Service, the U.S. Forest Service, the U.S. Fish and Wildlife Service, and the Bureau of Land Management for land acquisition and administration. The agencies have used these funds to extend legal protections to an estimated 3.4 million acres across the nation.

Purchases made with LWCF funds have included a number of areas that were subsequently incorporated into the national park system, including ecologically rich parks such as the Cape Cod National Seashore in Massachusetts, Padre Islands National Seashore in Texas, and Voyageurs National Park in Minnesota. The U.S. Forest Service has used LWCF funds to designate national recreation areas on its lands in almost every state. Similarly, the U.S. Fish and Wildlife Service has used LWCF funds to add approximately 750,000 acres to the National Wildlife Refuge system, including vital habitat for Florida panthers, sandhill cranes, and other endangered creatures (Nixon, "Paradise Lost?" 1998). Moreover, all four of the land management agencies in the United States have used LWCF funds to acquire inholdings and other private parcels within protected areas.

In addition, the Land and Water Conservation Fund has been an important asset for state governments looking to fund land preservation and outdoor recreation projects, for the trust includes a significant matching grant component. By the late 1990s the LWCF had contributed more than $3 billion in matching grants to state governments for more than 37,000 state, county, and local projects. In some cases, this matching grant money has been used for the development of recreation area

(continues)

the desire for the public to enjoy the scenic parks," stated one historian of the U.S. system. "Since the establishment of Yellowstone and other nineteenth-century parks, managers have had to deal not only with planning, development, construction, and maintenance of park facilities, but also with ever more demanding political, legal, and economic matters such as concession operations, law enforcement, visitor protection, and the influence of national, state, and local tourism interests. Such imperatives have *driven* park management" (Sellars, *Preserving Nature in the National Parks,* 1997).

facilities such as boat launches and playgrounds, but in many instances LWCF funds have been used to purchase natural areas that are at risk. An estimated 2.3 million acres have been acquired in this fashion, enabling state authorities to establish protected areas such as the Allagash Wilderness Waterway in northern Maine (ibid.).

Despite the evident value of the LWCF, however—and the wealth of oil and gas royalties generated in federal waters—the trust has been starved for funding for most of the past two decades. During the 1980s, Congress repeatedly diverted oil and gas revenues originally intended for the trust to other expenditures. The average authorization from Congress for the LWCF during this time was $250 million, less than 28 percent of the $900 million that could have been made available. Funding continued to dwindle during the early 1990s, and in 1994 the Republican-led Congress approved only $134 million for the LWCF, the smallest allocation since the trust's creation in 1965. One year later, Congress decided not to provide funding for the matching grant component of the LWCF, cutting off a significant financial resource for states. By the late 1990s, it was estimated that Congress had diverted $12.6 billion that could have gone to the LWCF for other purposes. During this same period, some lawmakers argued that the meager funds that did trickle into the LWCF should be used to pay for maintenance projects on federal lands rather than acquisition of new lands (ibid.).

In the last few years, however, lawmakers have shown increased appreciation for the value of the Land and Water Conservation Fund. Legislative support for full funding of the LWCF has increased markedly, and some lawmakers have explored ways to guarantee that the trust receives its full allotment of $900 million every year. This reassessment of the trust's worth has heartened many members of the environmental community who see the LWCF as a potentially invaluable weapon in the campaign to preserve at-risk natural areas and wilderness tracts.

Sources:

Nixon, Will. 1998. "Paradise Lost?" *Amicus Journal* (spring).

Zaslowsky, Dyan. 1994. *These American Lands: Parks, Wilderness, and the Public Lands.* Washington, DC: Island.

Although the Park Service has focused the bulk of its attention and funding on construction and other tourism-related expenditures, the infrastructure of the network of U.S. national parks has eroded slowly over time. By 1996 the National Park Service reported that it had immediate capital construction needs of $5.6 billion within the system, mostly in the areas of road, bridge, and building repairs. It also reported unmet capital needs of $1.1 billion for land restoration, $442 million for employee housing, and $304 million for utilities (National Park Service, "Recapitalization of the National Park Service," January 6, 1997). As conservationists noted, these figures included "no natural resource protection work. No funds are included to provide for the basic inventory and monitoring necessary to know the nature and condition of park resources. Nothing is included to support the management steps necessary to preserve the quality of these resources. The parks' physical infrastructure will be of little use if the natural and cultural resources the parks were established to protect are lost" (Natural Resources Defense Council and National Trust for Historic Preservation, *Reclaiming Our Heritage,* 1997).

Indeed, low levels of funding for scientific research—in fiscal year 1997 the United States spent as much to subsidize corporations growing cotton as it did on the national parks—make it impossible for the National Park Service to comply with its mandate of protecting flora and fauna within the parks. Not one national park in the U.S. system has a complete inventory of all its plants, animals, and historic artifacts, even though the NPS has been repeatedly criticized over the years—both internally and by independent experts—for inconsistent and sporadic support of science (National Park Service, *National Parks for the Twenty-first Century,* 1993; Wilkinson, "Climate Change," 2002). "Scientific information is critical to effective management of park resources," explained one analyst. "Without it, the Park Service cannot adequately assess the damage being done to park resources, let alone take the necessary steps to stop it" (Sellars, *Preserving Nature in the National Parks,* 1997).

Shortfalls in funding for research programs have also hobbled efforts to identify and protect important natural regions that are not currently represented in the park system. "The lack of a system-wide plan for park establishment has meant from the beginning that new park establishment typically is driven not by a need to protect unique ecological resources but by factors such as opportunity, aesthetics, local economic impacts, surrounding land uses, and political support. . . .[R]elatively few park areas—most notably Olympic, Everglades, and Denali National Parks—were selected primarily for their biological resources" (Wright and Mattson, "The Origin and Purpose of National Parks and Protected Areas," in Wright, ed. *National Parks and Protected Areas,* 1996).

The National Park System's financial difficulties are further exacerbated by lawmakers, who routinely insert their own funding priorities into the NPS budget. Every year, the Park Service is forced to spend more money on "Congressionally identified" initiatives than on projects recommended by its own personnel. In fiscal year 1997, for example, forty-one of the fifty-nine national park construction projects that received funding were stipulated by Congress rather than by Park Service officials. "Given that the Park Service budget has declined significantly in constant dollars, the new projects that Congress has required clearly take scarce resources from other critical needs. From fiscal year 1981 to fiscal year 1996, Congress required the Park Service to complete $1.1 billion of projects it had not planned to do. Often these Congressional add-ons are for new construction. As a result, not only does the backlog of existing repairs grow, but new maintenance responsibilities are added without additional funds to cover them" (Natural Resources Defense Council and National Trust for Historic Preservation, *Reclaiming Our Heritage*, 1997).

Other land management agencies are feeling the funding pinch as well. Nearly 390,000 miles of logging roads wind through U.S. national forests, but most of them do not meet minimal environmental and safety regulations. In fact, the U.S. Forest Service estimates that it has an $8.4 billion maintenance backlog to repair the roads and bridges that wind through the country's national forests and grasslands. Elsewhere, the U.S. Fish and Wildlife Service has reported an estimated maintenance backlog of $600 million in the country's national wildlife refuges. Desperate to augment their budgets, these agencies have introduced user fees and other income-generating schemes into their land management operations. Conservationists, meanwhile, have urged administrators and lawmakers to consider other budget-boosting measures, such as giving the National Park Service authority to issue bonds or keep all revenue generated in the parks. Full funding of the Land and Water Conservation Fund (LWCF), a federal trust that provides money for the acquisition of maintenance of lands for parks and recreation, has also been touted as an important element in any effective protected areas strategy (see sidebar on page 70).

Other legislative efforts to increase funding for protected areas are also underway, although not to levels recommended by the environmental community. The 1997 passage of the National Wildlife Refuge System Improvement Act has produced regular budget increases for the system, and in 2002 the Bush administration proposed a $56.5 million increase for the National Wildlife Refuge System, an 18 percent hike to cover maintenance and renovation of aging facilities. Legislators have also taken steps to boost the budget of the National Park Service, although conservationists and scientists observe that most of the increased allocations are earmarked for the system's huge maintenance and construction backlog. In addition, some lawmakers are trying to increase funding available specifically for the development of mass transportation systems in parks and other public lands. These systems—shuttle buses, light rail trams, and the like—are seen as an effective means of reducing the impact of visitors on park resources, but they are expensive to build, maintain, and operate; under the existing funding arrangement, most of the money that the Park Service receives for its transportation systems is explicitly targeted for the repair of existing roads. Only 5 percent of the total is earmarked for alternative transportation, and individual parks must compete with each other for this funding (Clarke, "The National Park or Parking System?" 2001). "America's existing . . . federal lands constitute one of its unique geopolitical features," summarized one analysis of its federal land management agencies.

> Nearly 30 percent of the nation's land is, in principle, dedicated to serving the *national* interest, and not private, sectional, regional, or exclusively local interests. Very few nations and peoples of the world are privileged in this manner. . . . Ultimately, though, it is crucial to realize how little we spend on public lands management, especially in the context of unprecedented economic growth. . . . The [2000] appropriation that sustains the four federal agencies amounts to only 0.37 percent of the $1.8 trillion federal budget! In other words, nearly 30 percent of the nation's land is protected, preserved, and maintained on less than 1 percent of the annual federal budget. As a result, the four federal land-managing agencies (particularly BLM and the Fish and Wildlife Service) operate without the resources necessary to fully implement the new ecosystems management and watershed planning models, models that hold much promise for resolving the present disputes over public lands policy. (Clark and Angersbach, "The Federal Four," in Davis, ed., *Western Public Lands and Environmental Politics,* 2001)

Managing Canada's Parks in an Era of Budget Cuts

To the north, Canada is grappling with many of the same park management issues as the United States. "The more the parks are used the more difficult it is to prevent abuse," summarized James B. Harkin, who directed Canada's national parks for a quarter-century. "There are increased demands for more and more roads, cheaper forms of amusement, commercial exploitations, and the danger is that if these demands are acceded to, the parks may lose the very thing that distinguished them from the outside world. The battle for the establishment of national parks is long since over but the battle to keep them inviolate is never won" (Harkin, "Reflections of a Parks Administrator," 1998).

According to the National Parks Act and the National Parks Policy, the primary mandate of Parks Canada is to maintain the ecological integrity of the natural resources under its care. But steep budget cuts implemented as part of governmentwide efforts to rein in spending have made it difficult for administrators to fully fund scientific research and habitat preservation programs, especially given the strong political pressure they face to accommodate evergrowing numbers of visitors. This dynamic has, in turn, increased pressure on the agency to generate revenue through other means, such as new user fees and corporate sponsorships and partnerships. Some observers believe that this state of affairs is undermining Canada's ability and will to make environmental stewardship its top priority in the management of protected areas. In 1996, for instance, the auditor general of Canada reported that Canada's national park management plans "emphasize social and economic factors over ecological factors" and asserted that vital scientific monitoring and research programs had been particularly affected by budgetary cutbacks (Auditor General of Canada, "Canadian Heritage—Parks Canada," 1996).

Subsequent reports, most notably the Banff-Bow Valley Study of 1996 and the 1999 report of the Panel on the Ecological Integrity of Canada's National Parks, have strongly recommended increased funding for Parks Canada, both to maintain resources within existing park units and to ensure smart decisionmaking in the creation of new protected areas. "Parks Canada lacks the financial resources to carry out adequate biophysical inventories and ecosystem analyses of new park candidates," stated the panel. "This means that Parks Canada begins negotiations for new parks without the conservation science needed to identify and advocate optimum park boundaries. In contrast, in the northern territories, Parks Canada spends ten times as much money on identifying potential mineral resources under the Mineral and Energy Resource Assessment (MERA) process as on basic wildlife, vegetation or ecosystem work" (Panel on the Ecological Integrity of Canada's National Parks, *Unimpaired for Future Generations?* 2000).

Analysts have also urged a greater emphasis on scientific management within Parks Canada. "Parks Canada has not systematically collected scientific data on natural resources and monitored changes in their condition over time for all the national parks," commented one government report. "Without this critical information, Parks Canada will have difficulty assessing the condition and trend of natural resources in these national parks, including species at risk. This increases the risk that Parks Canada will be unable to protect ecological integrity in these parks" (Auditor General of Canada, *Canadian Heritage—Parks Canada,* 1996).

The Canadian government has taken a number of steps to address these concerns in recent years, the most significant of which was the Canada National Parks Act. This act, which came into force in February 2001, had the stated intention of making maintenance and restoration of ecological integrity the first priority in all aspects of park management. The Minister of Canadian Heritage described the new act as a tool that would provide stringent new protections for national parks, and environmentalists and scientists voiced hope that it would prove an effective instrument in reprioritizing environmental protection ahead of tourism in Canada's management of protected areas.

A few months after the National Parks Act came into effect, however, the minister of Canadian heritage approved the construction of a 118-kilometer road through the middle of Wood Buffalo National Park, a UN World Heritage site that protects a vast wilderness area on the border of Alberta and the Northwest Territories. Supporters of the road project argued that it would provide economic benefits to the region and would have minimal impact on the park's natural resources. Opponents characterized the road as wholly incompatible with the ideals laid out in the National Parks Act. They charged that it would fragment important habitat and compromise the park's essential wilderness character. Both the Canadian Parks and Wilderness Society (CPAWS) and the Mikisew Cree First Nation launched separate legal challenges against the minister's decision. The society's assertion that the minister did not have the legal power to approve the road was dismissed (the organization subsequently announced that it would appeal), but Canadian courts upheld the Cree challenge, which claimed that the road would negatively impact tribal holdings in the park.

Secondary Uses in Protected Areas

Many protected areas in North America are managed to accommodate so-called secondary use of designated lands, in addition to nature conservation and habitat protection. These uses range from tourism and recreation to mining and logging. In the United States, for instance, "land protection in the past was intimately tied to commercial interests [so] no land was protected with the intention of keeping it untrammeled by humanity and permanently wild. The parks were expected to earn their budgets by catering to visitors. National forests were even more overtly commercial, as were the rangelands administered by the Bureau of Land Management. They were leased to lumber companies, ranchers, miners, and other developers." This state of affairs, "established long before terms such as *ecosystem* or *biodiversity* had even been coined," remains dominant within many land management agencies at the national, state, and provincial levels (DiSilvestro, *Reclaiming the Last Wild Places,* 1993).

In the U.S. national wildlife refuge system, for example, the Fish and Wildlife Service permits a wide array of secondary uses, even though the only explicit mandate of refuge management is to protect endangered species and migratory birds. According to a 1988 General Accounting Office report, secondary use was occurring on 92 percent of refuges in the system. These uses ranged from recreation-oriented uses such as hunting and fishing to mining, grazing, and practice bombing by the U.S. Air Force. According to the same GAO study, more than 70 percent of the refuges had at least seven different categories of secondary use, and 30 percent featured fourteen different uses within their boundaries. "Secondary use does not necessarily mean harmful use. A secondary use can be benign. However, uses that refuge managers believed harmful were reported on 254 refuges, 59 percent of all refuges" (ibid.).

The dominant secondary uses present in North America's national parks are tourism and recreation-related activities. But other uses are thoroughly integrated into the fabric of some parks. Most of Canada's parks in the Yukon and Northwest Territories, for example, accommodate First Nations subsistence hunting and fishing activities, and some U.S. parks, such as Grand Tetons National Park, were created only after specific allowances for grazing and other secondary uses were made to satisfy local business interests.

Private inholdings within protected areas are extensive as well. The National Park Service estimates that nearly 5.5 million acres of private land and leases are held within the park system, and many other federal lands are dotted with inholdings as well. In some cases, the presence of these inholdings has proven problematic for agencies trying to implement and enforce wilderness preservation programs. One option that the NPS and other agencies have pursued has been to negotiate purchase agreements with landowners in which the government takes possession of the land at the conclusion of a long-term lease (twenty-five years or more). But these types of arrangements can compromise efforts to protect fragile habitat. In Dinosaur National Monument in Colorado, for instance, cattle owned by an inholder with grazing rights destroyed a significant streamside wetland area within the monument in 2001. Moreover, ranchers with land and grazing rights within Dinosaur have threatened to develop a small resort on their property unless the government agrees to a selling price of almost $6 million. But the Park Service appraisal attaches a much lower value to the land, and the government cannot pay more than fair market value for land without congressional approval (Daerr, "Inholder's Cattle Destroy Wetland Area in Dinosaur," 2001).

Recreational activities within protected areas comprise the most environmentally friendly examples of "secondary use" in Canada and the United States. Activities such as backpacking, canoeing, kayaking, fishing, and camping can damage the environment when practiced carelessly, but they usually have a relatively minor impact on the surrounding environment, especially when practitioners adhere to the burgeoning "leave no trace" outdoor ethos that calls on visitors to tread lightly on the land by packing out all trash, choosing already established campsites, and so forth. Moreover, these activities often spark deeper understanding and appreciation of nature among participants and have helped foster the strong environmental ethic present among some segments of the U.S. and Canadian public. But while most recreational activities in parks and protected areas are seen as relatively benign when carried out in an environmentally sensitive fashion, the environmental community sees off-road-vehicle use as a notable exception.

Off-road vehicles (ORVs) include snowmobiles, jet skis, dirt bikes, jeeps, all-terrain vehicles (ATVs), and four-wheel-drive vehicles that leave roads. ORVs are tremendously popular, with sales of ATVs, snowmobiles, jet skis and other machines enjoying sustained growth throughout the 1980s and 1990s. But they have been criticized for emitting high levels of pollution, tearing up fragile land, and disturbing both wildlife and other visitors with their noise and their impact on the landscape. In the Wilderness Society's 2000 report entitled *15 Most Endangered Wildlands,* the organization identified ORV traffic as probably the fastest growing threat to wilderness in the United States and asserted that the country's federal land management agencies have shown little ability or inclination to halt illegal ORV intrusions into ecologically sensitive areas.

For their part, ORV enthusiasts resent limitations on where they can ride, and they accuse opponents of being elitists who are trying to lock up scenic areas for their own pleasure. In recent years, manufacturers and their political allies have actively lobbied for increased ORV access to protected areas that currently forbid their use. Alaska's congressional delegation, for instance, has attempted to pass legislation that would allow recreational snowmobiling in the wilderness core of Denali Park and Preserve. Opponents claim that such activity would disturb resident grizzly bears, wolves, and moose, and they point out that millions of acres in the surrounding area are already available for ORV use.

At the beginning of the twenty-first century, the status of ORV access to protected areas in North America is cloudy. Snowmobiling is permitted in some Canadian protected areas, but use of many other ORVs is restricted, especially in provincial and national parks. In the United States, ORV use is well established on many lands managed by the Forest Service and the BLM, but their presence in national parks has prompted considerable debate. During the Clinton administration, the NPS imposed a ban on snowmobiles in Yellowstone and Grand Teton national parks that would have begun in the winter of 2002. It also announced that jet skis, which discharge 25 to 30 percent of their fuel unburned into the water, would be outlawed in all but 10 of the country's 379 national parks by September 2002. But after President Bush assumed office, the snowmobiling ban was suspended by the Department of the Interior. The agency explained that the ban was withdrawn because of concerns that local communities and business owners had not been given adequate opportunity to explain their opposition. In April 2001 the Department of the Interior also rescinded jet ski bans at four national parks that had imposed restrictions on use, a decision that prompted speculation that the Clinton-era jet ski restrictions might also be scaled back or discarded.

Sources:

Agee, J. K., and D. R. Johnson. 1988. *Ecosystem Management for Parks and Wilderness.* Seattle: University of Washington Press.

Auditor General of Canada. 1996. "Canadian Heritage—Parks Canada: Preserving Canada's Natural Heritage." Ottawa: Auditor General of Canada, November.

Banff-Bow Valley Study. 1996. *Banff-Bow Valley: At the Crossroads.* Ottawa: Minister of Supply and Services Canada.

Beazley, Karen, and Robert Boardman, eds. 2001. *Politics of the Wild: Canada and Endangered Species.* Don Mills, ON: Oxford University Press.

Butler, R. W., and S. W. Boyd, eds. 2000. *Tourism and National Parks: Issues and Implications.* Chichester: John Wiley.

Canadian Environmental Advisory Council. 1991. *A Protected Areas Vision for Canada.* Ottawa: CEAC.

Chase, Alston. 1986. *Playing God in Yellowstone: The Destruction of America's First National Park.* Boston: Atlantic Monthly Press.

Clarke, Wendy Mitman. 2001. "The National Park or Parking System?" *National Parks* 75 (July–August).

Congressional Research Service. 2001. *Federal Land Management Agencies: Background on Land and Resource Management.* Washington, DC: CRS.

———. 2001. *National Monument Issues.* Washington, DC: CRS.

Daerr, Elizabeth. 2001. "Inholder's Cattle Destroy Wetland Area in Dinosaur." *National Parks* 75 (September).

Davis, Charles, ed. 2001. *Western Public Lands and Environmental Politics.* 2d ed. Boulder, CO: Westview.

DiSilvestro, Roger L. 1993. *Reclaiming the Last Wild Places: A New Agenda for Biodiversity.* New York: John Wiley.

Fretwell, Holly Lippke. 2000. "How to Improve Our Federal Parks." *Consumers' Research Magazine* 83 (April).

Hage, W. 1990. *Storm over Rangelands: Private Rights in Federal Land.* Bellevue, WA: Free Enterprise.

Halvorson, William L., and G. E. Davis, eds. 1996. *Ecosystem Management in the National Parks.* Tucson: University of Arizona Press.

Harkin, James B. 1998. "Reflections of a Parks Administrator." *Park News* 23, no. 5.

Lindholm, James, and Brad Barr. 2001. "Comparison of Marine and Terrestrial Protected Areas under Federal Jurisdiction in the United States." *Conservation Biology* (October).

National Park Service. 1993. *National Parks for the Twenty-First Century: The Vail Agenda.* Washington, DC: NPS.

———. 1995. *The National Parks: Index 1995.* Washington, DC: NPS.

———. 1996. *Statistical Abstract 1996.* Washington, DC: NPS.

———. 1997. "Recapitalization of the National Park Service." Washington, DC: NPS, January 6.

———. 1999. *Natural Resource Challenge: The National Park Service's Action Plan for Preserving Natural Resources.* Washington, DC: Department of the Interior, NPS, Natural Resource Stewardship and Science.

National Parks and Conservation Association. 1994. *Our Endangered Parks.* San Francisco: Foghorn.

Natural Resources Defense Council and National Trust for Historic Preservation. 1997. *Reclaiming Our Heritage: What We Need to Do to Preserve America's National Parks.* New York: NRDC, NTHP, July.

Nelson, Deborah, et al. 1998. "Trading away the West" series, *Seattle Times,* September 27–October 2.

Newmark, William D. 1987. "A Land-Bridge Island Perspective on Mammalian Extinctions in Western North American Parks." *Nature* 325.

———. 1995. "Extinction of Mammal Populations in Western North American National Parks." *Conservation Biology* 9 (June).

Nixon, Will. 1998. "Paradise Lost?" *Amicus Journal* (spring).

O'Brien, Bob R. 1999. *Our National Parks and the Search for Sustainability.* Austin: University of Texas Press.

Panel on the Ecological Integrity of Canada's National Parks. 2000. *Unimpaired for Future Generations? Conserving Ecological Integrity with Canada's National Parks.* 2 vols. Ottawa: PEICN.

Parks Canada. 1997. *State of the Parks 1997.* Ottawa: Parks Canada.

Peepre, J. S., and B. Jickling, eds. 1994. *Northern Protected Areas and Wilderness.* Whitehorse: Canadian Parks and Wilderness Society and Yukon College.

Rettie, Dwight F. 1995. *Our National Park System: Caring for America's Greatest Natural and Historic Treasures.* Urbana: University of Illinois Press.

Sadler, Barry. 1989. "National Parks, Wilderness Preservation and Native Peoples in Northern Canada." *Natural Resources Journal* 29, no. 1.

Savage, Candace. 2000. "A Highway Runs through It." *Canadian Geographic* 120 (July–August).

Searle, Rick. 2000. *Phantom Parks: The Struggle to Save Canada's National Parks.* Toronto: Key Porter.

Sellars, Richard West. 1997. *Preserving Nature in the National Parks: A History.* New Haven: Yale University Press.

Shaw, Jane S. 2001. "Perfect Spills." *American Spectator* 34 (September–October).

"Ten Most Endangered." 2000. *National Parks* 74 (May–June).

Wilkinson, Todd. 2002. "Climate Change." *National Parks* (January–February).

World Conservation Monitoring Centre. 1999. *Protected Areas Database.* Cambridge, UK: WCMC.

World Conservation Union. 1991. *1992 Protected Areas of the World: A Review of National Systems.* Gland, Switzerland: IUCN.

———. 1998. *1997 United Nations List of Protected Areas.* Gland, Switzerland: IUCN.

Wright, R. Gerald, ed. 1996. *National Parks and Protected Areas: Their Role in Environmental Protection.* Cambridge, MA: Blackwell.

Zaslowsky, Dyan. 1994. *These American Lands: Parks, Wilderness, and the Public Lands.* Washington, DC: Island.

Forests

Forestlands cover approximately one-quarter of North America's total land mass, and the continent holds approximately 12 percent of the globe's total forest area and 28 percent of the planet's temperate and boreal forests. Blessed with this abundance of valuable timberland, the United States and Canada have long held positions of world leadership in the production and export of forest products. But years of intensive logging and other development have raised concerns about long-term stewardship of the continent's forests, which provide essential habitat for wildlife and a host of other significant environmental benefits. Indeed, forest management practices have become flashpoints of controversy in both nations, as timber companies, logging communities, mill owners, environmental groups, wildlife biologists, and other interested parties debate the most appropriate measures for ensuring the future health and vitality of the continent's forestlands.

Economic and Environmental Benefits of Forests

North America's forest holdings are truly vast. The United States held an estimated 226 million hectares of forestland in 2000, while its neighbor to the north housed 245 million hectares of forest, approximately 53 percent of the continental total (UN Food and Agriculture Organization, *State of the World's Forests,* 2001). These forestlands encompass a great diversity of forest types, including boreal forests that span the continent's midsection from Canada's maritime provinces to the Alaskan interior; deciduous forests that dominate the landscape of the eastern United States; conifer forests that blanket the valleys of the Rocky Mountain region; and temperate rain forests that thrive in the rain-soaked Pacific Northwest. All told, the total forest area of North America is almost three times that of Europe (ibid.).

The U.S.-Canada Softwood Lumber Agreement

Since the 1980s, the United States and Canada have periodically locked horns over a bilateral treaty known as the Softwood Lumber Agreement (SLA). Under the terms of the SLA, Canada can ship 14.7 billion board feet of timber into the United States duty-free each year. Above that volume, duties are added on a sliding scale. These export-friendly terms have enabled Canada to increase dramatically its exports of softwood lumber into the United States over the past twenty-five years. By the late 1990s, Canada was exporting approximately C$10 billion ($U.S. 6.5 billion) of softwood lumber into the United States annually.

But the history of the SLA has not been a placid one. The final terms of this trade agreement were not formally concluded until 1996, after more than a decade of tense political, legal, and economic maneuvering. Since the SLA was finalized, it has been condemned by an unlikely alliance of critics from the U.S. timber industry and the U.S. and Canadian environmental communities. U.S. timber industry spokesmen insist that the SLA unfairly rewards Canadian logging companies with an "environmental subsidy" because their operations are not restricted by laws equivalent to the Endangered Species Act and other U.S. environmental laws. U.S. firms also note that the stumpage fees that Canadian logging companies pay to the provincial government for every tree they cut are set below market prices and are often reduced or returned to timber companies, enabling them to harvest high-grade timber at low-grade rates. U.S. timber companies point out that they do not benefit from such an arrangement (for their part, Canadian loggers are quick to respond that U.S. timber operations such as

(continues)

The economic value of timber harvested from these forests is significant. The United States is the world's largest producer of sawnwood, wood panels, wood pulp, and paper and paperboard, accounting for 25 to 30 percent of global production. In most of these product categories, Canada ranks second in production. As a result, the combined output of the two nations accounts for about 40 percent of the world's industrial roundwood and more than one-third of all processed wood products, including almost half the world's paper pulp (ibid.).

But while the United States is the world leader in timber harvesting, it also accounts for about one-third of global consumption of forest products (ibid.). In fact, the United States consumes wood products at a clip that exceeds domestic production rates. Canada has happily filled this gap, diverting 80 percent of its logged timber to U.S. destinations for use in the production of U.S. newspapers, backyard decks, and other wood and paper products (see sidebar on page 84). This state of affairs has made Canada the globe's leading exporter of major wood products. In 1997, for instance, forest product exports accounted for more than 10 percent of the total value of the nation's exports road-building are heavily subsidized by the U.S. government).

Environmentalists also believe that the SLA rewards Canadian timber companies for unsustainable or illegal practices. They charge, for instance, that British Columbia timber companies often clearcut up to the banks of rivers on public land in direct contravention of the Canadian Fisheries Act. In addition, the environmental community objects to the SLA because most of the timber exported to the United States via the pact is harvested from old-growth public forests in British Columbia, Alberta, Ontario, and Quebec.

In April 2001 the U.S.-Canada Softwood Lumber Agreement expired, setting the stage for another flare-up. In August 2001 the United States imposed a preliminary 19.3 percent duty on all softwood lumber imports from Canada's western provinces, claiming that those provinces provided unfair subsidies to its timber industry (the duty was not imposed on Canada's Atlantic provinces, where private ownership of forests is more extensive). Canada condemned the decision, warning that it could lead to significant sawmill closures and layoffs. It urged the United States to reconsider its decision, reminding U.S. policy-makers that cheap Canadian lumber had become a significant cog in the nation's economic engine. But U.S. timber companies and environmental groups have lobbied U.S. policy-makers to hold firm. They want the United States to negotiate greater restrictions on Canadian softwood exports and force Canada to change some of its environmentally questionable timber-cutting practices.

Source:

"U.S.-Canada Softwood Lumber Agreement," available online at www.ems.org/softwood_lumber_agreement (accessed November 2001).

(forest products accounted for only 2.1 percent of the value of U.S. exports). In recent years, the Canadian forest industry has generated between 2 and 3 percent of the country's total gross domestic product (UN Food and Agriculture Organization, FAOSTAT On-line Statistical Service, 1999, http://www.fao.org; Canadian Forest Service, *The State of Canada's Forests, 1999–2000,* 2000).

Logging is also a significant source of employment in North America, and especially in Canada. In fact, in 1998 Natural Resources Canada estimated that the nation's forest industry employed one in seventeen Canadians, either directly or indirectly, even though mechanization has significantly reduced industry payrolls over the years. The Canadian Council of Forest Ministers has estimated that approximately 1,600 Canadian communities have an appreciable dependence on forest industry jobs, with jobs in this sector accounting for more than 50 percent of employment in more than 330 of those communities (Canadian Council of Forest Ministers, *Criteria and Indicators of Sustainable Forest Management in Canada,* 1997). Timber industry workers are well paid, too, making well above national average earnings.

Wildfire and Disease in North America's Forests

Logging, mining, and other development activities are recognized as major influences on the health and character of North America's forests. Some of these activities result in serious environmental degradation, while others, when governed by a philosophy of stewardship and sustainability, can leave forest ecosystems relatively intact. But forest health is also profoundly influenced by a wide array of other factors. For example, air pollution in the form of acid rain has damaged many forest ecosystems, particularly in New England, Quebec, and Ontario. In the intermountain west, meanwhile, heavy livestock grazing has been a contributing factor in the decline of pine and conifer forests. And of course, North America's forests continue to be shaped by naturally occurring events such as wildfires, insect infestation, and disease. In fact, fires and insect infestations affect a far greater area of woodland than lumbering activities in North America. From 1980 to 1996, for instance, 69 million hectares of Canadian forest were harmed by insects (16.5 percent of the country's entire forest area) and 43 million hectares were damaged by fire, while only 16 million hectares were harvested. Moreover, infestations and wildfires are inextricably linked. Insect infestations create vast stretches of deadwood that becomes fuel for wildfires triggered by lightning strikes and unwatched campfires.

In recent decades, insect outbreaks in forested areas have declined significantly, although severe infestation outbreaks continue to occur. In 2001, for instance, British Columbia's rugged Caribou region suffered an infestation of mountain pine beetles that threatened to destroy more than 1.25 million acres of timber worth an estimated C$4 billion. As a general trend, however, the size and severity of infestations have diminished. For example, from 1976 to 1995, the total forest area affected by moderate to severe defoliation by insects in Canada declined from 65 million hectares to 7 million hectares. In 1998 only 5 million hectares were moderately to severely impacted by insects (Canadian Council of Forest Ministers, *Criteria and Indicators of Sustainable Forest Management in Canada,* 1997).

During this same period, however, wildfires have increased in size and number in both countries. Both the United States and Canada suffered through several of the most severe fire seasons in recorded history from the late 1980s through 2001. Many observers believe that the severity of these fire events can be attributed in part to Canadian and U.S. forestry policies. For decades, federal, state, and provincial forest managers actively worked to suppress wildfires whenever they erupted. Timber companies, foresters, and scientists believe that over time, that policy created excessive amounts of fire fuel in many areas.

Today, fire's role as a natural part of the life cycle of a forest has become more widely recognized and

(continues)

understood. As a result, some fires are left to run their natural course. But dangerous conditions persist in some areas, prompting increased use of prescribed burns and other fire-suppression activities. The U.S. Forest Service annually treats about 1.5 million acres through prescribed burning and other suppression actions. Another 4 million acres are treated in this manner by private landholders. Prescribed burns can be effective, but sometimes air quality concerns restrict the timing, location, and extent of burns. Moreover, prescribed burns can be difficult to control. In May 2000 a prescribed burn in New Mexico's Bandalier National Monument spread out of control, burning more than 200 houses and other structures at a government nuclear weapons laboratory near Los Alamos before finally being contained.

Foresters have also utilized various timber harvesting schemes, including "salvage" sales, to reduce fuel loads in areas that are vulnerable to fire. "After almost a century of intentionally excluding fire from Intermountain forests, wildfire is again gaining the upper hand," declared Steve Arno, a forest ecologist with the USFS Intermountain Fire Sciences Laboratory. "To regain control, we need to treat overstocked dead and dying timber stands that are fueling these fires. Thinning and controlled use of fire are the tools needed to restore natural processes that were present in forests that were here before we excluded fire. If we as a society decide not to use these tools, catastrophic fires will destroy the very forests we all love and are trying to save" (Arno, 1996).

These fuel removal efforts have been successful in some regions. But critics charge that some timber sales advertised as efforts to reduce fuel load have been, in actuality, only nominally concerned with deterring wildfires. In 1999, for instance, the General Accounting Office reported that U.S. Forest Service managers "tend to focus on areas with high-value commercial timber rather than on areas with high fire hazards" and "include more large, commercially valuable trees in a sale than are necessary to reduce the accumulated fuels." The GAO further concluded that the program is "largely driven by commercial rather than safety considerations."

But the timber industry and other logging advocates (including some forestry officials, silviculturalists, and lawmakers) contend that timber harvests should be further increased to address the threat of wildfires. Certainly, it has not escaped their notice that the severe fire seasons that have blackened portions of the U.S. West in recent years coincided with a dramatic downturn in timber volume harvested from those regions. Moreover, they argue that catastrophic wildfire events take a far greater toll on animal and marine habitat than logging activity. But opponents of increased logging activity deflect these arguments by citing scientific studies such as the 1996 Sierra Nevada Ecosystem Project Report, which stated that "timber harvest, through its effects on forest structure, local microclimate and fuel accumulation, has increased fire

(continues)

severity more than any other recent human activity." Indeed, environmental groups point to studies that indicate that forests in unroaded, unlogged areas experience fewer wildfire events than those that have seen road-building and logging activity (Ercelawn, *End of the Road,* 1999).

Sources:

Canadian Council of Forest Ministers. 1997. *Criteria and Indicators of Sustainable Forest Management in Canada.* Ottawa: Natural Resources Canada-Canadian Forest Service.

Ercelawn, A. 1999. *End of the Road—The Adverse Ecological Impacts of Roads and Logging: A Compilation of Independently Reviewed Research.* New York: Natural Resources Defense Council.

Global Forest Watch. 2000. *Canada's Forests at a Crossroads: An Assessment in the Year 2000.* Washington, DC: World Resources Institute.

Gorte, Ross W. 2000. "Timber Harvesting and Forest Fires." Congressional Research Service, CRS Report, August 22.

The forests of North America should not be seen solely as timber storehouses, however. In both the United States and Canada, forests provide a wide range of recreational benefits, many of which have significant economic value in their own right. "[Forests] generate wealth . . . in ways that have nothing to do with cutting them down," noted one environmental leader. "Billions are made through tourism, fishing, trapping, and other forest subsistence activities, all of which are heavily dependent on healthy forests" (May, *At the Cutting Edge,* 1998). "In some forest areas, the economic value of hiking, camping, fishing, hunting, wildlife viewing, and other recreational activities can rival or exceed returns from timber or other consumptive uses," added Global Forest Watch (*Canada's Forests at a Crossroads,* 2000). Indeed, money generated in America's national forests from recreational activities now dwarfs the value of timber sales taken from those public lands. In fact, national forests located near major urban areas such as Los Angeles, Seattle, Denver, and Atlanta have become so crowded on summer weekends that crime, traffic gridlock, garbage, loud partying, and other problems usually associated with urban settings have emerged as significant management issues. "We have about 1.7 million vehicles a day on the Forest Service's 386,000 miles of roads . . . and only about 15,000 are associated with timber harvesting," stated former U.S. Forest Service (USFS) chief Michael Dombeck (Sudetic, "The Forest for the Trees," 2001).

In addition, many U.S. and Canadian citizens feel that intact forests have an intrinsic spiritual and aesthetic value that eclipses their financial worth. This sentiment is particularly strong among hikers, anglers, canoeists, and other seekers of outdoor recreation, and within indigenous communities that have traditionally maintained close emotional ties to ancestral lands. In the mid-1990s, for example, British Columbia's Haisla Tribal Council rebuffed timber industry attempts to log the Kitlope Valley, their long-time spiritual home and one of the last unlogged rain forest watersheds in the province. Sacrificing much-needed employment for band members, the tribe instead worked with the federal government to establish the entire valley as a wilderness preserve.

Healthy forests also provide significant environmental benefits that ripple through entire ecosystems. For instance, watersheds with intact forests are less vulnerable to flooding during spring runoff or heavy thunderstorms (especially in mountainous regions), and they are better able to filter air- and waterborne pollutants before they reach populated areas. Forests also house rivers and streams that sustain fish and other aquatic species and provide essential drinking water (an estimated 80 percent of U.S. rivers originate within national forest watersheds). Forests even regulate climate by sequestering carbon dioxide from the atmosphere. And finally, forests serve as essential wildlife sanctuaries, providing food and shelter for creatures that subsist from ground level to the highest reaches of the forest canopy.

The Bountiful Forests of Canada

Canada is home to nearly 606 million acres (245 million hectares) of forest (UN Food and Agriculture Organization 2001). Most of Canada's forests—whether they are old-growth forests untouched by the lumberman's ax or lands that have been harvested—are Crown lands (that is, publicly owned). Approximately 94 percent of the country's forests are held in public ownership, with most of that land (71 percent) owned and managed by provincial governments. The remaining 29 percent of Canada's forests are owned by the federal government (23 percent) and private landowners (6 percent). The only province in which the majority of forestland is privately owned is Nova Scotia (Canadian Forest Service, *The State of Canada's Forests, 1999–2000,* 2000).

This distribution of ownership reflects Canada's constitution, which gives provinces primary responsibility for the forests within their borders. This arrangement has made it difficult for Canada to enact meaningful national forest stewardship programs, although the federal government does collect data on Canada's forest holdings and administer national and international forest agreements. Indeed, forest care philosophies vary considerably from province to province, shaped by economic trends, political ideology, the size and influence of regional timber interests, the level of environmental activism, and other factors.

Despite this sometimes unwieldy arrangement, however, the provinces of Canada still contain forestlands that are the envy of virtually every other nation

An old tree stump sprouting new growth, British Columbia, Canada COREL

on earth. Approximately 10 percent of the planet's total forest area lies within the country's borders, including 35 percent of the world's boreal forest and 20 percent of its temperate rain forest. Many of these forests remain virtually untouched by human hand. Global Forest Watch estimates that more than 60 percent of the nation's forests can still be found in undisturbed, roadless blocks of 10,000 square kilometers or more (Global Forest Watch, *Canada's Forests at a Crossroads,* 2000).

Most of these wilderness forests are located in Canada's northern realms, where human settlements are few and far between. Nonetheless, the extent of Canada's "intact" forestlands remains impressive, even after centuries of human activity. Ontario, for instance, has lost only 5 percent of its forestland to farming and human settlement, while British Columbia and Quebec have converted only 2 percent of their woodlands to those purposes. The provinces that have converted the largest portions of their forests to farms, towns, and cities are Prince Edward Island (46 percent) and Alberta (21 percent) (ibid.). Logging has impacted a greater area of Canada's forests than agriculture or municipal development. But even after more than a century of industrial logging, the World Resources Institute estimates that Canada holds one-quarter of the globe's remaining "frontier forests"—that is, those that still exist in large, intact ecosystems (Bryant et al., *The Last Frontier Forests,* 1997). These wild lands serve as essential feeding and calving areas, migration corridors, and refuges for a tremendous array of flora and fauna, including threatened or endangered grizzly, wolf, cougar, caribou, and wolverine populations. These same forests also house rivers and streams that still run clear and cold, sustaining salmon, trout, and myriad other aquatic species.

Of the estimated 245 million hectares of forestlands in Canada—which make up about half of its total land area—approximately 9 million hectares are contained in parks and preserves that do not allow commercial logging. Less than half of the remaining 235 million hectares are classified by the Forest Service as "productive"—that is, commercially viable and accessible forest land (Canadian Council of Forest Ministers, *Compendium of Canadian Forestry Statistics, 1996*, 1997). The remainder are located on mountainsides, in marshlands, and in other inhospitable areas that present forbidding technical challenges to commercial timber harvesters.

Still, enormous tracts of forestland remain within easy reach of the timber industry. Indeed, few forested regions of southern Canada—where the overwhelming majority of Canadians live and work—have been left unmarked by clearcuts or logging roads during the past two centuries. Using Canadian Forest Service data, Global Forest Watch estimates that approximately 20 percent of Canada's commercial timberlands had been logged by the close of the twentieth century, and that an additional 1 million hectares were being cut on an annual basis in the late 1990s. About three-quarters of this timber harvest currently takes place in Quebec, Ontario, and British Columbia. British Columbia accounts for the country's highest annual harvest rates by volume (45 percent of the national total, due to the impressive size of the trees in the region), but Quebec logs a greater area of land than any other province.

The size of Canada's annual timber harvest is unlikely to diminish appreciably in the near term, in part because logging rights to more than 50 percent of Canada's forests have already been handed out via "tenure" contracts—license agreements between provincial governments and timber companies that give the companies rights to the timber in a given area. In fact, thirteen corporations had Canadian tenure holdings larger than the area of Switzerland (41,000 square kilometers) in the late 1990s. These corporations feature integrated operations that encompass all phases of the timber harvesting process, including logging, saw-milling, and pulping (Global Forest Watch, *Canada's Forests at a Crossroads*, 2000).

To date, most of Canada's forests that have been converted for agriculture, settlement, and industrial development or affected by extractive industries such as mining and logging have been located in the nation's southern reaches. But timber and mining companies and other developers are increasingly casting their gaze northward, where an estimated 1.9 million square kilometers of untouched boreal and taiga forestland containing huge bounties of timber and mineral wealth rolls to the horizon (see sidebar on page 84).

Environmental groups and scientists fear that unless development restrictions are imposed on those forests, which are particularly sensitive to outside disturbances because of their fragile soils and brief growing seasons, they will eventually resemble the nation's heavily used southern forests. Indeed, most Canadian forests outside the Yukon and Northwest Territories have already been altered by roads, pipelines, power lines, railways, mines, hydropower dams, settlements, and other permanent or semipermanent manifestations of human activity.

Global Forest Watch Canada reports that 88 percent of New Brunswick's remaining forests have been accessed in this manner, and that forests in other provinces such as Alberta (83 percent), British Columbia (63 percent), and Nova Scotia (62 percent) are in similar condition. Less than 30 percent of the vast forests of Ontario (28 percent) and Quebec (21 percent) bear these access signs, but conservation groups hasten to note that in both of those provinces, the percentage of forest likely to be affected by human activity soars upward when tenure agreements are added to the equation. In fact, it has been estimated that 62 percent of Canada's total forest area is already either tenured or located within 10 kilometers of a road, settlement, dam, mine, or other development (Global Forest Watch, *Canada's Forests at a Crossroads,* 2000). This percentage is expected to increase as extractive industries exhaust resources in areas of current operation and move northward to establish new operations. One study estimates that as much as one-fifth of the country's untouched wild forests in the north are already under imminent pressure from logging, mining, and other human activities (Bryant et al., *The Last Frontier Forests,* 1997).

Most U.S. Forests Held in Private Ownership

According to the FAO, an estimated 560 million acres (226 million hectares) of forestlands carpet the United States (UN Food and Agriculture Organization, *State of the World's Forests,* 2001). The U.S. Forest Service puts the total forested area somewhat higher, at 628.5 million acres, with the bulk of those forestlands—393 million acres—held in private ownership by timber companies, Native American communities, and an estimated 9.9 million nonindustrial private owners. Only 15 percent of America's forests are owned by commercial timber companies, but those lands account for about one-third of the nation's total timber harvest, in part because rich timberlands in the West were purchased by private interests prior to the creation of the National Forest

Table 4.1 Forest Conversion and Access by Province in Canada

Province	*Converted Land (000 Hectares)*	*Percent Converted*	*Total Remaining Forest (000 Hectares)*	*Accessed Forest (000 Hectares)*	*Percent Accessed Forest*
Northwest Territories	1	0	46,517	1,217	3
Yukon Territory	1	0	12,929	1,252	10
British Columbia	849	2	48,184	30,137	63
Quebec	1,468	2	80,948	16,898	21
Newfoundland	15	0	16,813	668	4
Ontario	3,858	5	78,721	21,849	28
Nova Scotia	203	4	4,879	3,035	62
New Brunswick	239	3	6,612	5,797	88
Prince Edward Island	211	46	250	153	61
Alberta	9,035	21	33,259	27,518	83
Saskatchewan	7,270	19	31,558	5,841	19
Manitoba	3,304	8	40,289	5,074	13
Nunavut	0	0	1,977	0	0
Total	*26,454*	*6*	*402,936*	*119,439*	*30*

SOURCE: GFW Canada

System in 1905 (Berger, *Understanding Forests,* 1998). According to the Forest Service, another 94 million acres are held by states and local governments, with Western states possessing the greatest landholdings. The remaining 141 million acres are part of the nation's National Forest System, which encompasses 192 million acres, including 51 million acres of grasslands and other nonforest terrain.

The United States is far more heavily populated than Canada and contains a smaller amount of total forest area, so its forestlands are considerably more fragmented than those of its neighbor to the north. According to one study, only 6.3 percent of U.S. "frontier" forests—large, natural forest ecosystems that have remained relatively undisturbed—are original old-growth forest, whereas 56.5 percent of Canada's forests meet that definition (Bryant et al., *The Last Frontier Forests,* 1997). Most of the frontier forest that remains in U.S. territory is in the Pacific Northwest and Alaska (the latter is home to Tongass National Forest, the largest national forest in the U.S. system).

The future of these undisturbed forestlands is uncertain. Numerous forests that are held in private ownership, both in the Pacific Northwest and other parts of the country, will undoubtedly be logged at some point in time. But pressure to preserve old-growth stands that are in private ownership (usually held by timber companies) has escalated in recent years, leading public officials to approve several land swaps and outright purchases of vulnerable forests in the 1990s. Some of these acquisitions have been mired in controversy, however. In the spring of 1998, for instance, the federal government and the state of California agreed to pay the Pacific Lumber company $480 million for 7,500 acres of northern California redwoods that the company had targeted for harvest, including the 4,500-acre Headwaters Grove, a stand of ancient redwoods that is home to endangered species such as the northern spotted owl and the marbled murrelet. Some members of the environmental community hailed the acquisition, but others slammed the agreement. Critics complained that the company used extortionist tactics to inflate the purchase price of the land and charged that Headwaters could have been saved from logging simply by enforcing provisions of the Endangered Species Act.

Some publicly owned forests in the United States are protected—according to the World Conservation Monitoring Centre (WCMC), 6.7 percent of the nation's tropical forests and 10.4 percent of its nontropical forests are shielded from resource extraction and other development—but many other mature forests are vulnerable to logging, mining, and other extraction activities. In early 2001 the Clinton administration placed additional protections on 58.5 million acres of old-growth national forest land, but opposition to the measures from the timber industry and prologging lawmakers, including the Bush administration, has cast doubt on the future of these ancient forests. Indeed, the vast system of U.S. national forests has emerged as the primary battle-ground in the fight over forest use and preservation.

The Clash over National Forests

The U.S. network of national forests includes nearly 192 million acres of forestland in forty-two states and accounts for approximately 8 percent of the total U.S. landmass. Approximately 34.7 million acres of this land has been formally designated as "wilderness" and is thus off-limits to road-building, logging, mining, and other habitat-altering activities. In addition, approximately 4,348 miles of waterway that are part of the U.S. national "Wild and Scenic Rivers" system weave through national forest territory, so public forestlands bordering those rivers are managed with an emphasis on preservation.

But the future of much of the remaining land in the National Forest System is up in the air. Historically, these forests have been an important source of timber for logging companies and oil and gas for energy companies. "For over fifty years [since World War II], we assessed the economic value of our national forests based mostly upon the value of commodities produced from them: the board feet of timber, the tons of coal, the barrels of oil and cubic feet of gas," said former USFS chief Michael Dombeck (Sudetic, "The Forest for the Trees," 2001). Indeed, Forest Service policies were so hospitable to logging and other resource extraction activities that the Forest Service became perceived in some quarters as a de facto subsidiary of the timber and energy industries. But during the 1980s and 1990s environmental groups, scientists, and lawmakers expressed mounting concern about the country's vanishing old-growth forests and the condition of other forest-lands within the system, and industry access to those public forests eroded. According to Forest Service records, the amount of timber harvested in U.S. national forests fell from 11 billion board feet in 1965—with a peak of 12.7 billion board feet in 1987—to 2.9 billion board feet in 1999, less than 4 percent of all timber harvested in the country.

This trend is a disquieting one to the timber industry, which would like to increase its rate and volume of cut in the national forests. Logging opponents, however, continue to campaign for increased protection of forests and their attendant ecosystems. Consequently, environmental groups and timber interests (and the many scientists, foresters, politicians, and communities that have taken sides on the issue) remain locked in a bitter, highly litigious, and occasionally violent clash to stamp the U.S. Forest Service with their own vision of forest stewardship. Neither side has yet been able to generate decisive public support for their position, even though three events of the past decade or so—the spotted owl controversy, the salvage logging rider of 1995, and a federal plan to ban road-building and logging on more than 58 million acres of federal land—have received extensive news media coverage. "The owners of the national forests—the public—remain as confused and uninvolved as ever: vaguely opposed to logging yet consuming more wood products than any other people on earth and, for the most part, completely clueless as to why or how the government is selling their trees" (Roberts, "The Federal Chain-Saw Massacre," 1997).

Spotted Owls and Old-Growth Forests in the Pacific Northwest

During the 1970s, new environmental laws forced the Forest Service to change its mandate to put increased management emphasis on nontimber uses and stewardship of wildlife. But the long-simmering debate over management of U.S. national forests did not boil over until the early 1990s, when concerns over the future of the Northern spotted owl and other endangered species forced timber companies in the Pacific Northwest to dramatically curtail their logging of valuable old-growth forests on federal land.

Opposition to logging the remaining old-growth forests of the Pacific Northwest had been growing for some time prior to the late 1980s, when environmentalists took the federal government to court for failing to protect the endangered Northern spotted owl—which relies on the region's old-growth forest for nesting and breeding habitat—in accordance with the requirements of the Endangered Species Act. This legal action was a milestone, and both sides of the logging debate recognized its potential importance. "[Environmentalists argued that the Northern spotted owl] was an 'indicator species,' a canary in the mine, whose decline was a barometer of the failing health of the planet. To loggers, it was a Trojan horse, deliberately constructed to breach the walls and bring ruin to their culture" (Chase, *In a Dark Wood,* 2001).

On May 23, 1991, U.S. District Judge William Dwyer ruled that the Forest Service and other federal agencies had repeatedly violated national environmental laws by treating forests as timber reserves and giving short shrift to their ecosystem stewardship responsibilities. The judge barred the Forest Service from selling any of its trees in the Pacific Northwest until it could demonstrate how it could do so without further endangering the Northern spotted owl. The Dwyer decision immediately halted logging on 24 million acres in seventeen national forests in the region. As federal sales of Pacific Northwest lumber dried up, timber-dependent communities simultaneously braced for the economic impact and denounced the environmental groups that had spearheaded the drive to protect the spotted owl.

Northern spotted owl, Oregon KEVIN SCHAFER/CORBIS

Since the Dwyer decision, assessments of the ruling and its impact on the Pacific Northwest have varied widely. Everyone agrees that the amount of federal timber cut in Oregon and Washington dropped dramatically in the aftermath of the ruling (new limitations on logging of old-growth forests on federal land managed by the U.S. Fish and Wildlife Service also contributed to the decline). But the economic repercussions of the logging ban continue to be hotly debated. Environmental groups and other supporters of the Dwyer ruling contend that dire warnings about economic ruin and rampant unemployment in the region were overstated. They note that both Oregon and Washington enjoyed significant economic expansion during the 1990s despite the downsizing of the timber industry. According to one economic study, when the spotted owl lawsuits were first filed in 1988, timber jobs accounted for 3.6 percent of total employment in Oregon and Washington. By 1994 the number of jobs added each year in all sectors in the two states was

Climate Change and Canada's Northern Forests

Many observers believe that global climate change will dramatically alter the character of the forests of northern Canada—indeed, all of Canada's woodlands. Some scientists believe that Canada's temperature could increase by more than three times the global average (as much as 10 degrees Celsius) over the next century, as regions at higher latitudes are generally expected to feel the impact of global warming more acutely. A temperature change of that magnitude would fundamentally transform the landscape of Canada, but even a modest increase in temperature would have serious repercussions (Canadian Forest Service, *The State of Canada's Forests,* 1999; Canadian Forest Service, *Climate Change and Forests,* 1999).

First, scientists warn that projected climate changes will increase Canada's vulnerability to wildfires, including catastrophic wildfires of truly awesome proportions (Flannigan and Wagner, "Climate Change and Wildfire," 1991; Canadian Forest Service, *Climate Change and Forests,* 1999). In addition, climate change would drastically alter the mix of tree species in various geographic regions of Canada. "On the southern fringe [of the country], northern deciduous species and balsam fir may displace the current mix of spruce, pine, larch, poplar, and birch. In mid-continental areas, grasslands may replace the southern boreal forest. And in the eastern boreal regions, the tree line may advance into areas previously occupied by tundra. Boreal tree species would have to migrate northward at between 1.5 and 5.5 kilometers per year over the next 50 to 100 years to remain within similar climate conditions, which is most likely

(continues)

more than total timber industry employment (Niemi et al., "The Sky Did NOT Fall," 1999). Some supporters even described the suspension of federal timber sales as a boon to the region because it made the area more attractive in "quality-of-life" terms to new businesses and their employees. These factors led some observers to conclude that the ubiquitous "owls versus loggers" characterization of the conflict was a "brilliantly misleading slogan promoted by industry—and conveyed uncritically by the media" (Roberts, "The Federal Chain-Saw Massacre," 1997).

But this was by no means the only perspective on the conflict. Other analysts charged that the logging ban visited severe economic and emotional pain on timber-dependent communities. By all accounts, thousands of loggers and mill-workers lost their jobs in the wake of the Dwyer ruling and were forced to accept new jobs, some of which were not as financially rewarding (estimates of job losses range from 6,000 to more than 20,000, depending on the source).

beyond the adaptive capabilities of most tree species" (Global Forest Watch, *Canada's Forests at a Crossroads,* 2000). For one thing, tree species migration would be severely curtailed by the soil quality of Canada's northern latitudes. "Although the weather may shift, it will take centuries for soil quality to improve. The thin soils of the far north will not be able to support forests, even if the temperature readings suggest they should. The stress created by changing temperatures, shifting rainfall patterns, drought where rain used to be abundant, increased rainfall in areas adapted to be dry, all point to a lengthy period of readjustment for Canada's forests. It is possible that, with time, forests will adapt to the new regime. After all, much of Canada's forest stands on areas once covered in ice. But such transitions usually move at geological speed. These changes will happen too fast for the earth—and too fast for Canadian society" (May, *At the Cutting Edge,* 1998).

Sources:

Canadian Forest Service. 1999. *Climate Change and Forests.* Ottawa: Natural Resources Canada.

———. 1999. *The State of Canada's Forests: 1998–1999 Innovation.* Ottawa: Natural Resources Canada.

———. 2000. *The State of Canada's Forests, 1999–2000: Forests in the New Millennium.* Ottawa: Natural Resources Canada, 2000.

Flannigan, M. D., and C. E. Van Wagner. 1991. "Climate Change and Wildfire in Canada." *Canadian Journal of Forest Research* 21.

Global Forest Watch. 2000. *Canada's Forests at a Crossroads: An Assessment in the Year 2000.* Washington, DC: World Resources Institute.

May, Elizabeth. 1998. *At the Cutting Edge: The Crisis in Canada's Forests.* San Francisco: Sierra Club.

Many timber towns also suffered because of their longtime reliance on a 1908 law that distributes 25 cents of every USFS dollar in forest-related revenue to local communities for school and road expenditures. Critics of the ban on federal timber sales also pointed out that whereas large timber companies with extensive private landholdings were able to weather the loss of federal logs, smaller outfits that depend on national forests for their livelihood were sometimes forced to close their doors. According to one critic, the Dwyer ruling "transform[ed] the region into a western Appalachia, dotted with pockets of poverty. As these towns die, they experience more crime, greater drug use, more suicides, spousal abuse and divorce, more limited public services, and worse or fewer schools" (Chase, *In a Dark Wood,* 2001).

Finally, logging advocates charged that the Dwyer decision forced the United States to import increased quantities of timber from Canada and other countries. "As federal logging in the Pacific Northwest is slowed to a virtual standstill, species extinction in tropical forests has accelerated at a thunderous rate," claimed one forester. "Is saving the spotted owl and the marbled murrelet worth the loss of 8,000 to 10,000 species in the Philippines, Malaysia, Indonesia, and Madagascar?" ("Congress Debates the Endangered Species Act," 1995). But this assertion has not gone unchallenged, either. "From 1991 to 1995, when the federal timber harvest was cut in half by owl litigation, America's total timber production (public and private) actually climbed by more than a billion board feet and timber companies were somehow able to export to Asia tens of thousands of 'raw,' or unprocessed, logs—and with them, the processing jobs previously held by American workers" (Roberts, "The Federal Chain-Saw Massacre," 1997).

The battle to shape public perceptions of the Dwyer ruling and its impact on the economies of Pacific Northwest states is unlikely to end anytime in the near future. In the meantime, wildlife biologists state that the future of the region's Northern spotted owl—the small bird that triggered the entire controversy—remains uncertain. Scientists believe that the bird's rate of population decline is slowing, but they admit that the long-term outlook for the owl is shrouded in doubt.

The Salvage Rider of 1995

The struggle over U.S. national forests further intensified in 1995, when the Republican-controlled Congress passed—and President Bill Clinton, a Democrat, signed—a bill that directed the Forest Service to triple its volume of "salvage logging" in national forests over a two-year period. The rider triggered angry denunciations from the environmental community and an explosion of logging activity across the country.

"Salvage logging" involves the culling of dead trees and the thinning of live ones from forests. This practice helps prevent forest fires by removing "fuel load"—dead and dying trees, dense undergrowth, and stands of small trees that carry surface fires into the forest canopy, creating crown fires of dangerous speed and size—and it is a standard tool in the management arsenal of many foresters. But critics of Forest Service policy claim that "salvage" became a preferred designation in the 1980s because it circumvents normal 40-acre limits on clear-cut size, permits logging in areas where harvesting is usually prohibited, and enables the agency to keep all receipts from sales, unlike regular timber sales, which are fed into the Treasury. In fact, the popularity of "salvage sales" surged in the late 1980s, a time when timber sales in the Pacific Northwest and elsewhere began to drop because of legal challenges from environmental groups. Between 1988 and 1989, USFS salvage receipts quadrupled, from $32 million to $144 million. By 1990 salvage sales accounted for 26 percent of the federal timber program. And by 1993, salvage accounted for 42 percent of federal timber sales (this percentage was skewed in part by the steep decline in regular sales from Pacific Northwest forests, most of which had been closed to logging by the Dwyer ruling).

The Forest Service attributed this sharp rise in salvage sales to costly wildfire seasons—due in part to sharp declines in federal timber sales—that highlighted the need to remove fuel loads from vulnerable forests. Indeed, advocates characterized the 1995 salvage program as an overdue response to a brewing forest health crisis (see sidebar on page 98). But critics interpreted increased use of the salvage designation as a cynical maneuver to skirt ongoing environmental litigation against regular timber sales. Opponents decried the loss of ecologically valuable old-growth forests that were opened to logging by the rider, and they bitterly objected to provisions in the rider that essentially suspended public, administrative, and judicial oversight of timber sales. Indeed, the bill suspended applicable environmental laws for the duration of the rider's existence.

Certainly, the 1995 salvage logging rider took use of the salvage timber classification to new heights. It not only mandated a dramatic increase in sales of salvage timber in national forests but also made it possible for loggers to take large quantities of healthy forest as well. "The bill authorized the agency to sell not just dead or dying trees but any 'associated' green trees, a wonderfully ambiguous term that effectively permitted *any* tree to qualify as 'salvage'" (Roberts, "The Federal Chain-Saw Massacre," 1997). During the two-year life of the rider, massive salvage operations were undertaken in national forests in Alaska, Idaho, the Pacific Northwest, and the northern Rockies.

Predictably, the expiration of the salvage logging rider on December 31, 1996, prompted widely divergent reviews of its efficacy. Timber companies and other prologging advocates characterized the salvage logging campaign as a tremendous success that simultaneously aided the industry and lessened U.S. vulnerability to catastrophic wildfires. The environmental community, on the other hand, saw it as a terrible event that degraded large expanses of forest wilderness at public expense. Indeed, the Congressional Research Service later reported that the Forest Service overestimated the selling price of salvage timber by nearly 100 percent and stated that the two-year rider may have cost the U.S. Treasury more than $200 million.

Roadless Protection in the National Forests

The next high-profile battle for the future of U.S. national forests rumbled to life in the late 1990s. During that period, the Clinton administration began weighing proposals to ban road construction—and by extension, logging, mining, and other resource extraction activities—from some as-yet-undisturbed forestlands in the system. The Forest Service subsequently held more than 600 public meetings nationwide and solicited volumes of scientific testimony on the potential benefits and drawbacks of such a ban. A record total of 1.6 million comments were received on the proposed measure, with 96 percent of respondents expressing support for the ban. Polling on the issue, meanwhile, showed strong support for roadless area conservation across all regions and demographic groups, including hunters, anglers, hikers, canoeists, and other frequent recreational users of national forest land (*Roadless Area Conservation Final Rule and Record of Decision*, 2001). In the meantime, the Forest Service placed an eighteen-month moratorium on new road-building in 33 million acres of national forests in February 1999. This decision halted road construction in 130 of 156 national forests and heightened anxiety within the timber industry and among prologging advocates.

In January 2001, President Clinton announced a ban on road-building (and most logging and mining) in 58 million acres of roadless forest in the National Forest System, approximately one-third of the total land area managed by the USFS. This so-called roadless rule was hailed by environmental groups as one of the most significant conservation measures of the past century and attacked by the timber industry and its allies as a blatant federal land grab that would have severe economic repercussions for numerous Western communities.

Proponents of the ban immediately attempted to defuse the economic arguments against implementing the roadless rule. Conservation groups and economists pointed out that few timber harvests took place in unprotected roadless areas during the 1990s, yet nearby communities enjoyed steady population and economic growth during those years (Power, "The Economic Impact of National Forest Roadless Areas," 2000).

Other objections to the road ban centered on the loss of local control of national forests. Conservation groups and other supporters of the ban, however, contend that forest authorities at the state and local levels were too often influenced by powerful corporate and political interests. "Where permitted, local control of national forests has brought economic and environmental ruin: landslides, sprawling clearcuts, silted rivers, endangered fish and wildlife, and single-species plantations subject to pest infestations and inhospitable to native fauna," claimed one supporter of the ban (Williams, "Clinton's Last Stand," 2000). For its part, the Forest Service admitted that "[w]hile individual decisions to build roads may achieve local management objectives, collectively they may result in a continued net loss of the quality and quantity of inventoried roadless areas nationally" (*Roadless Area Conservation Final Rule and Record of Decision*, 2001).

Supporters of the roadless rule also noted that it included numerous provisions that allowed for local discretion in forest management (such as regulation of off-road-vehicle use), and that it included a number of notable exceptions to the roadless ban. For instance, the roadless rule still permitted the logging and selling of small trees in roadless areas to reduce fire risk, for personal use, or for administrative purposes. The rule also "grandfathered" in an enormous pipeline of mostly roadless area sales in the Tongass National Forest in Alaska, despite the ready availability of substantial timber in previously roaded portions of the Tongass. The ban also included provisions allowing road-building when needed to address imminent threats to property or human life; allowed expansion of oil and gas operations in roadless areas, including new areas, within the perimeter of existing or renewed leases; left grazing regulations untouched; and closed no existing logging roads (ibid.).

The roadless rule also received support from those who claimed that the federal timber program as currently constituted was a significant drain on the U.S. Treasury, because receipts from timber sales were outpaced by administrative costs associated with those sales, including road-building. Indeed, this aspect of logging on national forest lands came under heightened scrutiny during the 1990s. According to the General Accounting Office, the federal timber program operated at an average revenue deficit of $330 million from 1992 to 1997. In 1998, the last year for which the Forest Service issued a detailed financial statement on its timber sales, it reported a loss of $126 million on the program. According to some analysts, however, the actual cost of the program was much greater. In 2001, Taxpayers for Common Sense, a national budget watchdog group, issued a report in which it claimed that the federal timber program cost taxpayers $407 million more than it received for timber sales in 1998. The group claimed that 105 of 111 national forests failed to return as much money as they spent managing their timber program. It also reported that the Siuslaw National Forest in Oregon, which did the most restoration and cut the fewest old-growth trees of any forest in the national system, made the greatest profit ($11.5 million), while the forest that proposed the most old-growth logging—Willamette National Forest, also in Oregon—was the biggest money loser in the national system ($30 million) (Taxpayers for Common Sense, *From the Ashes,* 2001). Finally, many critics contend that these figures underestimate the true economic cost of the timber program because they do not take into account the indirect costs of logging, such as reduced water quality and lost fisheries revenue.

The Forest Service also cited the state of its existing forest roads in defending the roadless rule. Nearly 390,000 miles of logging roads wind through U.S. national forests, but by the Forest Service's own admission, only about 20 percent of them are currently maintained in accordance with environmental and safety regulations. In fact, the Forest Service has a road and bridge reconstruction and maintenance backlog of more than $8.4 billion. By ending road-building in wilderness forest areas, the agency stated that it would be better able to repair long-neglected roads in previously established timber-cutting areas (*Roadless Area Conservation Final Rule and Record of Decision*, 2001). Finally, Clinton administration Forest Service chief Mike Dombeck stated that "there is another reason to stop building roads, and it is the same reason that the roadless areas are still roadless in the first place. The most valuable timber that was easy to reach is already gone. Of the 58.5 million acres protected by the road-building ban, only 9 million are classified as suitable timberlands, and those are generally low-productivity areas where access is very difficult because the terrain is so steep or because the trees are at the tops of the mountains. In many instances, it would cost more to prepare and harvest the forest than the lumber is worth" (Sudetic, "Forest for the Trees," 2001). Indeed, the Forest Service estimated that the roadless policy would affect less than 0.5 percent of the nation's overall timber production and an even smaller fraction of oil and natural gas production (*Roadless Area Conservation Final Rule and Record of Decision*, 2001).

The Forest Service announced the road-building ban in the waning days of the Clinton administration. But when President George W. Bush assumed office in January 2001, his administration initially delayed implementation of the rule, then said that it intended to modify the ban to provide for greater local input and forest-by-forest decisions on logging, road-building, and other development. These announcements sparked another hail of suits and countersuits by industry, state governments, and environmental groups. The latter constituency has voiced particular concern that the Bush administration seeks to eliminate ecosystem health as a top priority in national forest management, remove specific requirements for scientific review when making forest management decisions, curtail public comment periods on agency policies and management, and undermine the Endangered Species Act by weakening ties between the Forest Service and federal agencies that protect endangered species. For its part, the Bush administration states that it is dedicated to managing U.S. national forests in an environmentally responsible manner.

The ultimate fate of the road-building ban will be decided in the U.S. court system. In May 2001, an Idaho district court temporarily halted implementation of the road-building ban with an injunction, citing a "grossly inadequate" comment period and a rule-making process that violated provisions of the National Environmental Protection Act. The district ruling was praised by protimber advocates and denounced by environmental groups. Since that time, the legal battle over implementation of the original 58.5-million-acre road ban has remained at a fever pitch, with the final outcome in doubt. But even if the road-building ban is eventually instituted, environmental groups have expressed concern that their victory will be brief. They note that in 2001, the Forest Service launched and completed yet another comment period at the behest of the Bush administration. The second comment period is widely regarded as a precursor to a potentially major revision of the rule.

North American Logging Operations and Their Environmental Impact

By many measurements, the state of U.S. forests has improved dramatically since the beginning of the twentieth century, when the nation was in the midst of a sustained campaign of indiscriminate logging that devastated forests throughout the eastern United States, from Maine to the Midwest and beyond. This drive to clear forestland for farming and provide timber for rapidly expanding cities was so ruthlessly efficient that only scattered patches of old-growth forest remain in the East, outside the Great Smoky Mountains and the Adirondacks. In Michigan, for instance, federal researchers estimated that more than 92 percent of the state's original timber stands had been felled by the late 1920s (Dempsey, *Ruin and Recovery*, 2001). Over time, however, the majority of these logged-over lands gradually recovered from this abuse and degradation and sprouted young forests. Indeed, the number of total trees in the United States increased steadily after World War II, boosted by intensive forest management and the reversion of idle farmland to woodlands.

Canadian lumber ROBERT SEMENIUK/CORBIS

Today, many U.S. forests—whether publicly or privately owned—are managed in a more enlightened manner than in generations past, with an emphasis on sustainability and environmental stewardship that was wholly absent in previous eras. Large swaths of forestland owned at the federal and state levels enjoy some form of protection from logging, mining, and other resource extraction activities, while those areas that are open to timber harvest are subject to state and federal safety and environmental regulations. In addition, some states provide tax incentives for private landowners to protect forested areas (via conservation easements, for instance) or maintain cooperative forest management programs that bring together public and private landholders. Timber certification programs have also taken root, boosted by the increased participation of major retailers that have heeded consumer demands for "eco-friendly" wood products. By 2000 approximately 1.78 million hectares (4.4 million acres) of commercial forestland in the United States had been certified by the Forest Stewardship Council, an international nonprofit organization devoted to "environmentally appropriate, socially beneficial, and economically viable management of the world's forests" (Forest Stewardship Council, On-line Data Service, 2000, http://www.fscoax.org). Encouraged by such incentives—and the long-term economic value of maintaining healthy forests—some members of the timber industry have adopted meaningful sustainable forestry initiatives such as major reseeding programs. U.S. forests of notable ecological significance have also been preserved through the efforts of the Nature Conservancy and other conservation organizations that acquire ecologically sensitive land. In 2001, for example, the New England Forestry Foundation purchased more than 762,000 acres of forest in Maine—an area larger than Rhode Island—to protect it from development.

In Canada, timber companies and other logging advocates also maintain that their country strikes an appropriate balance between resource extraction and environmental protection. Defenders of Canadian logging activities and policies note that several provinces have adopted progressive forest management policies—such as Quebec's 1994 Forest Protection Strategy and British Columbia's 1995 Forest Practices Code—to curtail careless "cut and run" logging and other destructive harvesting practices that characterized earlier decades. Some companies, especially smaller logging and mill operations, have also adopted operating practices that stress sustainable and environmentally sensitive use of the land. By 2000 more than 212,000 hectares of Canadian timberland had been certified by the Forest Stewardship Council.

Despite these and other conservation-oriented initiatives, however, timber harvesting practices in Canada and the United States have drawn withering criticism from environmental groups, scientists, tourism-dependent businesses, and other constituencies in recent decades. These sectors contend that North America is frittering away its abundant forest resources by supporting forest management policies and practices that take an unacceptable toll on the environment. This sentiment is based on several factors, but one of the most frequently cited targets for criticism is the North American timber industry's penchant for "clearcutting." Under this method of tree harvesting, a tract of forest—usually of significant size—is cleared of all its trees at the same time. In most years, more than 90 percent of the territory logged in Canada is cleared in this fashion, according to Environment Canada and the Canadian Forest Service. In the United States, meanwhile, "clearcutting is the principal regeneration harvest system used in the national forests, and is particularly important in . . . the eastern half of the country and Alaska" (Backiel and Gorte, "Clearcutting in the National Forests," 1992).

Clearcutting

Clearcutting does have its defenders. Timber companies cite it as the safest and most efficient means of gathering raw materials, and they claim that resorting to other methods of harvest would reduce profits, trigger higher prices for wood products, and jeopardize jobs. Proponents also cite it as a legitimate forest management tool. The Society of American Foresters, for example, describes clearcutting as "an appropriate silvicultural method for regenerating species that are shade-intolerant and the optimum method to achieve other management objectives. . . . Clearcutting properly applied, though at times unsightly, does not cause or promote environmental degradation" (Society of American Foresters, "Clearcutting," 2001). Some defenders of the practice also claim that clearcutting simply mimics large wildfires and other natural events that consume large expanses of woodlands every year. Finally, advocates point out that some species of flora and fauna—including popular game animals such as grouse and rare species such as Kirtland's warblers—actually fare much better in clearcut areas, which often regenerate over time into young woodlands, than they do in mature, closed-canopy forestlands.

Nonetheless, clearcutting draws heavy fire from Canadian and U.S. environmental groups, aboriginal communities, some scientists, and various other constituencies. Opponents charge that large clearcuts destroy wilderness ecosystems by fragmenting vital migration corridors and sanctuary areas, removing forest canopies that provide vital shade over salmon and trout streams, and taking ancient trees that provide habitat for cavity-nesting birds and other species. "Species that prefer old-growth and closed canopy forest, such as martens, California red-backed voles, northern flying squirrels, and red-backed salamanders, to mention a few, have declined in abundance in logged forests relative to unlogged forests. These species' decline in turn has impacts on other parts of the ecosystem. For instance, a reduction in salamander populations (which are an integral part of the forest food chain) affects bird and mammal species that rely on them as food, as well as forest floor ecology and nutrient cycles" (Ercelawn, *End of the Road,* 1999).

Figure 4.1 Area Logged Annually in Canada, 1920–1995

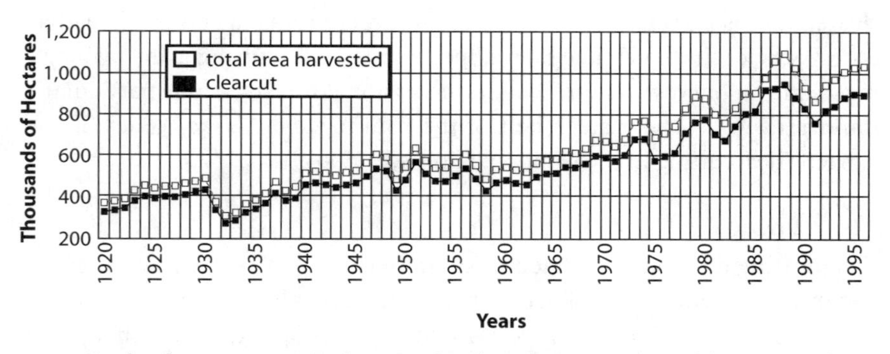

SOURCE: For data from 1920–1992: Environment Canada. 1995. *Sustaining Canada's Forests: Timber Harvesting, Technical Supplement No. 95-4.* Ottawa: Environment Canada. For data from 1993–1996: Canadian Council of Forest Ministers. 2000. "National Forestry Database Program: Silviculture: Table 6.1.1." Online at: http://nfdp.ccfm.org (January 19).

Critics also take issue with comparisons between clearcutting and wildfires. "Fires do not leave behind a network of logging roads, landings and skid trails, creating a long-lasting risk of landslides. Fires and other natural disturbances rarely do substantial damage to the soil. Clearcuts often do. The heavy mechanization of clear-cuts gouges the soil, often removes the top layer of organic material, exposes mineral soils, and compacts the soil beneath the heavy equipment" (May, *At the Cutting Edge,* 1998). Opponents also claim that the timber industry makes extensive use of the "clearcut-as-substitute-for-wildfire" rationale even in regions that rarely see major wildfires, such as the coastal rain forests of British Columbia and southern Alaska. Finally, many people oppose clearcutting for aesthetic reasons, since the practice transforms forests into stump-riddled clearings, albeit temporarily.

Plantations and Old-Growth Forest

Postharvest forest regeneration schemes, which transform expanses of forestland into tree plantations consisting solely of commercially desirable species, have also been excoriated by some environmental groups. Logging advocates fiercely defend the use of tree plantations. "America's major timberland owners have been investing in plantation-related biotech research since the 1960s, funding university-led research cooperatives that have perfected numerous strains of genetically superior trees. Such trees grow faster, display greater resistance to disease and climatic extremes, and typically exhibit better form—an important consideration for both lumber and paper manufacturers" (A Word about 'Frankentrees'" 2001). Defenders of monocultural forestry also contend that the timber generated from these operations might otherwise be culled from wild forests. "Fast growing forest plantations are central to meeting soaring global demand for wood fiber while also protecting the world's wild forests from further exploitation" (ibid.).

But opponents of the practice insist that in the greater scheme of things, tree plantations have done little to slow timber-cutting incursions into virgin forestland, either in North America or elsewhere. Indeed, Environment Canada reports that approximately 90 percent of all territory logged in Canada has never been cut before (Environment Canada, *Sustaining Canada's Forests,* 1995), and gaining access to timber-rich old-growth forests remains a primary focus of the logging industry throughout North America. In Alberta, for instance, logging operations are sweeping through the province's publicly owned old-growth forests so swiftly that trees over 150 years of age may soon be totally eradicated from Crown lands (Timoney, *The Old-Growth Forests of Alberta,* 1998).

Figure 4.2 Importers of Canadian Forest Products

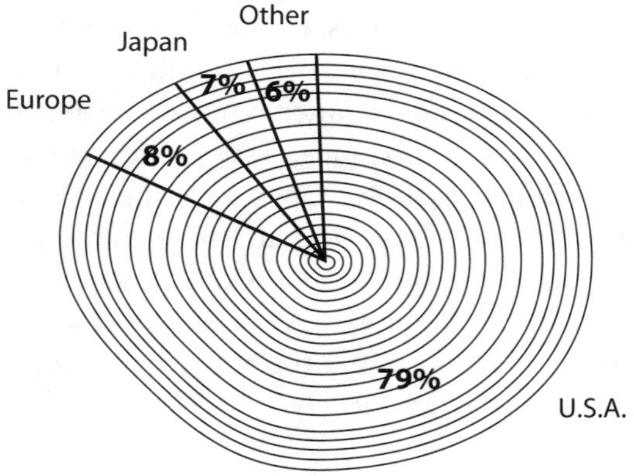

SOURCE: Canadian Forest Service. 1999. *The State of Canada's Forests: 1998–1999 Innovation.* Ottawa: Natural Resources Canada.

Farther west, British Columbia has long touted its extensive system of heavily forested parks and preserves, now 12 percent of its total land area. In 2001 it also agreed to protect 1.5 million acres of the Great Bear Rain Forest—a beautiful region of rain forests, mountains, and coastal islands in central B.C.—from logging, mining, and hydropower interests (a development moratorium has been placed on another 2 million acres of the Great Bear to study possible land use and protection measures for the region). By all accounts, this agreement, cobbled together by provincial officials, environmental groups, industry groups, First Nation representatives, and other local community leaders, is a conservation landmark for Canada. One of the world's largest remaining tracts of intact temperate rain forest, the region supports grizzlies, wolves, and a tremendous array of other creatures. It is also the only known home of a rare white-furred variation of the black bear known to international environmental groups as the Spirit Bear (an estimated one in ten black bears in the region is born with a double-recessive gene that makes its fur snow white).

But despite such set-asides, environmental groups contend that British Columbia's forest policies encourage conversion of forest areas to monocultural tree farms. By the late 1990s, more than 80 percent of the coastal forestland of British Columbia had been allocated to logging companies for harvest. Some of the tracts technically included within these allocations are probably safe from harvest because of surrounding mountainous terrain, but significant sections of these ancient forests will eventually be logged (Global Forest Watch, *Canada's Forests at a Crossroads*, 2000).

Rate of Cut

North America's timber industry also has been criticized for harvesting the nation's trees at a fundamentally unsustainable rate. Some studies indicate that while actual logging rates in Canada usually fall below the total Annual Allowable Cut (AAC)—the amount of timber made available for cutting by individual provinces—many Canadian AACs have been deliberately set above long-term sustainable harvest levels so that companies can log large tracts of primary and old-growth forests, which yield higher timber volumes (ibid.; Clark, *Timber Supply and Endangered Spaces,* 1995). This dynamic has been particularly problematic in timber-rich provinces such as British Columbia, where about 90 percent of Crown forests managed as "timber supply areas" were being logged at an unsustainable pace in the late 1990s (Marchak et al., *Falldown,* 1999). The environmental community also contends that the amount of Canadian forest certified as "well-managed" by the Forest Stewardship Council is paltry given the total size of the nation's holdings. In the United States, meanwhile, environmental groups charge that several states enforce timber sale mandates that are fundamentally unsustainable over the long term.

Logging Roads

"Of all the things that we do on national forests, road building leaves the most lasting imprint on the landscape," stated former USFS chief Michael Dombeck in January 1997. These words echo the sentiments of many environmental groups and members of the scientific community who describe the vast network of logging roads criss-crossing North America's forests as a major threat to wilderness habitat. "[There is a] cascade of damaging effects that follow a bulldozer into the forest, including diminished water quality, fragmentation of wildlife habitat, and a loss of ecological integrity," charged one writer. "By changing the hydrology of an area, roads inexorably damage fish habitat by accelerating the silting over of spawning grounds, reducing the quality of wintering habitat by filling in deep pools, and warming streams where temperature-sensitive species live" (Glick, "Disturbing the Peace," 1998). Indeed, the National Marine Fisheries Service has cited logging road construction as a significant factor in the decline of the Pacific Northwest salmon.

Alteration and fragmentation of wilderness areas from roads, meanwhile, take many forms. For instance, studies indicate that logging roads displace species sensitive to disturbance or dependent on forest interior habitat. "Species like grizzly bears, wolves, and elk avoid otherwise suitable habitat near roads. They may modify their home range, and they have been shown to select areas with lower road densities than the average on the landscape. As a result, high-quality habitat becomes effectively unavailable to them" (Ercelawn, *End of the Road,* 1999). This can be a particularly harsh blow for threatened or endangered animal species that can ill afford the loss of calving areas, migration corridors, and other wilderness sanctuaries. In addition, logging roads also increase the incidence of destructive debris slides, especially in mountainous regions. After winter storms in 1995–1996, for instance, 70 percent of the more than 400 landslides that rumbled out of the mountains of Idaho—many of them pouring into rivers located in valleys below—were directly linked to the presence of Forest Service logging roads. Finally, numerous scientific studies indicate that invasive species are more likely to establish themselves in roaded areas, permanently altering forest ecosystems.

Oversight of Public Forests

Another charge leveled by opponents of logging is that control of public forests in the United States and Canada is too often ceded to timber companies without ensuring adequate regulatory oversight or public input. In the United States, these accusations intensified in 2001, when the U.S. Forest Service published a proposal that would allow national forest supervisors to approve small timber sales, road construction, mining projects, and off-road vehicle (ORV) trails without seeking public comment. That same year, the Forest Service sought to complete the largest postfire logging plan in the agency's history without providing any public comment period. The plan called for the sale of 44,000 acres of timber (an estimated 176 million board feet) that had been scorched by wildfire within Montana's Bitterroot National Forest. But a coalition of conservation groups objected to the sale, which would have harvested more than double the amount of timber taken from the forest over the previous decade. They argued that the massive logging plan was not based on sound forestry practices and would decimate habitat for trout and other threatened species in the region. In January 2002 a federal judge halted the sale, saying that the Forest Service violated the public's right to be involved in decisions affecting public lands. A few weeks later, the two sides reached a court-mediated deal that permitted logging of about two-thirds of the timber in the original proposal in return for protection of 15,000 acres of roadless wilderness that environmental groups saw as crucial habitat for endangered trout species.

Debate over public input into management of U.S. forests escalated in 2003 when the Bush administration touted a new "Healthy Forests Initiative." Backers tout the proposal as a badly needed thinning program that will reduce wildfires, but opponents characterize it as a windfall for loggers, noting that the initiative streamlines environmental rules and curtails the public's legal rights to contest timber sales. In Canada, meanwhile, environmentalists charge that logging restrictions contained in British Columbia's Forest Practices Code and the Canadian Fisheries Act have been rendered meaningless by lax enforcement. Elsewhere, Ontario's provincial leadership ordered the transfer of nearly all Crown land forests to industry control via long-term leases in the 1990s, while simultaneously proposing the removal of any limitations on clearcut size and imposing personnel cuts on forest management agencies responsible for ensuring industry compliance with logging laws. And critics contend that the Quebec Forest Act gives wood processing plants near-perpetual cutting rights over many provincial forests without adequate consideration of environmental or social impact.

Industry spokesmen, though, counter opposition to long-term leases by pointing out that such arrangements provide timber companies with economic incentive to be good stewards of the land. Even the executive director of the Sierra Club of Canada acknowledged that there is "a certain persuasiveness to the argument. . . . With forests requiring anywhere from forty to eighty years, depending on the ecosystem, before another round of logging can be undertaken, private companies argue that it is only logical that if they had a long-term stake, such as they would have in their own land, they would be more likely to take responsibility for the future productivity of the forest" (May, *At the Cutting Edge,* 1998).

Given the acrimony and distrust that has characterized the debate over logging practices in the United States and Canada in recent years, many loggers, environmentalists, scientists, and other observers have become openly skeptical about the values and motives of their opponents. But as one Canadian government report noted, "[B]oth sides have common interests. A forest worker may also use the forest for hunting and fishing, and may take domestic water supply from a creek downstream from a timber-harvesting site; an environmentalist's job and quality of life may exist because of the economic contribution of the forest industry to community prosperity" (Commission on Resources and Environment, "A Sustainability Act for British Columbia," Ministry of Sustainable Resource Management, 2000).

Increased recognition of this dynamic has led some people to conclude that common ground can be found if hatred and suspicion can be replaced with empathy and a spirit of cooperation. This belief has been nurtured by specific instances in which timber interests and environmental organizations have been able to hammer out agreements that have addressed both environmental and economic concerns. In the 1990s, for example, citizens of Quebec's Gaspé Peninsula formed the Coalition for the Integrated Management of the

Cascapédia Watershed when excessive logging on a key tributary of the Grande Cascapédia River caused increased spring flows and heightened sedimentation and erosion of essential salmon spawning habitat. "[The organization] obtained a one-year moratorium on logging to assess its impact on the watershed. Since then the coalition has worked with logging companies on improvements, including better road planning and logging practices. In 2000 more than 20 sites in the watershed were upgraded, and repairs were completed on logging roads that had been carrying sediment into waterways" (Burke, "On the Brink," 2001). These and other efforts to institute environmentally sustainable timber harvesting practices reflect a recognition that "logging . . . is neither all good nor all bad. It must be evaluated in the context of the ecosystem where it takes place and the manner in which it is practiced" (Wilcove, *The Condor's Shadow*, 1999).

Sources:

American Lands Alliance. 1999. *National Forest Yearbook 1999.* Washington, DC: ALA.

Arno, Steve. 1996. *Evergreen* (September–October).

Backiel, Adela, and Ross W. Gorte. 1992. *Clearcutting in the National Forests.* Washington, DC: Congressional Research Service.

Berger, John. 1998. *Understanding Forests.* San Francisco: Sierra Club.

"The Bountiful Harvest: Securing America's Forest Future." 2001. *Evergreen* 15 (fall).

Bryant, Dirk, D. Nielson, and L. Tangley. 1997. *The Last Frontier Forests: Ecosystems and Economies on the Edge.* Washington, DC: World Resources Institute.

Burke, Monte. 2001. "On the Brink." *Audubon* 103 (November–December).

Canadian Council of Forest Ministers. 1997. *Compendium of Canadian Forestry Statistics, 1996.* Ottawa: Natural Resources Canada-Canadian Forest Service.

———. 1997. *Criteria and Indicators of Sustainable Forest Management in Canada.* Ottawa: Natural Resources Canada-Canadian Forest Service.

Canadian Forest Service. 1999. *Climate Change and Forests.* Ottawa: Natural Resources Canada.

———. 1999. *The State of Canada's Forests: 1998–1999 Innovation.* Ottawa: Natural Resources Canada.

———. 2000. *The State of Canada's Forests, 1999–2000: Forests in the New Millennium.* Ottawa: Natural Resources Canada.

Chase, Alston. 2001. *In a Dark Wood: The Fight over Forests and the Myth of Nature.* New Brunswick, NJ: Transaction.

Clark, Tom. 1995. *Timber Supply and Endangered Spaces.* Toronto: World Wildlife Fund.

Commission on Resources and Environment. 2000. *A Sustainability Act for British Columbia.* Vancouver: Ministry of Sustainable Resource Management.

"Congress Debates the Endangered Species Act." 1995. *Evergreen* (May–June).

Cooper, Mary H. 1998. "National Forests." *CQ Researcher* 8 (October 16).

Dempsey, Dave. 2001. *Ruin and Recovery.* Ann Arbor: University of Michigan Press.

Environment Canada. 1995. *Sustaining Canada's Forests: Timber Harvesting SOE Bulletin 95–4.* Ottawa: Environment Canada.

Ercelawn, A. 1999. *End of the Road—The Adverse Ecological Impacts of Roads and Logging: A Compilation of Independently Reviewed Research.* New York: Natural Resources Defense Council.

Glick, Dan. 1998. "Disturbing the Peace." *Wilderness* (annual publication).

Global Forest Watch. 2000. *Canada's Forests at a Crossroads: An Assessment in the Year 2000.* Washington, DC: World Resources Institute.

Gofte, Ross W. 1996. "The Salvage Timber Sale Rider: Overview and Policy Issues." Washington, DC: Congressional Research Service, Report of the CRS, June 24.

Kimmins, Hamish. 1992. *Balancing Act: Environmental Issues in Forestry.* Vancouver: University of British Columbia Press.

Lee, Robert G. 1990. "Social and Cultural Implications of Implementing 'A Conservation Strategy for the Northern Spotted Owl.'" College of Forest Resources, University of Washington, June 21.

MacCleery, Douglas W. 1992. *American Forests: A History of Resiliency and Recovery.* Durham, NC: Forest History Society.

Marchak, M. Patricia. 1995. *Logging the Globe.* Montreal: McGill-Queen's University Press.

Marchak, M. Patricia, S. Aycock, and D. M. Herbert. 1999. *Falldown: Forest Policy in British Columbia.* Vancouver: David Suzuki Foundation and Ecotrust Canada.

May, Elizabeth. 1998. *At the Cutting Edge: The Crisis in Canada's Forests.* San Francisco: Sierra Club.

Mitchell, John G. 1997. "Our National Forests: In the Line of Fire." *National Geographic* 196 (March).

Niemi, Ernie, Ed Whitelaw, and Elizabeth Grossman. 1999. *The Sky Did NOT Fall: The Pacific Northwest's Response to Logging Reductions.* Eugene, OR: ECONNorthwest.

Power, Thomas Michael. 1998. *Lost Landscapes and Failed Economies: The Search for a Value of Place.* Washington, DC: Island.

———. 2000. "The Economic Impact of National Forest Roadless Areas." *Earth Island Journal* 14 (winter).

Rauber, Paul. 2000. "Buzz Cut." *Sierra* 85 (September–October).

Roadless Area Conservation Final Rule and Record of Decision. 2001. Final Environmental Impact Statement, January 12 (66 Fed. Reg. 3245–3246).

Roberts, Paul. 1997. "The Federal Chain-Saw Massacre." *Harper's Magazine* 294 (June).

Ross, Monique. 1995. *Forest Management in Canada.* Calgary: Canadian Institute of Resources Law.

Sedjo, Roger A., ed. 2000. *A Vision for the U.S. Forest Service: Goals for Its Next Century.* Washington, DC: Resources for the Future.

Society of American Foresters. 2001. "Clearcutting—The Position of the Society of American Foresters." http://www.safnet.org/archive/clearcut.htm.

Sudetic, Chuck. 2001. "The Forest for the Trees." *Rolling Stone* 871 (June 21).

Taxpayers for Common Sense. 2001. *From the Ashes: Reducing the Rising Costs and Harmful Effects of Western Wildfires.* Washington, DC: TCS.

Timoney, K. P. 1998. *The Old-Growth Forests of Alberta.* Sherwood Park, AB: Treeline Ecological Research.

UN Food and Agriculture Organization. 1999. FAOSTAT On-line Statistical Service. http://www.fao.org.

———. 1999. *State of the World's Forests 1999.* Rome: FAO.

———. 2001. *State of the World's Forests 2001.* Rome: FAO.

Wilcove, David S. 1999. *The Condor's Shadow: The Loss and Recovery of Wildlife in America.* New York: W. H. Freeman.

Williams, Ted. 2000. "Clinton's Last Stand." *Audubon* 102 (May–June).

"A Word about 'Frankentrees.'" 2001. *Evergreen* (fall).

World Wildlife Canada. 1999. *Canada's Commitment to Forest Protected Areas: A WWF Status Report.* Toronto: WWF-Canada.

5

Agriculture

—Illisa Kelman

North America covers 14 percent of the earth's land area. Though only 27 percent of the continent is devoted to agriculture, North American farms—with their unprecedented output channeled through increasingly open markets, trade, and aid—feed and clothe people around the globe (UN Environment Programme, *Global Environment Outlook 2000,* 1999). The United States accounts for the majority of agricultural production on the continent. Nearly 82 percent of North American cropland and all but 10 percent of the land in permanent pasture lies south of the Canadian border, while only 7 to 8 percent of Canada is farmable (Environment Canada, "Cultivating a Secure Future," 2000).

Privately owned farmland covers 907 million of the 1.893 billion acres of the United States. Ranchers control the largest portion of U.S. farmland, with 35 percent, followed by farmers with 27 percent (U.S. Department of Agriculture, *1997 National Resources Inventory,* 2000). U.S. production is increasingly concentrated among the few largest agricultural operations. Likewise, the number of very large farms in Canada more than doubled from 1981 to 1996 (Statistics Canada, *2001 Census of Agriculture,* 2002). But small farms account for the majority of agricultural land in Canada and play a critical role in conservation and environmental quality.

In 1999–2000, the United States led global export market shares in wheat (27.3 percent), corn (67 percent), soybeans (56 percent), and cotton (25 percent). That same year, the U.S. led the world's poultry export market (42 percent), and was second in beef production (19 percent), while Canada (18 percent) and the United States (17 percent) placed second and third in global market shares of pork. In 2001, Canada produced and exported the largest share of canola in the world, and accounted for 17.9 percent of the world's wheat exports (ibid.).

Combines harvest rows of cotton in a Mississippi cotton field RICHARD HAMILTON SMITH/CORBIS

Burgeoning technological innovations in the context of a growing global marketplace have driven a threefold to fourfold increase in North American productivity over the past fifty years. These vast yields have sprung from a diminishing number of acres, concentrated on fewer, larger farms, run by an ever decreasing percentage of citizens. In fact, only about 2 percent of U.S. citizens and 3 percent of Canadians now farm (Environment Canada, "Cultivating a Secure Future," 2000; Farm Bureau, *Farm Facts,* 2002). A downside of this surge in productivity, however, has been the impoverishment of the natural resource base. As one expert noted: "One of the greatest challenges facing agriculture for the foreseeable future is to resolve conflicts caused by a growing competition for the services of the soil, water, and other natural resources on which agriculture depends—driven by growing demands for food, fiber, and for non-agricultural services that these resources provide" (Antle and Capalbo, "Agriculture as a Managed Ecosystem," 2001).

Forces of the political economy—such as increasing population and suburbanization, rising demand for goods and services, consolidation of farming with the processing, retailing, and chemical industries, and market globalization—conspire to simultaneously enhance and imperil the North American cornucopia (Busch, *Food Security in the United States,* 1984). To sustain itself, agriculture must exploit and protect its natural resource base and balance its social, economic, and environmental objectives. "The sector must be economically viable if it is to conserve the environment and support the social systems upon which it is based," stated one observer (Agriculture and Agri-Food Canada, *National Environment Strategy for Agriculture and Agri-Food,* 1995).

Agriculture's Nonrenewable Resource Base

North Americans have converted land, soil, water, germ plasm, and fossil fuel into tremendous quantities of food and other products. Simultaneously, however, they have also delivered an array of pollutants and nutrients back through this same resource stream.

Land

Between 1982 and 1997, 22 million acres of prime U.S. agricultural land were converted for residential and commercial development and for other nonfarming uses. This total comprises more than 18.5 million acres of cropland, nearly 2.2 million acres of pasture, and 1 million acres of rangeland. Much of the converted land surrounds traditional urban areas. However, a land-hungry demographic shift toward smaller cities and rural subdivisions is also devouring farmland in traditionally rural regions (Sorensen et al., *Farming on the Edge,* 1997). Current conversion levels of high-quality farmland to nonagricultural uses reflect North America's rising standard of living, which encourages sprawl more aggressively than does population growth.

An "increasing pattern of small [parcel] ownership in many rural areas means a dramatic increase in the 'edge effect,' as urban land use patterns press into rural ones," wrote one observer. "Rural homesites and 'ranchettes' increasingly mix with prime farm and forestland. The conflicts that develop between rural residents and agriculture make commercial production more expensive and difficult. Increasing taxes, regulations, and land prices often lead farm and forest landowners to give up and sell out" (Barrios, "Agriculture and Water Quality," 2000). However, evidence suggests that many people living on the urban/rural fringe value open space preservation and the attendant sprawl mitigation that farms provide, and have demonstrated some willingness to protect farmland from development (Krieger, "Saving Open Spaces," 1999).

Canada has maintained its total farm area at about 68 million acres since the 1980s, primarily because virtually all of the land that is suitable for farming and has not been otherwise developed is already being used for agricultural purposes. However, this surface stability masks the continuing loss of prime farmland to urban development, which in turn has led some farmers to turn to environmentally sensitive lands for crop production. Indeed, the amount of cultivated land in Canada increasingly exceeds the amount of dependable farmland. This increase reflects growing urbanization and may indicate intensification of cultivation (Agriculture and Agri-Food Canada, *Agriculture in Harmony with Nature II,* 2002). Pressure for land has also led to conversion of an enormous amount of the continent's wetlands. By the middle of the twentieth century, 85 percent of the decline in Canada's original wetland area was attributed to drainage for agricultural purposes (Rubec, "Canada's Federal Policy on Wetland Conservation," 1994).

Some financially strapped farmers fall victim to practices that do not reflect high standards of environmental stewardship. Determined to squeeze the greatest possible immediate financial return from their holdings, they may strip-mine the topsoil, overexploit regional water sources, and cultivate marginal lands. "As much as agricultural landowners may want to protect environmental values on their lands, they have a powerful inducement not to do so," one expert explained. "The market economy offers landowners a strong incentive to manage their holdings for the highest and best *economic* return. . . . Of course, landowners are not *forced* to seek the highest profit obtainable. That is their choice. But if one can profit by converting land from native habitat to agriculture and from agriculture to condominiums, chances are land will be converted" (Evans, *A New Look at Agriculture,* 2001).

In the United States, an evolving cadre of land protection programs have effectively blunted some farmland conversion. Between 1982 and 1997, for example, more than 9 million acres were put into the Department of Agriculture's Conservation Reserve Program (CRP) (U.S. Department of Agriculture, *Agriculture and Environment,* 2002). The CRP and the similar Wetland Reserve Program (WRP) pay farmers to take land out of production, thus providing them with the financial wherewithal to retain ownership of agriculturally non-productive land. In the Farmland Protection Program, the federal government partners with state, tribal, and local governments to purchase development rights to keep productive farmland in agriculture.

In Canada, the Agricultural Environmental Stewardship Initiative (AESI) is a three-year (2000–2003) program under the Canadian Adaptation and Rural Development fund. Intended to accommodate Canada's immense physiographic variation, AESI addresses "the regional impacts of agricultural practices on water, soil, and air quality, biodiversity, and greenhouse gas emissions . . . through education and awareness, technology transfer, and stewardship tools including environmental clubs, environmental management systems, and land use planning" (Agriculture and Agri-Food Canada, *Agriculture in Harmony with Nature II,* 2002).

Soil

Healthy, productive soils teem with life: soil organic matter, earthworms, insects, fungi, bacteria, and decaying vegetation that replenishes nutrients utilized by plants. Good soils regulate flows of water, energy, and nutrients through an ecosystem, and support vigorous plant growth. "Soil quality is the foundation of agricultural productivity and land health," summarized the U.S. Department of Agriculture. "If soil quality is stable or improving, we have a good indicator that the ecosystem is sustainable. If soil quality is deteriorating, the larger ecosystem will almost certainly decline with it" (U.S. Department of Agriculture, *Agriculture and Environment,* 2002).

Forces of soil degradation include compaction from heavy machinery, salinization from excessive irrigation, and wind- and water-induced erosion of topsoil. This is a significant problem in North America, where agricultural production has intensified markedly in recent decades. By the early 1990s, wind- and water-induced soil erosion had degraded an estimated 95,000 square kilometers of North American farmland (UN Environment Programme, *World Map of the Status of Human-Induced Soil Degradation,* 1991). Farming practices that exacerbate erosion include clean cultivation, where the soil is mechanically disturbed and cleaned of all vegetation prior to planting; cultivation of marginal land; and irrigation. Eroded soils contain insufficient organic matter, hold fewer nutrients and soil organisms, and exhibit reduced water-holding capabilities. Eroding soils thus lead to increased sedimentation and contamination of surface and groundwater.

The severe droughts of the 1930s Dust Bowl, when the ruined soil of the prairies became airborne and blew to the Atlantic Ocean, spurred efforts to improve soil and water quality across the continent. Through careful and considerate farming practices and numerous conservation programs, North America has begun to hold on to its topsoil. Between 1981 and 1996, the risk of wind erosion decreased 30 percent across Canada's vulnerable prairie provinces, and regional rates of water erosion also dropped (Environment Canada, "Cultivating a Secure Future," 2000). Erosion from water and wind also declined significantly during this period (U.S. Department of Agriculture, *1997 National Resources Inventory*, 2000).

Conventional tilling methods have been a major force in soil depletion; conservation tillage combats this loss. Unlike the clean cultivation technique, conservation tillage leaves plant residue on the soil as a physical deterrent to erosion to retain nutrients and water storage capacity. Crop damage is minimized, and farmers save on labor, fuel, and equipment costs. In 1998, 109.2 million of the 293.4 million acres of farmed land in the United States were cultivated using some mode of conservation tillage, up from just over 70 million acres in 1989. The jump in conservation tillage is mostly due to the adoption of no-till practices on conventional farms, suggesting an increasing reliance on herbicides or herbicide resistant crops (Farm Bureau, "Farm Facts," 2002). In the no-till method, only herbicides and cover crops are used. Cotton, soybeans, and wheat grown under no-till cultivation actually produce higher profit margins than those grown on tilled fields. With mulch-till and ridge-till methods, soils are turned over once prior to planting, and herbicides or cover crops are used to supplement weed control.

Other practices that maintain and enhance soil quality include fertilizing with animal waste (manure), plant debris (compost), and manufactured nutrients; planting leguminous species—plants that convert ambient nitrogen into a biologically useful form—in rotation with market crops; and planting cover crops that stabilize the soil.

Water

Across the continent, urban sprawl and industry compete with agriculture for water. In many areas, agriculturalists dangerously deplete ground and surface water by diverting aquifers and rivers with insufficient regard for the natural cycle that maintains stable water availability (Gold, *Sustainable Agriculture*, 1999). In the United States, agriculture accounts for more total freshwater withdrawals (42 percent) than any other sector, including power generation (39 percent), municipal use (11 percent), and industrial use (8 percent) (U.S. Geological Survey, "Estimated Use of Water in the United States in 1995," 1997; Organization for Economic Co-operation and Development, *Environmental Performance Reviews, United States*, 1996). Canadian agricultural interests, on the other hand, take a significant but much smaller share of total freshwater withdrawals—approximately 8 percent (Organization for Economic Co-operation and Development, *Environmental Performance Reviews, Canada*, 1995).

Observers fear that the agricultural heartlands of both countries are draining freshwater resources for irrigation at unsustainable rates. The Council on Environmental Quality estimates that the amount of irrigated land in the United States rose from 1.5 million hectares in 1890 to 21 million hectares in 1995, with the bulk of the development taking place in the country's Western reaches, where light annual rainfalls and other arid conditions prevail. In fact, many Western states—including California, the biggest of them all—use 80 percent or more of their freshwater sources for farming. In the United States in 1990, Western farmers withdrew 45.6 trillion gallons of water from streams and aquifers—almost 1 million gallons per acre—for irrigation alone. This total is over 71 percent more water than was withdrawn from the system for all other human uses (MacDonnell, *From Reclamation to Sustainability*, 1999).

Figure 5.1 Fertilizer Use in North America (kg/hectare arable land/yr)

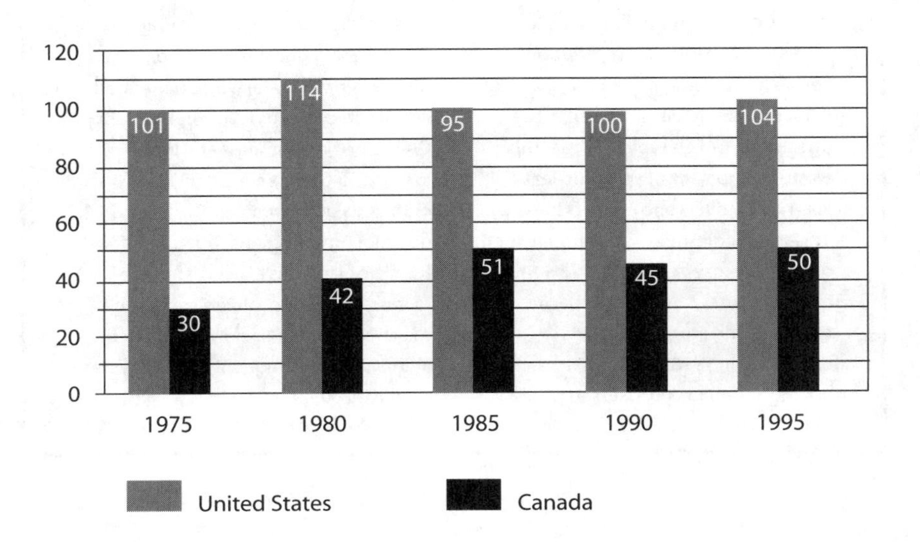

SOURCE: UNEP GRID Geneva from FAO 1997a.

Controversy over Concentrated Animal Feeding Operations

Concentrated animal feeding operations (CAFO), also known as intensive livestock producers, are facilities in which at least 1,000 "animals units" are confined for eventual slaughter and consumption (though the number of animals produced in these settings often reaches 10,000 or more). In addition, smaller livestock operations that are shown to pollute national waterways via the direct discharge of pollutants into waterways or into waters that come into direct contact with the confined animals are also sometimes placed under the CAFO umbrella by environmental and public health groups (Utah AFO Advisory Committee, "A Utah Strategy to Address Water Pollution from Animal Feeding Operations," 2000).

In recent years these livestock and poultry "factories" have come under intense criticism for polluting water and air resources. Most of this pollution comes from prodigious amounts of animal waste that is produced in the operations. CAFOs typically store this waste in lagoons, but spills and leaks into nearby rivers and aquifers have poisoned some local water supplies and damaged ecosystems. Indeed, twenty-two states that categorized specific types of agricultural pollution concluded in 1998 that animal wastes pollute about 35,000 assessed river miles (Environmental Protection Agency, *Draft Unified National Strategy for Animal Feeding Operation,* 1998). Moreover, domestic animal waste has been cited as a far greater contributor to excess nitrogen levels in waterways than either municipal or industrial discharges in the United States (Environmental Protection Agency, *Feedlots Point Source Category Study,* 1998). Noxious odors emanating from these operations have also been a frequent target of criticism from nearby homeowners and communities. In addition, these facilities are owned by large agribusiness corporations that have been blamed for forcing small family farms out of business.

The location of CAFOs can also be a significant contributor to waste disposal problems. Many Midwestern CAFOs are part of larger operations that produce their own feed grain, in part by using phosphorus- and nitrogen-rich animal waste generated in CAFO facilities as fertilizer. But U.S. CAFOs in the Southeast and West are located far from the nutrient-needy croplands of the prairies. The decoupling of livestock operations from cropland has exacerbated the manure disposal problem created by the sheer volume of closely confined animals (Barrios, "Agriculture and Water Quality," 2000).

(continues)

In recent years, some industry practices seen as particularly egregious in their environmental impact—such as saturating the land with nitrogen-heavy waste or polluting groundwater—have been restricted or banned in the United States, and some states have imposed new regulations on storage and disposal of CAFO animal waste. These developments have led some environmental groups to speculate that the hog industry intends to intensify its activities in Canada. Alberta, for instance, already has a $C600 million pork industry, and provincial leaders have signaled their enthusiasm for a significant increase in CAFO operations, citing economic benefits. In 2002 the province streamlined its approval process for new livestock operations in an effort to attract investment from Canadian and international CAFO operators. But fears about air and water pollution associated with these operations have influenced governmental policies in other provinces. In June 2002, for example, Quebec imposed an eighteen-month moratorium on the opening of new industrial-scale hog facilities across the province, even though the industry is the second-largest revenue producer in Quebec's overall agriculture sector and already employs about 30,000 people. Industry representatives and other supporters of hog facility expansion characterized the moratorium as capitulation to environmental fear-mongering. Environmental and community groups said that the decision would help protect provincial waterways and associated freshwater habitat from potentially ruinous levels of degradation.

Sources:

Barrios, Anna. 2000. "Agriculture and Water Quality." American Farmland Trust, Center for Agriculture in the Environment, June.

U.S. Environmental Protection Agency. 1998. *Feedlots Point Source Category Study, Preliminary Data Summary.* Washington, DC: EPA.

U.S. Environmental Protection Agency and U.S. Department of Agriculture. 1998. *Draft Unified National Strategy for Animal Feeding Operation.* Washington, DC: EPA and USDA.

U.S. Senate Committee on Agriculture, Nutrition, and Forestry. 1997. "Animal Waste Pollution in America: An Emerging National Problem. Environmental Risks of Livestock and Poultry Production." Washington, DC: U.S. Senate Committee on Agriculture, Nutrition, and Forestry, December.

Utah AFO Advisory Committee, Utah State University Extension. 2000. "A Utah Strategy to Address Water Pollution from Animal Feeding Operations." http://extension.usu.edu/aems/cafo.htm

Agriculture is also responsible for almost half of the pollution in the U.S. groundwater system. Indeed, farming operations constitute the largest single nonpoint source of water pollutants in the United States, spewing out large volumes of sediments, salts, fertilizers (nitrates and phosphorus), pesticides, and manures (see sidebar on page 124). "Pesticides from every chemical class have been detected in groundwater and are commonly found in groundwater beneath agricultural areas; they are widespread in the nation's surface waters. Eutrophication and 'dead zones' due to nutrient runoff affect many rivers, lakes, and oceans" (Gold, *Sustainable Agriculture,* 1999). For example, U.S. Food and Drug Administration (FDA) studies have found that between 33 and 39 percent of the U.S. food supply in any given year contains detectable (though not illegal) levels of pesticide residue (U.S. Food and Drug Administration, *Pesticide Program Residue Monitoring, 1987–1994,* 1996). The humid croplands of southeastern Canada suffer similar contamination problems.

Moreover, while the safety of drinking water is an issue in many parts of Canada and the United States, it is particularly problematic in agricultural regions. Rural families are more reliant on private wells and small water systems, which are most at risk of contamination from farming activities. Many of these rural communities also do not have the financial resources necessary to ensure compliance with safe drinking water standards (National Research Council, *Safe Water from Every Tap,* 1997).

Soil conservation practices and policies have reduced sedimentation throughout most of North America, however, and more prudent pesticide and fertilizer applications have reduced industrial inputs in some regions. Mandated in the 1977 amendments to the U.S. Clean Water Act, best management practices (BMPs) explicitly link water quality and higher productivity to conservation practices. They specify soil and crop testing toward the timing of irrigation and fertilizer and pesticide applications to minimize inputs and to contain contaminants without stressing crops. BMP conservation strategies include cover crops, green manure crops, conservation tillage, and strip-cropping to control erosion; crop nutrient management; and conservation buffer strips around cultivated fields. These undisturbed parcels of land are beneficial because the vegetation that resides there intercepts pollutants and protects against wind and water erosion, thereby maintaining water quality while providing wildlife habitat (Gold, *Sustainable Agriculture,* 1999; Barrios, "Agriculture and Water Quality," 2000).

Integrated pest management (IPM), meanwhile, is an environmentally sensitive approach to pest (animal and weed) control that has experienced increased acceptance in recent years. IPM integrates practices such as crop rotation, use of resistant cultivars, biological control organisms, prophylactic seed treatments, certified disease-free seed and rootstock, carefully timed cultivation and pesticide applications, eradication of infested organisms, and local knowledge to combat infestations of weeds and insects (Gold, *Sustainable Agriculture,* 1999). To counter concerns that genetically altered varieties could drive the evolution of super-pests, the U.S. Environmental Protection Agency (EPA) instituted guidelines for integrated resistance management (IRM) in 1999. For example, the guidelines specify that non-GMO (genetically modified organism) refuges should be planted next to GMO fields of similar species to dilute pesticide resistance in the general pest population (Pretty, "Rapid Emergence of Genetic Modification," 2001).

Irrigators and legislators have even begun to improve notoriously wasteful water-delivery systems—by some estimates, more than half of the water withdrawn by Western states is lost through systemic inefficiencies before it ever reaches the fields. The costs associated with meaningful improvements in this area are great, but proponents believe that long-term economic and environmental advantages will result. "[These systems are being upgraded] because of the direct economic gains [they make] possible—measured in terms of increased irrigated acreage, a more reliable water supply for existing irrigated lands, the cultivation of more water-intensive [higher value] crops, and reduced labor" (MacDonnell, *From Reclamation to Sustainability,* 1999).

Transgenic Crops and Biodiversity

Market demand for plentiful and uniform products has driven North American agricultural enterprises to rely increasingly on genetically uniform crop and livestock breeds. Simultaneously, habitat conversion, degradation of soil and water, and other ecosystem disruptions created by farming operation have reduced biodiversity levels in the wild.

The most recent addition to the agricultural toolkit comes from biotechnology. Although selective breeding results in loosely constructed genotypes, genetic modification permits the transfer of genetic material across taxonomic kingdoms to obtain designer characteristics. In 2002, for example, the Canadian Agriculture Department approved a new selectively bred hybrid species of wheat, *Brassica juncea*. Unlike traditional selective breeding, carried out by farmers in field environments, government scientists derived these new varieties in the laboratory. They converted mustard plants to canola by lowering the erucic acid and glucosinolate levels. They thus created a species that resists blackleg, a disastrous canola disease, as well as heat and drought, facilitating the expansion of canola cultivation into more marginal land (Holmes, "Canada Creates New Drought-Tolerant Canola Species," 2002).

The most commercially important GMO applications to date involve crops that are developed for herbicide resistance, insect resistance, or both. Soybean, canola, cotton, corn, and sugar beets altered to withstand glyphosate and glufosinate ammonium (such as Monsanto's Round-up Ready varieties) permit broad spectrum herbicide spraying on the standing crops. In 1999, 28 million hectares of these herbicide-resistant crops were planted. Insect resistance induced by *Bacillus thuringiensis* (Bt), mostly in maize and cotton, renders insecticides almost unnecessary. Some 8.9 million hectares of insect-resistant crops were cultivated in 1999, and an additional 2.9 million hectares of crops with both herbicide resistance and Bt genes were cultivated that year (Pretty, "Rapid Emergence of Genetic Modification," 2001). Bacteria have been engineered to produce drugs for livestock, and animals themselves are being engineered to produce novel pharmaceuticals and fibers.

Commercial cultivation of GMOs began in 1995 with soybeans, and since that time the technology has experienced tremendous growth. Most of this growth has been driven by North America, however—and the United States, in particular, because of the country's ability to invest in GMO technology and governmental efforts to create a friendly regulatory environment for GMO food and crops. By 2000, 44.5 million global hectares of GMO crops had been planted worldwide, with 68 percent in the United States and 7 percent in Canada. More than half of the current transgenic crop is soybean, followed by maize, cotton and canola, potato, and squash (ibid.). About 60 percent of Canada's canola crop is transgenic (Holmes, "Canada Creates New Drought-Tolerant Canola Species," 2002). Likewise, bulk commodity farmers in the United States appear to be sold on GMOs. The USDA estimated that in 2002, three-quarters of the nation's 73 million acres of soybeans and 34 percent of the 79 million acres of corn will be raised from genetically modified or "transgenic" seeds. Planting of transgenic cotton accounted for 71 percent of the overall U.S. crop in 2002. The National Academy of Sciences and various environmental and public health groups remain skeptical about associated risks, however, and they urge close scrutiny of genetically altered crops before commercial approval is granted.

Proponents of genetically modified crops believe that they open the door to greater volumes of crops; more nutritious crops; crops with increased resistance to insect infestation, drought, or other stresses; and crops wired to carry a host of other desirable traits. For example, analysts believe that genetically modified foods such as corn, lettuce, tomato, cowpeas, and potatoes could eventually be used as an inexpensive vehicle to vaccinate people against certain diseases. Proponents also tout potential environmental benefits associated with transgenic crops, such as reduced reliance on pesticides that are carried by runoff into rivers and lakes. U.S. farmers planting transgenic cotton with engineered pest resistance, for instance, have been able to cut their pesticide sprayings from four to six per crop to zero (James, "Global Status of Transgenic Crops," 1997; Paarlberg, "Promise or Peril?" 2000).

But environmental and consumer groups and other detractors see numerous potential flaws with GMO or "bio-tech" foods and other farm products, including "horizontal gene flow to wild relatives; new forms of resistance and pest problems; recombination to produce new pathogens; direct and indirect effects of novel toxins; loss of biodiversity from changes to farm practices; allergic and immune system responses; and antibiotic resistant marker genes" (Pretty, "The Rapid Emergence of Genetic Modification," 2001).

Energy and Productivity

Like soil, water, and genetic material, energy flows through agricultural ecosystems. In modern agriculture, "relatively cheap and abundant supplies of fossil fuel have been substituted for human energy. Thus, man-made fertilizers and pesticides as well as machinery have helped our farmers and diminished the level of personal energy they must expend to farm" (Pimentel and Pimentel, "Land, Energy, and Water," 1995).

In large-scale, single-species, or limited rotation systems, continued high yields require cheap and abundant fossil energy—including synthetic additives, fertilizer, pesticides, irrigation, and vehicle fuel (ibid.). After all, fossil fuels run the heavy machinery needed to prepare, fertilize, water, and harvest massive monocultures. The resulting vast quantities of food and fiber then require fleets of fuel-guzzling trucks for distribution from the centralized places of production. Indeed, the regionalization of crop production—corn in Iowa, tomatoes in California, oranges in Florida, dairy products in New York and Wisconsin, wheat across the prairies, and so forth—has contributed to the development of North America's vast, petroleum-dependent transportation network. According to one analysis, a typical feedlot steer, ingesting corn for three-quarters of its total calories, is responsible for the consumption of 284 gallons of oil in its lifetime. "We have succeeded in industrializing the beef cattle, transforming what was once a solar-powered ruminant into the very last thing we need: another fossil-fuel machine" (Pollan, "Power Steer," 2002).

Fossil fuel inputs have counterbalanced the productivity declines otherwise associated with soil erosion. However, they may have reached their upper efficiency limit: applying more fertilizer to counter declining soil health may no longer increase crop productivity proportionately to its cost. In addition, agricultural impacts on freshwater systems and potential impacts on human

Cattle at a watering hole in New Mexico CRAIG AURNESS/CORBIS

Grazing and the Environment

"For many people, the scene of cattle and sheep grazing languidly upon endless ranges depicts the quintessential essence of the American West and its colorful history" (Smith, "To Graze or Not to Graze," 1999). But conservationists contend that standard ranching practices, most notably grazing, actually take a significant toll on wildlife habitat and other aspects of the environment. Manifestations of grazing's impact on public lands have attracted particular concern from environmentalists. "Unlike pronghorn, elk, and deer, cattle will not move very far from water if they are not forced to, nor are they inclined to abandon an area until just about every bit of forage has been ingested," charged one critic. "In the process, they trample whatever hasn't been eaten, crumble riverbanks, foul water, and otherwise make life miserable and sometimes impossible for the plants, birds, fish, and amphibians dependent upon these rivers of life. The impact of generations of that kind of use, particularly in the arid Southwest, has been devastating" (Watkins, "High Noon in Cattle Country," 2000). Other environmental problems associated with livestock ranching include the historical eradication of potential predators of domestic livestock, and the transmission of diseases to which indigenous animals have no immunity. For example, pulmonary diseases transmitted by domestic sheep have driven several species of native bighorn sheep to the brink of extinction (Smith, "To Graze or Not to Graze, 1999).

These concerns have been confirmed in numerous studies conducted by U.S. agencies responsible for public lands. A 1990 EPA report, for example, stated that "extensive field observations in the 1980s suggest riparian areas throughout much of the West were in the worst condition in history. Many once-productive fish and wildlife populations have been eliminated or greatly reduced over wide areas of land." A 1994 U.S. Forest Service report, meanwhile, claimed that livestock grazing was the fourth leading cause of species endangerment in the country—and the leading culprit in arid regions such as the Colorado/Green River plateau. This perspective was confirmed by a 1994 National Wildlife Federation study which reported that grazing contributed directly or indirectly to a minimum of 340 species being listed or becoming candidates for listing under the Endangered Species Act (National Wildlife Federation, *Grazing to Extinction*, 1994). "Cattle grazing has converted many of the riparian habitats in the arid West into communities dominated by habitat generalists and weedy species such as dandelions, cheatgrass, cowbirds, and smallmouth bass, and by upland or abundant species such as sagebrush, juniper, and speckled dace," summarized one opponent. "As a result, both habitat quality and native species diversity have been severely reduced. . . .

(continues)

Nearly all scientific studies, both observational and experimental, refute [claims that grazing benefits natural areas]. Livestock do not benefit stream and riparian communities, water quality, or hydrologic function in any way" (Belsky et al., "Survey of Livestock Influences on Stream and Riparian Ecosystems," 1999).

These critical findings have sparked repeated calls for fundamental reform of U.S. grazing laws and the modest grazing fees that the government charges ranchers to put their stock on public land. But ranchers and their supporters insist that the environmental impact of grazing on public lands has been wildly overstated. They note that more than 96 percent of the beef generated in the United States comes from private farmland or feedlots, and that many ranchers manage their herds in order to ensure the long-term viability of public and private land, both for economic and ecological reasons. Moreover, the continued existence of livestock ranches—some of which would not be able to maintain profitable operations without access to public land—has been cited as a key factor in limiting residential and commercial development and other incarnations of urban sprawl. Grazing advocates also assert that active management of livestock on the range can deter the spread of noxious weeds, reduce the likelihood of catastrophic fire, and benefit prairie birds, deer, and elk by maintaining open grasslands. Some conservation-minded ranchers even maintain that ranching has the capacity to regenerate long-neglected Western rangelands (Knight et al., *Ranching West of the 100th Meridian*, 2002).

Sources:

Belsky, A. J., A. Matzke, and S. Uselman. 1999. "Survey of Livestock Influences on Stream and Riparian Ecosystems in the Western United States." *Journal of Soil and Water Conservation* 54.

Council for Agricultural Science and Technology. 1996. "Grazing on Public Lands." CAST, December.

DiSilvestro, Roger L. 1993. *Reclaiming the Last Wild Places: A New Agenda for Biodiversity.* New York: John Wiley.

Knight, Richard L., Wendell C. Gilgert, and Ed Marston, eds. 2002. *Ranching West of the 100th Meridian: Culture, Ecology, and Economics.* Washington, DC: Island.

National Wildlife Federation. 1994. *Grazing to Extinction.* Washington, DE: NWF.

Smith, Ed. 1999–2000. "To Graze or Not to Graze: The Issue." *Loma Prietan* (December–January).

Watkins, T. H. 2000. "High Noon in Cattle Country." *Sierra* 84 (March–April).

Wilkinson, Todd. 2000. "The Beef with Livestock." *National Parks* 74 (May–June).

Wuerthner, George, and Mollie Yoneko Matteson, eds. 2002. *Welfare Ranching: The Subsidized Destruction of the American West.* Washington, DC: Island.

health are encouraging more careful cultivation practices and driving the implementation of new environmental regulations on fertilizer and pesticide use. For example, persistent organic pollutants (POPs) contained in products used on cotton, fruits, vegetables, and nuts have been linked to higher rates of cancer and neural, genetic, and behavioral abnormalities in humans. As a result, major restrictions—including outright bans—were placed on many of these compounds in both Canada and the United States. In 2001, delegates from the United States, Canada, and 120 other nations agreed to a treaty calling for a worldwide phaseout of the twelve worst POPs. The pact covers dioxin, PCBs, DDT, aldrin, chlordane, dieldrin, endrin, heptachlor, mirex, toxaphene, hexachlorobenzene, and furans. New regulations governing a plethora of other farming activities, from pesticide applications to waste disposal from factory farms, have also been introduced at the regional and federal levels in both Canada and the United States.

The Changing Face of North American Agriculture

Agriculture is a vital sector of the regional, national, and international economies, producing about 15 percent of the U.S. gross domestic product (GDP) and 4.3 percent of Canada's GDP (Evans, *A New Look at Agriculture,*

Planes are used to spray pesticides over large areas such as this Arkansas farm. U.S. DEPARTMENT OF AGRICULTURE

2001; Agriculture and Agri-Food Canada, *Profile of Production Trends and Environmental Issues,* 1997). As a result, environmental problems associated with agriculture are closely intertwined with economic and social changes within North America's farming and ranching communities (see sidebar on page 131). And in recent years, the dominant characteristics of many of these communities have undergone considerable changes.

> Economically, the U.S. agricultural sector includes a history of increasingly large federal expenditures and corresponding government involvement in planting and investment decisions; widening disparity among farmer incomes; and escalating concentration of agribusiness—industries involved with manufacture, processing, and distribution of farm products—into fewer and fewer hands. Market competition is limited. Farmers have little control over farm prices, and they continue to receive a smaller and smaller portion of consumer dollars spent on agricultural products. . . .Economic pressures have led to a tremendous loss of farms, particularly small farms, and farmers during the past few decades—more than 155,000 farms were lost from 1987 to 1997. This contributes to the disintegration of rural communities and localized marketing systems. (Gold, *Sustainable Agriculture,* 1999)

In response, some U.S. and Canadian farmers and ranchers are increasingly pressing for noncommodity (NC) goods and environmental services to be effectively measured and afforded economic value. NC services include secondary functions of agriculture that nonetheless have a moral, cultural, or environmental value in their own right. These include open space; preservation of cultural heritage and traditional lifestyle; wildlife habitat; soil, water, and air quality; flood control; carbon sequestration; food security; and future agricultural productivity (Antle and Capalbo, "Agriculture as a Managed Ecosystem," 2001). Under these types of value systems, the value of a dairy would be based not only on its production of milk but also on the intrinsic value of its bucolic pastures. Similarly, crop and hay fields within forested regions would be more valuable because of their importance in providing songbird habitat (Mullarkey, "Multifunctionality and Agriculture," 2001; Evans, *New Look at Agriculture,* 2001).

Over the last several decades, however, the prevailing trend in North American agriculture has been toward one of two economically, socially, and environmentally distinct types of operation. "One pole is industrial agriculture comprising the major agricultural chemical and equipment companies, the principal grain, processing and packing companies, the major grocery and restaurant outlets, and the majority of farm producers. The other pole is alternative or sustainable agriculture, which is a loose network of organic and regional producers, chefs, and ordinary food customers" (Thompson, "The Reshaping of Conventional Farming," 2001). In the practices of farming, however, the differences are composed of values and nuanced world views rather than of absolute opposites.

Meeting long-term agricultural objectives such as food and economic security, or environmental and human health, requires all agriculturalists—conventional as well as alternative—to consider the notion of sustainability. "A sustainable agriculture is one that produces the food, fiber, energy, and other crops that the nation needs, including a marketable surplus that can be sold abroad," one writer stated.

> It produces this in an average year, not just during times of good weather. It weathers a bad year by drawing on stored fertility and moisture in the soil; stored water in reservoirs; stored wealth in financially secure farms; and stored food products in the granaries of farmers, industries, and government. It profits from a good year by setting aside extra commodities or making an extra effort to see that they are sold abroad, without driving prices through the floor and creating financial hardship or ruin among producers. In addition to meeting domestic food needs and a substantial export market, a sustainable, regenerative agriculture could reduce the waste and pollution of water, provide better wildlife habitats, slow the advance of desertification and salinization, reduce the loss of prime farmlands and fragile topsoils, and, in general, make rural America a far more healthy, satisfying, and financially rewarding place to live." (Sampson, "America's Agricultural Land," 1984)

Conventional Farming Methods

All of the major commodity crops in North America—including corn, wheat, soybeans, and cotton—are most commonly grown using so-called conventional methods. Common characteristics of conventional or industrial farming systems include extensive use of heavy machinery and technological innovation; large capital investments in those machines and technological innovations; reliance on single crops or row crops over many seasons; heavy utilization of high-yield hybrid or GMO crops; extensive use of pesticides and fertilizers; high labor efficiency; and high economic dependence on agribusiness (Gold, *Sustainable Agriculture,* 1999). The extreme economy of scale in larger operations of this type requires huge levels of inputs to maintain soil function and to suppress disease and pests. Monocropping indulges in limited genetic variety—in the United States, for example, half of the wheat crop is produced using only nine varieties, and 46 percent of the corn crop is produced using only six. Furthermore, factory farming has encouraged the spatial disassociation of livestock and croplands (Union of Concerned Scientists, Food and Environment Program, 2002).

Small farms continue to dominate North American agriculture in sheer numbers, but their share of the economic bounty has declined dramatically. For instance, 8 percent of Canadian farms occupy about 43 percent of all farmland (Government of Canada, *The State of Canada's Environment,* 1996), and the influence of giant farms is even greater in the United States. Today, large agribusinesses control a steadily expanding share of farm production in both countries, and agricultural production is increasingly controlled by corporations and contract farms rather than by farmers-owners. In many cases, a single corporation controls all aspects of the agricultural supply chain in conventional operations, from planting and harvesting to retail sales (Hudson and Herndon, "Cooperatives Consolidate," 2001).

Alternative Farming Methods

Sustainable or holistic agriculture aspires toward "no soil erosion, no chemical contamination of the countryside, no fossil fuel dependency, a return of people to the land, to the small towns and rural communities" (Jackson, *Becoming Native to This Place,* 1994). "This approach is holistic: the emphasis is on the farm as an integrated whole, not as a set of inputs and outputs. It is also scientific: it relies on knowledge about the elements of the system, and their interactions to achieve its results. It is a powerful approach that can produce high yields and profits for farmers" (Union of Concerned Scientists, Food and Environment Program, 2002).

Most alternative farming methods take the form of organic agriculture, the "primary goal" of which is to "optimize the health and productivity of the interdependent communities of soil life, plants, animals, and people" (Codex Alimentarius Commission, *Organically Produced Foods,* 2001). Indeed, organic agriculture is based on principles that place a high value on biodiversity and natural biological cycles, and it emphasizes sustainability in all operational aspects.

Growing numbers of conventional farmers have incorporated organic agriculture practices into their own efforts, albeit in simplified form. These practitioners are attracted to organic farming not only because of its benefits to the local and broader environment but also because of the growing popularity of organic products in the marketplace. In 1996, 49 percent of organic farmers in the United States intended to place more land under organic farming, whereas only 4 percent intended to reduce their acreage devoted to organic crops (Gold, *Sustainable Agriculture,* 1999). Organic farming has become mainstream enough to warrant federal standards in the United States and in Canada.

Incorporating Sustainability into Agricultural Practices

Both the United States and Canada have vowed to pursue environmental sustainability as a central focus of their agricultural operations. The U.S. Department of Agriculture, for example, claimed a mandate to balance the goals of improved production and profitability with stewardship of the natural resource base and economic development of rural communities. Similarly, Agriculture and Agri-Food Canada (AAFC) promotes sustainable agriculture as one of its main goals, citing objectives such as "improving the environmental sustainability of natural resources, promoting a prosperous and viable [agricultural] sector where growth is achieved in an environmentally sustainable manner, and contributing to sustainable communities . . . integrating sustainable development into its own departmental decision-making process, as well as greening its own operations" (Agriculture and Agri-Food Canada, *Agriculture in Harmony with Nature II,* 2002).

Despite good intentions and ongoing successes, however, the long-term health of North American agriculture—from ecological, economic, social, human health, and philosophical perspectives—remains insecure. Agriculture policy must determine whether to increase or decrease subsidies and other financial assistance for farmers and ranchers, find a balance between protection of habitat and efficiency of agricultural production, find ways to integrate new conservation applications into normal farming operations, and seek an appropriate level of support for agricultural research and extension education programs (Hallberg et al., *Food, Agriculture, and Rural Policy into the Twenty-First Century,* 1994).

Historically, most government efforts have primarily benefited major commodity agriculture. Critics contend that the less immediately lucrative "broader political issues"—such as improving farmers' standards of living and correcting poor land use practices—have too often been relegated to the fringes of the general debate (Doering, "An Overview of Conservation and Agricultural Policy," 1998). In 2002 the United States government signaled that farming subsidies for agribusiness remained an integral part of its agricultural policy-making, but it also gave significant attention to conservation issues. It approved a farm bill that will distribute an estimated $190 billion to the country's agricultural interests over a ten-year period, most of it in the form of subsidies. The bill, which authorizes a $73.5 billion increase over existing programs, marks a visible retreat from the 1996 Freedom to Farm Law, which was designed to wean farmers from subsidies. Critics charge that it will encourage overproduction of grain, cotton, and other crops, and that it will send more than 60 percent of total subsidies to farms that rank in the top 10 percent by size. But the bill also contains an 80 percent increase in funding for land-conservation programs. It expands the Conservation Reserve Program, which pays farmers for stewardship of "working lands," to 39.2 million acres, and boosts funding for the Environmental Quality Incentives Program, which shares the expense of controlling fertilizer, manure, and other agricultural runoff into lakes and streams. Other conservation measures contained in the bill include increases in the federal government's wetland reserve and wildlife habitat improvement programs.

Despite increased funding for environmentally sustainable forms of agriculture, however, observers believe that environmentalists and farmers must better coordinate their efforts with one another to encourage the best stewardship of the land. "One of the best ways to support and encourage environmental value . . . is to take advantage of the strong stewardship ethic of many . . . farmers and ranchers, and adjust programs to improve the ability of these owners and operators to nurture the ecological values associated with the lands under their care" (Evans, *A New Look at Agriculture,* 2001).

Sources:

Agriculture and Agri-Food Canada. 1995. *National Environment Strategy for Agriculture and Agri-Food.* Ottawa: AAFC, August.

———. 1997. *Profile of Production Trends and Environmental Issues in Canada's Agriculture and Agri-Food Sector.* Ottawa: AAFC.

———. 2002. *Agriculture in Harmony with Nature II: Sustainable Development Strategy 2001–2004.* Ottawa: AAFC.

American Farmland Trust. "Fact Sheet: The Farmland Protection Toolbox." Farmland Information Center. http://www.farmlandinfo.org (accessed March 20, 2002).

Antle, John M., and Susan L. Capalbo. 2001. "Agriculture as a Managed Ecosystem: Policy Implications." University of Montana. http://www.climate.montana.edu/pdf/AgManagedEcosystem.pdf (accessed February 27, 2002).

Barrios, Anna. 2000. "Agriculture and Water Quality." Washington, DC: American Farmland Trust, Center for Agriculture in the Environment, June.

Berk, Alexander, ed. 2001. *Agriculture Issues and Policies,* vol. 1. Huntington, NY: Nova Science.

Busch, Lawrence, and William B. Lacy, eds. 1984. *Food Security in the United States.* Boulder, CO and London: Westview.

Codex Alimentarius Commission, Joint FAO/WHO Food Standards Programme. 2001. *Organically Produced Foods: Guidelines for Production, Processing, Labeling, and Marketing.* Rome: Codex.

Doering, Christopher. 2002. "U.S. Farmland, Forests Can Absorb Greenhouse Gases." Reuters News Service, April 24. http://www.planetark.org/dailynewsstory.cfm/newsid/15625/story.htm.

Doering, Otto. 1998. "An Overview of Conservation and Agricultural Policy: Questions from the Past and Observations about the Present." Washington, DC: American Farmland Trust, Center for Agriculture in the Environment.

Environment Canada. 2000. "Cultivating a Secure Future: Rural Development and Sustainable Agriculture in Canada. A Canadian Contribution to the Land Use Dialogue at the Eighth Session of the United Nations Commission on Sustainable Development, April 24 to May 5, 2000." Conservation Priorities and Planning Branch. http://www.ec.gc.ca/agenda21/2000/agriculteng.htm.

Evans, Craig. 2001. *A New Look at Agriculture: A Discussion Paper Devoted to Redefining Agriculture's Role in Our Economy, Landscape, Environment, and Social Culture.* Boca Raton: Florida Stewardship Foundation, March.

Farm Bureau. 2002. *Farm Facts.* http://www.fb.org/brochures/farmfacts/ (accessed March 20).

Gold, Mary V. 1999. *Sustainable Agriculture: Definitions and Terms.* Washington, DC: U.S. Department of Agriculture, Agriculture Research Service, September.

Government of Canada. 1996. *The State of Canada's Environment, 1996.* Ottawa: Supply and Services Canada.

Hallberg, Milton C., Robert G. F. Spitze, and Daryll E. Ray. 1994. *Food, Agriculture, and Rural Policy into the Twenty-First Century: Issues and Trade-Offs.* Boulder, CO: Westview.

Holmes, Kanina. 2002. "Canada Creates New Drought-Tolerant Canola Species." Reuters News Service, April 24. http://www.planetark.org/dailynewsstory.cfm/newsid/15640/story.htm.

Hudson, Darren, and C. W. Herndon Jr. 2001. "Cooperatives Consolidate: Response to the Changing Structure of the U.S. Food Industry." *Choices: The Magazine of Food, Farm and Resource Issues* 16, no. 3.

Hurt, R. Douglass. 1996. *American Farms: Exploring Their History.* Malabar, FL: Kreiger.

Jackson, Wes. 1994. *Becoming Native to This Place.* Louisville: University of Kentucky Press.

Jackson, Wes, and Marty Bender. 1984. "An Alternative to Till Agriculture as the Dominant Means of Food Production." In Lawrence Busch and William B. Lacy, eds., *Food Security in the United States.* Boulder, CO: Westview.

James, C. 1997. "Global Status of Transgenic Crops in 1997." ISAAA Brief no. 4. Ithaca, NY: International Service for the Acquisition of Agri-Biotech Applications.

———. 1999. "Global Review of Commercialized Transgenic Crops: 1999." ISAAA Report no. 12. Ithaca, NY: International Service for the Acquisition of Agri-Biotech Applications.

Korves, Ross. 1999. "The Voice of Agriculture Issues." Washington, DC: American Farm Bureau Federation, December.

Krieger, Douglas J. 1999. "Saving Open Spaces: Public Support for Farmland Protection." DeKalb, IL: enter for Agriculture in the Environment, April.

LeVeen, E. Phillip. 1984. "Domestic Food Security and Increasing Competition for Water." In Lawrence Busch and William B. Lacy, eds., *Food Security in the United States*. Boulder, CO: Westview.

Lyson, Thomas A. 2000. "Moving toward CIVIC Agriculture." *Choices: The Magazine of Food, Farm and Resource Issues* 15, no. 3.

MacDonnell, Lawrence J. 1999. *From Reclamation to Sustainability: Water, Agriculture and the Environment in the American West*. Niwot: University Press of Colorado.

McRae, T., C. A. S. Smith, and L. J. Gregorich, eds. 2000. *Environmental Sustainability of Canadian Agriculture: Report of the Agri-Environmental Indicator Project. A Summary*. Ottawa: Agriculture and Agri-Food Canada, Minister of Industry, Science and Technology.

Mullarkey, Daniel, J. Cooper, and D. Skully. 2001. "Multifunctionality and Agriculture." *Choices* (first quarter).

National Research Council. 1989. *Alternative Agriculture*. Washington, DC: National Academy.

———. 1997. *Safe Water from Every Tap: Improving Water Service to Small Communities*. Washington, DC: National Academy.

Ockenden, Jonathan, and Michael Franklin. 1995. *European Agriculture: Making the CAP Fit the Future*. London: Pinter.

Organization for Economic Co-operation and Development. 1995. *Environmental Performance Reviews, Canada*. Paris: OECD.

———. 1996. *Environmental Performance Reviews, United States*. Paris: OECD.

Paarlberg, Robert. 2000. "Promise or Peril: Genetically Modified Crops in Developing Countries." *Environment* 42 (January–February).

Pimentel, David. 1984. "Energy Inputs and U.S. Food Security." In Lawrence Busch and William B. Lacy, eds., *Food Security in the United States*. Boulder, CO: Westview.

Pimentel, David, and Marcia Pimentel. 1995. "Land, Energy and Water: The Constraints Governing Ideal U.S. Population Size." Negative Population Growth Forum Series: Environment. January. http://www.npg.org/forum_series/land_energy&water.htm (accessed February 15, 2002).

Pollan, Michael. 2002. "Power Steer." *New York Times Magazine*, March 31.

Pretty, Jules. 2001. "The Rapid Emergence of Genetic Modification in World Agriculture: Contested Benefits and Risks." *Environmental Conservation* 28, no. 3.

Rubec, C. D. A. 1994. "Canada's Federal Policy on Wetland Conservation: A Global Model." In W. J. Mitsch, ed., *Global Wetlands: Old World and New*. Amsterdam: Elsevier.

Sampson, Neil. 1984. "America's Agricultural Land: Basis for Food Security?" In Lawrence Busch and William B. Lacy, eds., *Food Security in the United States*. Boulder, CO: Westview.

Sorensen, A. Ann, Richard P. Greene, and Karen Russ. 1997. *Farming on the Edge.* Washington, DC: American Farmland Trust, Center for Agriculture and the Environment, March.

Soule, Judith D., and Jon K. Piper. 1992. *Farming in Nature's Image: An Ecological Approach to Agriculture.* Washington, DC: Island.

Statistics Canada. 2002. *The 2001 Census of Agriculture.* Ottawa: Statistics Canada.

Thompson, Paul B. 2001. "The Reshaping of Conventional Farming: A North American Perspective." *Journal of Agriculture and Environmental Ethics* 14, no. 2.

Thrupp, Lorin Ann. 1997. "Linking Biodiversity and Agriculture: Challenges and Opportunities for Sustainable Food Security." Washington, DC: World Resources Institute.

Union of Concerned Scientists. 2002. Food and Environment Program. http://www.ucsusa.org/food/foo-home.html.

UN Environment Programme. 1999. *Global Environment Outlook 2000.* London: Earthscan.

UN Environment Programme and International Soil Reference and Information Centre. 1991. *World Map of the Status of Human-Induced Soil Degradation.* 2d rev. ed. Nairobi, Kenya: UNEP; and Wageningen, Netherlands: ISRIC.

U.S. Department of Agriculture. 2002. *Agriculture and Environment.* Washington, DC: USDA.

U.S. Department of Agriculture, Natural Resources Conservation Service. 2000. *1997 National Resources Inventory.* Washington, DC: USDA.

U.S. Food and Drug Administration. 1996. *Pesticide Program Residue Monitoring, 1987–1994.* Washington, DC: FDA.

U.S. Geological Survey. 1997. "Estimated Use of Water in the United States in 1995." Washington, DC: U.S. Department of the Interior, USGS.

Vanden Heuvel, Richard M. 1996. "The Promise of Precision Agriculture." *Journal of Soil and Water Conservation* 51, no. 1.

Vorman, Julie. 2002. "U.S. Biotech Crop Plantings Rise Again in 2002." Reuters News Service, April 2. http://www.planetark.org/dailynewsstory.cfm?newsid=15271.

6

Freshwater

The North American nations of Canada and the United States contain between 13 and 17 percent of the world's total renewable freshwater resources, according to various governmental and scientific estimates. Renewable surface sources (in the form of lakes and rivers) and groundwater sources (aquifers) together provide the two nations with an estimated 5,300 cubic kilometers of freshwater on an annual basis, giving North America more readily accessible freshwater than any other continent. Indeed, Canada alone has an estimated one-fifth of the world's freshwater, although only 10 percent of it is classified as "renewable" (that is, freshwater that is continually replenished by natural hydrological cycles such as precipitation or snowmelt runoff). The continent's wealth of freshwater is unevenly distributed, however, and some of its greatest population and economic growth is taking place in its most arid, water-scarce regions, such as the U.S. Southwest.

World Leaders in Freshwater Supply and Use

Water demand and use are considerable in both Canada and the United States. In fact, Canadians and U.S. citizens use about twice as much water per person as the average in the industrialized world (although they pay far less than European consumers), and they use a far greater amount than individuals from developing nations. Steady population growth on both sides of the border has triggered increasing municipal demands for water, while U.S. irrigation-dependent agriculture networks and the energy-hungry industries present in both the United States and Canada also rank as major water consumers. According to the Organization for Economic Co-operation and Development (OECD), Canadian freshwater withdrawals can be broken down as follows: power generation (58 percent), industrial use (27 percent), municipal use (8 percent), and agriculture (7 percent). In the United States, agriculture accounts for the greatest use by sector (42 percent of total withdrawals), followed by power generation (39 percent), municipal use (11 percent), and industrial use (8 percent) (U.S. Geological Survey, "Estimated Use of Water in the United States in 1995," 1997; Organization for Economic Co-operation and Development, *Environmental Performance Reviews, Canada*, 1995; Organization for Economic Co-operation and Development, *Environmental Performance Reviews, United States*, 1996).

Canada's history and its sense of self-identity are closely intertwined with the mighty rivers and lakes that cover much of its land mass. But Canada's population, which has roughly ten times the water resources of the United States on a per capita basis, consumes water at a prodigious rate that is often attributed to a general sense that the nation's water supply is virtually inexhaustible. Approximately, 7.6 percent of Canada is covered by lakes and rivers, and British Columbia alone, replenished by annual rainfalls that can reach 200 inches, is estimated to hold at least 4 percent of the world's accessible, renewable freshwater. Canada also shares the Great Lakes, repository of 18 percent of the world's fresh surface water, with the United States. In addition, Canadian rivers carry as much as 9 percent of the world's renewable freshwater, with four of North America's eight largest rivers running in whole or in part through the Canadian provinces bordering the United States. One of these, the Fraser River, gathers nearly twice the runoff of all of California. But 60 percent of Canada's freshwater drains northward into Arctic seas, while 90 percent of the Canadian population lives within 300 miles of the Canada-U.S. border.

This sense of plenty is partly responsible for Canada's casual perspective on water use and its historically anemic efforts at water conservation. Many Canadian communities, for example, still do not meter water use, even though Canadian households paying for water by volume use significantly less than those paying a flat rate. Certainly, recent trends in water use support the arguments of critics who charge that Canada exhibits a fundamentally complacent attitude in this area. Between 1972 and 1991, Canada's water withdrawal increased from 24 billion cubic meters to more than 45 billion cubic meters annually. This increase, propelled by increased industrial and power generation demand, occurred during a period when the Canadian population increased by less than 5 percent (Government of Canada, *The State of Canada's Environment*, 1996).

Water use efficiency improved in Canada during the 1990s, but the average Canadian household was still using about 26,000 liters of water per month in the latter part of the decade. These trends have led conservation groups, scientists, municipal planners, and other observers to call for a fundamental reassessment of the nation's assumptions regarding its rate of water use. As one study warned: "We [Canadians] now consider our unsustainable use of aquatic resources as acceptable" (Rawsom Academy of Aquatic Science, *Ecological Security and Canada's Freshwater Resources,* 1992).

Canada's neighbors to the south have a similar spendthrift history regarding water use. Blessed with abundant freshwater resources of its own across much of its length and breadth (although its arid Southwest and High Plains regions are notable exceptions), the United States consumes great amounts of water daily. For example, it is estimated that Americans use more than 4.8 billion gallons of water every day just to flush their toilets. Moreover, few meaningful steps have been taken to reduce consumption by the agricultural sector, the largest—and arguably the most inefficient—consumer of freshwater resources in the country. Still, the picture is not entirely bleak. Analysts note that regional water scarcities and increased environmental awareness have sparked incremental reform and conservation efforts that have blunted U.S. consumption in some important respects. According to a 1998 study by the U.S. Geological Survey, for instance, U.S. industries have decreased their water consumption by nearly 35 percent since 1950, while overall U.S. water consumption decreased by 9 percent between 1980 and 1995. Regulatory efforts to improve water quality, such as the landmark Clean Water Act of 1977, have also made more water available.

Nonetheless, the United States is expected to continue to be a world leader in freshwater consumption for the foreseeable future, in part because U.S. communities and individual consumers alike commonly continue to view freshwater as a limitless and inexpensive commodity. Indeed, the nation's current pricing systems for water consumption provide little incentive for users to conserve. "When people are charged nothing for water, or farmers get it for as little as one cent per 1,000 gallons, it should surprise no one that water is squandered," wrote former U.S. senator Paul Simon (*Tapped Out,* 1998). Moreover, the United States already has a massive water allocation infrastructure in place, a vast network of dams, reservoirs, and canal systems that harness the country's water for a wide array of uses and a vast range of users. Many constituencies have a vested interest in keeping this infrastructure in its present form.

In North America, then, the perception of water wealth has created an environment in which excessive, wasteful water consumption is rarely penalized. "With respect to water, Canadians and Americans suffer from the same disease: We say that it is priceless, but act as if it were absurdly cheap," lamented the *Toronto Globe and Mail* in a May 23, 1998, editorial. "Most North Americans pay far less for their water than even just the cost of supplying it, cleaning it up and returning it to the environment. Yet subsidizing water use is economically and ecologically disastrous. In fact, heavy subsidization of water in the U.S. is the cause of any water 'shortages' that may exist there. In California, for example, agriculture consumes 80 percent of the state's water, often growing low-value and water-intensive crops in the desert. If everyone paid the true value of the water they used, they would use less, freeing more for those who need it."

Water Pollution a Continuing Problem

North America made significant improvements in cleaning up its rivers and lakes during the last three decades of the twentieth century. During that time, the United States and Canada introduced regulatory reforms at federal and state/provincial levels that reduced the levels of pollutants in watersheds from industrial, agricultural, and municipal sources. Nonetheless, as recently as 1997, the U.S. Environmental Protection Agency (EPA) estimated that half of America's lakes and one-third of its rivers were unfit for swimming or fishing.

Pollution from municipal water systems and manufacturing facilities remains a major problem in some regions of North America. Acid rain caused by industrial emissions, for example, has done extensive harm to ecosystems in lakes all across eastern Canada and the northeastern United States over the last forty years. Meanwhile, countless rivers spanning the continent continue to be beleaguered by collateral damage from harmful logging, mining, and agricultural practices. Detailed studies of these river systems have given credence to criticism from scientists and conservation groups that water diversions, runoff from fertilizers and pesticides, erosion-inducing practices like clearcutting (harvesting all timber in a given area, irrespective of size or age), and inadequate wastewater treatment systems are all contributing to the steady deterioration of numerous freshwater ecosystems.

In the United States, the quality of drinking water has steadily improved with the introduction and implementation of new treatment technologies for phosphates and point source pollution. But a report commissioned by *USA Today* in 1998 found that 40,000 of 170,000 drinking water systems did not meet purity guidelines. Of these, 9,500 water systems serving almost 25 million people had "significant violations," defined by the EPA as posing "serious threats to human health." America's practice of disposing of large quantities of liquid hazardous waste in deep underground wells—an estimated 34 billion liters of heavy metals, radioactive materials, and chemicals annually—has also been blamed for creating drinking water contamination problems in several states.

Figure 6.1 America's Most Endangered Rivers, 2002

SOURCE: American Rivers, Annual Report.

In addition, many cities have sanitary and storm water systems that are groaning under the weight of rampant development and population growth. This growth not only taxes existing systems (which are often antiquated) but also paves over wetlands and other water-absorbent natural areas that could help filter polluted runoff before it flows into rivers and lakes. As a result, many municipal systems discharge large amounts of untreated sewage into natural water bodies when overwhelmed by wet weather (in some communities, even ordinary levels of rainfall can wreak havoc). These types of over-

Las Vegas: Watery Oasis in the Desert

As debates over water use in the American West have intensified, the glittering city of Las Vegas has emerged as a frequent target of discussion. Las Vegas is located in the southern corner of Nevada, in one of the most arid regions of North America. A desert city, Las Vegas receives only four inches of rainfall annually. But its voracious consumption of water from the Colorado River has enabled it to defy geographic realities and become North America's fastest-growing city. Boosted by the perennial popularity of its many casinos—most of which use extraordinary amounts of water for ornamental purposes—the city attracts 30 million tourists every year. In addition, its population passed 1.1 million in the late 1990s, and the Las Vegas Center for Business and Economic Research projects a population of 1.86 million by 2010. This record of explosive growth delights the city's business community, but it is a source of concern to members of the scientific and environmental communities, who view the city as an outrageous symbol of profligate water use in the West. "Las Vegas is America's city of fantasy, and water, not wealth, is its greatest fantasy of all," wrote Jacques Leslie. "The city that Hoover Dam made possible is the nation's fastest-growing metropolis in the country's driest state, the perfect manifestation of the notion that water will never run out" (Leslie, "Running Dry," 2000).

Las Vegas historically has laid claim to Nevada's total annual allotment of Colorado River water—300,000 acre feet a year. This water, which is distributed to the city via Lake Mead, accounts for 88 percent of its total water use (groundwater sources account for the remaining 12 percent). Both of these sources are in some jeopardy, however. The Colorado River is already severely oversubscribed, making it difficult for Nevada to negotiate a greater share of its flow. Additional access to the region's limited groundwater aquifers is also uncertain. Indeed, Las Vegas Valley Water District is engaged in fierce, ongoing battles with rural farm-based communities in neighboring counties over unallocated groundwater rights in the region. In the meantime, the city continued to use water at three times the rate of other U.S. cities located in similar climates as recently as the mid-1990s.

(continues)

flows are cited as a key reason why the United States was forced to close beaches more than 11,000 times for pollution reasons in 2000, according to one Natural Resources Defense Counsel report. But efforts to correct these problems and incorporate improved water treatment systems are hampered by the great expense of such endeavors. In 2001, for example, the Southeast Michigan Council of Governments estimated that it will cost $20 billion to fix the century-old water and sewer system that currently serves more than 4.2 million people in southeast Michigan.

These realities, coupled with the city's reputation as an extravagant waster of water, spurred Las Vegas to belatedly introduce a variety of water conservation measures. They ranged from a system of recapturing wastewater for irrigation and hydroelectric power to a water conservation plan, introduced in 1995, that has pared more than 15 percent off the city's projected water use. This conservation program instituted tiered water rates that targeted residential users, which continue to use more than 60 percent of the city's total. Las Vegas also supplemented this consumption scheme with a mix of mandatory and voluntary conservation measures, ranging from ordinances that prohibit residents from outdoor water use between noon and 7:00 P.M. to programs that offer cash incentives to homeowners who replace conventional, water-thirsty lawns with native cactus and other desert plants and shrubs. Critics note, however, that restrictions on water use have not been levied against the city's casinos and hotels, which continue to utilize massive water fountains and artificial waterways as centerpieces of their architectural designs.

Other steps taken by Las Vegas to meet its future water needs include construction of a new $2 billion water treatment plant on Lake Mead, repairs to existing pipelines, and greater efficiencies in pumping methods. The city is also exploring the possibility of obtaining some of California's allocation of Colorado River water in exchange for bankrolling the construction of state desalination facilities, or purchasing water from Arizona, which has managed to save some of its Colorado allotment over the years. Many critics of Las Vegas's extraordinary growth contend, however, that these measures will only delay—not negate—a future water crisis of serious dimensions for the city.

Sources:

Couret, Christina. 1998. "Las Vegas: Beyond the Neon." *American City and County* 113 (September).

Davis, Mike. 1995. "House of Cards." *Sierra* 80 (November–December).

De Villiers, Marq. 2000. *Water: The Fate of Our Most Precious Resource.* New York: Houghton Mifflin.

Leslie, Jacques. 2000. "Running Dry." *Harper's Magazine* 297 (July).

Simon, Paul. 1998. *Tapped Out: The Coming World Crisis in Water and What We Can Do About It.* New York: Welcome Rain.

In rural areas of the United States, agrochemical runoff is the main source of water pollution. According to the OECD, fertilizers and pesticides used in farming operations account for about 60 percent of total stream and lake impairment in the entire United States (Organization for Economic Cooperation and Development, *Environmental Performance Reviews, United States,* 1996). Excess nitrogen content, a by-product of fertilizers (the United States used 20 million tons of fertilizer in its agricultural operations in 1997 alone) and livestock manure, is regarded as a particularly troublesome development in many regions. Excess quantities of nitrogen in waterways starve downstream areas of oxygen, creating sterile zones that are unable to sustain any aquatic life. This growing problem is most evident in the Gulf of Mexico, a vital commercial and recreational fishing region that hosts myriad species of fish and shellfish and provides habitat for 75 percent of North America's migratory waterfowl. The Gulf is fed by the Mississippi River, which drains 40 percent of the continental United States, including much of its most productive farmland. The Mississippi has now deposited so much excess nitrogen into the Gulf from agricultural operations farther upstream (as well as various industrial and municipal sources) that a massive "dead zone" has been created. The size of this sterile zone varies with weather changes and other environmental conditions, but in July 2000 it was estimated to be larger than the state of New Jersey and to span the length of Louisiana's coastline.

The status of the Great Lakes, the massive freshwater lake system shared by the United States and Canada, is mixed. Studies indicate that it is far cleaner than in earlier decades, in large measure because of regulatory initiatives undertaken on both sides of the border. But the Sweetwater Seas, as they are regionally known, remain reservoirs of agricultural and chemical runoff. Each year 50 to 100 million tons of hazardous waste are generated in the watershed for the lakes, including 25 million tons of pesticides. In the late 1990s, the International Joint Commission (IJC), an independent agency that is charged with monitoring and resolving water issues between the United States and Canada, even found radioactive contaminants from nuclear power plant discharges in Great Lakes waters. The IJC also issues annual warnings against eating Great Lakes sport fish, consumption of which can lead to birth anomalies and other health problems for children and women of child-bearing age (International Joint Commission, *Tenth Biennial Report on Great Lakes Water Quality,* 2000). The viability of these warnings was underscored in early 2001, when the University of Wisconsin released a study showing that high levels of polybrominated diphenyl ether (PBDE), a common flame retardant found in various plastics and textiles, had been discovered in Lake Michigan salmon.

According to the study's authors, the concentrations were among the highest reported in the entire world for salmon in open waters.

These perennial pollution problems led the IJC, in its 2000 report on Great Lakes water quality, to declare that unless the U.S. and Canadian governments take swift and resolute action to address pollution problems, their professed desire to "restore and maintain the chemical, physical, and biological integrity of the water of the Great Lakes Basin ecosystem" is doomed to failure. In conjunction with this warning, the IJC also offered a blunt assessment of both countries' level of commitment to earlier agreements to clean up the Great Lakes: "The power of the vision captured in the [Great Lakes Water Quality Agreement of 1978, the principal international environmental legislation protecting the lakes] has not been reflected in the two governments' implementation efforts. . . . [Without] the provision of adequate resources for Great Lakes Water Quality Agreement programs, there can be little hope of fully restoring and protecting the Great Lakes" (ibid.).

Water pollution also looms as a serious issue in other areas of Canada. "By almost any measure, Canada does not treat its water very well," wrote Marq De Villiers. "We unload an extraordinary amount of trash into our rivers, counting on the fact that rivers are effective natural flushing mechanisms. . . . Few major Canadian rivers are safe to drink in their 'natural' state. Inflows of agricultural herbicides and pesticides are virtually unregulated" (De Villiers, "Water Works," 2000). Perhaps the most stark example of Canada's neglectful record in this realm can be found in the provincial capitals of Halifax, St. Johns, and Victoria. None of these capital cities have sewage treatment systems in place. As a result, all three cities continue to pour their raw sewage into the oceans, as they have for generations (Hinrichsen, *Coastal Waters of the World*, 1998).

The residents of those cities are not unique within Canada, however. Indeed, an estimated one-third of Canadians are not served by waste-treatment plants. Many of these people reside in small towns and other rural areas, where the safety of drinking water has emerged as a growing concern in recent years. The government of Canada reported in 1996, for instance, that as many as 40 percent of the nation's rural water wells may be contaminated by fecal coliform bacteria and nitrates. Four years later, the potential seriousness of this situation was underscored in Walkerton, Ontario, where *E. coli* contamination of the town's water supply killed 7 residents and sickened another 2,000.

Observers note that Canada's groundwater and freshwater resources are most contaminated in the nation's southern reaches, where the overwhelming majority of its populace lives. But even Canada's Arctic watersheds, largely unpopulated but for scattered aboriginal communities, have not escaped pollution from agricultural or industrial operations located hundreds or even thousands of miles away. Many of Canada's remote Arctic rivers and lakes have registered rising levels of lead, mercury, petroleum hydrocarbons, and other pollutants in recent years as a result of airborne contamination.

Unsustainable Groundwater Use in the American West

North America relies extensively on groundwater sources to meet the water needs of many of its communities. Approximately half of the municipal water supplies in both the United States and Canada are drawn from groundwater sources. This percentage is even higher in rural areas. Approximately two-thirds of rural Canadians rely on groundwater to wash their dishes and take their showers, while more than 95 percent of rural U.S. citizens utilize wells that tap into groundwater aquifers for their household needs.

Groundwater aquifers are also used as an irrigation resource to support agricultural operations in both countries. In Canada, the agriculture-dependent prairie provinces of Alberta, Manitoba, and Saskatchewan account for the overwhelming majority of all irrigation demand. To meet their irrigation needs, farmers in this region make heavy withdrawals from groundwater aquifers, in conjunction with freshwater diversions from rivers and lakes. Concerns have been raised about western Canada's entrenched pattern of withdrawing groundwater for agricultural purposes at a rate greater than natural replenishment. But the existence of alternative water resources, the region's relatively small population centers (when compared with the United States), and its smaller farming industry all act to rein in its groundwater mining practices to varying degrees.

The United States devotes a far greater volume of water to agriculture. According to the Council on Environmental Quality, the amount of irrigated land in the United States rose from 1.5 million hectares in 1890 to 21 million hectares in 1995, ranking it third in total irrigated area in the world (after India and China). Most of this development has taken place in the West, a fundamentally arid region that has, over the course of several generations, been transformed by irrigation practices into some of the world's most valuable and productive farmland. In fact, California, Arizona, Colorado, New Mexico, Kansas, Nevada, Nebraska, Idaho, and North and South Dakota all use about 80 percent (or better) of the water at their disposal from renewable and fossil water sources for farming. This agricultural development laid the foundation for the transformation of the region into one of the country's major economic and population growth areas. But critics warn that in its zeal to maintain the agricultural empire that it constructed out of some of the most inhospitable country in the United States, the West is depleting its groundwater and surface water sources at an unsustainable rate.

California laid the groundwork for this state of affairs, for it was the first Western state to harness the region's water and bend it to its purposes. In fact, historians such as Marc Reisner claim that, "as is the case with most western states, California's very existence is premised on epic liberties taken with water" (Reisner, *Cadillac Desert,* 1993). In the 1930s California initiated an era of massive water diversion projects that nurtured its explosive growth and, even today, remains the backbone of the state's agricultural, industrial, and municipal infrastructure.

> Every year the state moves 14 trillion gallons of water, in directions mostly south, capturing it behind 1,200 dams on every river and stream of any size, before fluming it hundreds of miles, lifting it over some mountain ranges and pumping it under others, fitting the sere landscape with a caul of pipes, ditches, and siphons that irrigates an agricultural empire far greater but not unlike the one that bloomed in the deserts of Babylon and ancient Egypt. And if wealth has tamed the water, then the water has made California wealthier still. If it were a nation, the state's $1 trillion economy ranks it seventh among national economies, and in addition to providing 55 percent of America's fruit, nuts, and vegetables, California has managed to become the sixth-largest agricultural exporter in the world by intensively farming a region that receives less than 20 inches a year. (Graham, "A Hundred Rivers Run through It," 1998)

The Colorado River, which covers 630,000 square kilometers and carries an average flow of about 14 million acre-feet annually as it winds through the Western states, remains the most important of the renewable water resources used by California and neighboring states. After all, it is the largest major river system in a region that has cast much of its economic fortunes with water-dependent agriculture. Not surprisingly, the Colorado and its tributaries have suffered enormously from the water demands of the region's growing population. Almost all of its annual flow is already spoken for by the seven Western states through which it flows, its waters diverted to supply drinking water for Phoenix, golf courses for Tucson, casino fountains for Las Vegas, and sustenance for the crops of California's San Joaquin Valley (see sidebar on page 148). In addition, Mexico is entitled to 1.5 million acre feet of Colorado River water annually by virtue of a formal agreement with the United States. With all of these demands placed on it, the Colorado has become so oversubscribed that its Pacific Ocean delta, once home to a rich aquatic ecosystem, is now a parched echo of its former self. Yet perennial squabbling among the Colorado Basin states over the river's finite supply of water has intensified in recent years, as growing cities like Las Vegas demand a greater share of the river's water.

The major source of groundwater in the U.S. West, meanwhile, is the Ogallala Aquifer, the largest discrete aquifer on the planet. This aquifer, which underlies as much as 580,000 square kilometers of the Great Plains stretching from Texas to South Dakota, helped transform otherwise poor farming land in Texas, Oklahoma, Nebraska, Kansas, Colorado, and New Mexico into productive cropland during the middle decades of this century. Today, the Ogallala alone waters one-fifth of the nation's total irrigated land. But this resource, upon which Great Plains agricultural enterprises—and communities—depend for their livelihood, is vanishing swiftly. According to some estimates, perhaps 60 percent—an amount of water equivalent to one-third the total volume of Lake Huron or the annual flow of eighteen Colorado rivers—is already gone, sucked out of the ground at a rate that far exceeds rates of natural replenishment. Even a cursory review of rates of withdrawal illustrates the problem dramatically. For example, in the late 1950s, Nebraska was irrigating fewer than a million acres; less than twenty years later, it was irrigating seven times that acreage, almost entirely with water pumped from the Ogallala. This surge in withdrawal was reflected up and down the aquifer, as Marc Reisner noted: "By 1975, Texas was withdrawing some eleven billion gallons of groundwater—per *day* [from the aquifer]. In Kansas, the figure was five billion; in Nebraska 5.9 billion; in Colorado, 2.7 billion; in Oklahoma, 1.4 billion; in New Mexico, 1.6 billion. In places, farmers were withdrawing four to six feet of water per year, while nature was putting back half an inch" (Reisner, *Cadillac Desert,* 1993). Since that period, the population in many of these states has risen significantly, putting even greater pressure on the Ogallala.

No one knows when the Ogallala Aquifer will be exhausted. One study carried out in the early 1980s estimated 2020, but many analysts believe that this projection is overly optimistic. Whenever the time arrives—in ten, twenty, or sixty years—many local and regional economies will have to undergo wrenching transitions to non–water dependent economies and lifestyles, barring strict new conservation programs that lengthen the usable life of the aquifer, or water importation/diversion schemes that, at least in the early years of the 21st century, seem economically or politically untenable. Moreover, experts worry that the loss of millions of acres of formerly productive farmland, if it occurs, will have a strong negative impact on worldwide food supplies.

Not surprisingly, these calamitous scenarios have sparked considerable criticism of the region's post–World War II agricultural policies. "Strictly regulated, the Ogallala could have been made to last hundreds of years instead of decades," wrote Reisner. "The opportunity for economic stability offered by the world's largest aquifer, however, was squandered for immediate gain. The only inference one can draw is that the states felt confident that when they ran out of water, the rest of the country would be willing to rescue them" (ibid.). Indeed, as far back as 1982, a Six-State High Plains-Ogallala Area Study sponsored by the U.S. Department of Commerce and carried out by regional officials declared that "the only long-term solution to declining groundwater supplies and maintaining a permanent irrigated agricultural economy in most of the High Plains region is the development of alternate water supplies. . . . Although emerging technologies for local water supply augmentation offer some potential for alleviating the overdraft of the aquifer, none can provide sustained and replenishable supplies to meet the region's needs. [Therefore] regional water transfer potentials . . . should be continued and expanded to feasibility and planning levels."

Today, as the Great Plains states begin a new century of farming, proposed solutions to the problem of unsustainable water use have included increasing

Water Exports and Diversions

"Americans and Canadians have a long history of more or less amicable relations on water matters," wrote Marq De Villiers. "Partly because the politicians of both countries have seen eye to eye on the value of exploiting water and controlling recalcitrant rivers, and partly because Canada's sheer abundance—or perceived abundance—of water has made it difficult to generate much political heat over water matters" (De Villiers, *Water*, 2000). In 1999, however, a small Ontario company roiled this usually placid area of relations between the two countries when it secured a permit to make annual 600-million-liter deliveries of Lake Superior water to clients in Asia. News of this development triggered angry outcries from statehouses in Michigan, Ohio, and other Great Lakes states. Moreover, the issuance of the permit sparked a wave of vocal opposition from within Canada itself. The image of freighters laden with Great Lakes water disappearing over the horizon to distant ports resurrected old fears among the populace that Canadian rivers and lakes, among the country's most potent and valued symbols of national self-identity, might someday be diverted to meet the expanding water appetites of the U.S. West. Opposition to the water export scheme soon reached such a pitch on both sides of the border that Ontario's

(continues)

the expense of water consumption, making greater efficiencies in irrigation, switching to less water-dependent crops, and ending subsidies of some crops. But it appears that water transfers—whether from the Great Lakes or some other source—remain the region's principal hope for staving off the crippling shortage of water that otherwise awaits them some unknown period down the road, even though resistance to such schemes would be fierce in the Great Lakes states or other targeted areas on both environmental and economic grounds (see sidebar on page 155). This potential for deadlock has led still others to point to Pacific Coast desalination plants—facilities that remove salts from ocean water—as the long-term solution to the West's water woes. "While demand management and efficiency options are still far more cost-effective, desalination may ultimately prove to be the best new supply option for high-valued uses of water in coastal regions where efforts to maximize efficiency

provincial government rescinded the permit and announced a ban on future exports of Great Lakes water. Ontario's decision averted a potential crisis between Canada and its southern neighbor. But this incident, combined with similar attempts to export water out of Newfoundland and British Columbia, has led both nations to examine the various benefits and pitfalls of proposed diversions from the Great Lakes and other waterways with renewed vigor.

Proposals to export Canadian water to the United States or other nations for financial gain first appeared in the 1950s, when private industries proposed erecting a huge dike across James Bay and diverting many of eastern Canada's river systems into the Great Lakes for use by municipalities, agricultural sectors, and hydroelectric power plants. That proposal faded away, but in the 1970s a new plan, called the North American Water and Power Alliance (NAWAPA), proposed to dam many of British Columbia's mightiest free-flowing rivers and turn them backward into a monstrous Rocky Mountain storage reservoir that would irrigate America's Great Plains states and illuminate the living rooms of western Canada. Ultimately, the prohibitive expense and unfathomable ecological impact of both of these proposals seemed to relegate them to the realm of fantasy. Still, some Canadian and U.S. industrialists and politicians periodically attempt to revive various incarnations of these plans, armed with a steadily accumulating mountain of data about encroaching water shortages and the potential future value of freshwater.

The issue of water exports subsided as a topic of discussion for much of the 1990s. But the Ontario permit episode brought the subject back into the spotlight with a vengeance, fueled by a growing recognition that water

(continues)

are being made and where absolute supply constraints are severe," wrote water expert Peter H. Gleick (*The World's Water 2000–2001*, 2000).

Depletion of Wetlands

Wetlands are a major natural resource in North America. They act as filters to improve water quality, absorb water for groundwater renewal and flood control, and are recognized as vital wildlife habitat in both the United States and Canada. The U.S. National Marine Fisheries Service, for instance, has estimated that about 70 percent of the annual $45 billion commercial fish catch of the United States is dependent upon inshore-wetland habitats. Wetlands serve an important role in flood control, for they have the capacity to soak up rain and water runoff, then slowly release it back into the rivers, streams, lakes, and groundwater as flood conditions subside. Not surprisingly, then,

shortages are becoming more acute across much of the world. Since that time, supporters and opponents have argued bitterly over the political, social, economic, environmental, and legal implications of bulk water exports from the Great Lakes or other Canadian freshwater sources. Conservation groups decry the ecological damage that such exports might do. They also charge that under the North American Free Trade Agreement (NAFTA) and other international treaties, completion of a single water export transaction would render Canada powerless to prevent even the most environmentally insupportable bulk water shipments. Supporters, however, contend that these trade rules only prevent governments from adopting discriminatory practices in the event that they do decide to export water resources. Moreover, they contend that a prohibition on water exports is an immoral response to the plight of water-deprived peoples around the world.

For its part, Canada's federal government has stated its unconditional opposition to water export schemes to the United States, Asia, or anywhere else. But it is reluctant to impose a federal ban on such transactions because of concerns that such an action might constitute a violation of NAFTA and WTO (World Trade Organization) trade rules, which prohibit such blanket export bans. Unable to rely on the protection of a federal export ban, Canada's provincial governments have sought to address the issue themselves. In 1999, for instance, Ontario introduced amendments to the International Boundary Waters Treaty Act prohibiting bulk water removals from the Great Lakes and other bodies of water shared by the United States and Canada. The provinces are also debating a proposed Canada-wide accord that would

(continues)

the conversion of millions of acres of marshes, ponds, and other wetlands to agriculture, commercial development, and other uses over the past century has triggered or exacerbated an array of problems associated with flooding. The severity of the 1997 Red River flood, which devastated North America's midsection, for example, was attributed in large part to the fact that 75 percent of the wetlands in the Red River basin have been drained over the years.

After decades of undisciplined drainages and conversions, efforts to conserve wetlands intensified in both the United States and Canada during the 1990s. Triumphs in this area include the North American Waterfowl Management Plan (NAWMP), a joint effort of Canada, the United States, and Mexico. This program is credited with preserving hundreds of thousands of acres of wetlands used by migratory waterfowl in those three countries. But despite a slowing rate of conversion, wetland losses continued to outstrip wetland gains in most of North America.

Canada is currently home to about one-quarter of the world's wetlands, with its largest wetland areas in Ontario, Manitoba, and the Northwest

prohibit bulk transfers from Canadian watersheds, even if the final destination remains within Canada. Five provinces—British Columbia, Alberta, Manitoba, Saskatchewan, and Quebec—balked at this initiative, although British Columbia, Alberta, and Quebec already have bans in place that cover much the same ground. Provincial representatives say, however, that such setbacks do not reflect disagreement about the wisdom of protecting Canadian rivers and lakes but rather differing perspectives on the best ways to go about meeting that goal. In the United States, meanwhile, the Great Lakes region has become increasingly suspicious of water-hungry Western states. As a result, political leaders, business interests, and conservation groups are all exploring a variety of state and federal regulations that would protect the waters of Lake Superior and its sister lakes from the predations of the West.

Sources:

De Villiers, Marq. 2000. *Water: The Fate of Our Most Precious Resource.* New York: Houghton Mifflin.

———. 2000. "Water Works." *Canadian Geographic* 120 (May–June).

Farid, Claire, John Jackson, and Karen Clark. 1997. *The Fate of the Great Lakes: Sustaining or Draining the Sweetwater Seas?* Buffalo, NY: Canadian Environmental Law Association, United Buffalo State College.

Geddes, John. 2000. "Water Wars: Should Canada Sell Its Most Precious Resource?" *Maclean's* (March 6).

International Joint Commission. 2000. *Tenth Biennial Report on Great Lakes Water Quality.* Windsor, ON: IJC, July.

Territories. It contains approximately 127 million hectares of wetlands within its borders, even though it has converted about one-seventh of its marshes, swamps, and bogs to other land uses over the course of the twentieth century. The most severe losses have been in major metropolitan and agricultural areas. For example, nearly 70 percent of all wetlands in southern Ontario, Canada's most populous region, have been drained or converted to other uses. Western provinces dependent on agriculture, such as Alberta, have lost similar percentages (Government of Canada, *The State of Canada's Environment,* 1996).

Of the wetlands that remain, 29 percent are under federal jurisdiction, primarily in Canada's northern territories. These lands have come under increased protection from the federal government, which announced several major wetland conservation goals during the 1990s, including no net loss of existing wetlands on federal lands and increased rehabilitation of degraded wetland areas. These initiatives have been instituted in concert with a number of new provincial wetland protection programs.

Figure 6.2 Wetland Losses by State

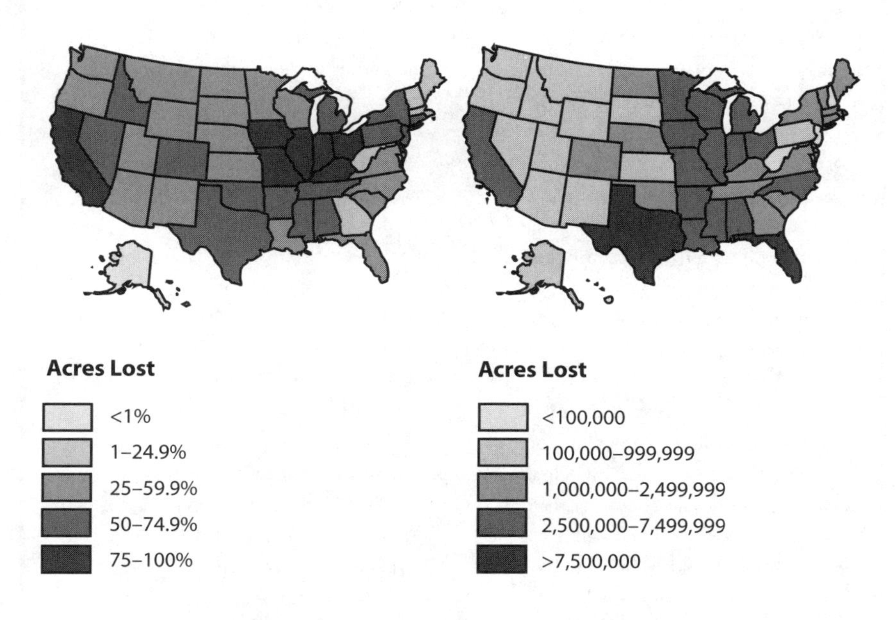

SOURCE: Stein et al. 2000. *Precious Heritage: Status of Biodiversity in the United States*, NatureServe.

The Fight over Salmon and Dams on Washington's Lower Snake River

The fish ladder at Ice Harbor Dam in the Snake River in Washington State
U.S. ARMY CORPS OF ENGINEERS

One of the most contentious, emotional fights over dam removal in North America is taking place in the Pacific Northwest, where a battle has raged over four federal dams on the Lower Snake River since the early 1990s. The Columbia River system, of which the Snake River is the greatest tributary, once housed one of the world's greatest salmon fisheries. According to some estimates, up to 15 million wild salmon and steelhead once returned to spawning grounds in the Columbia and Snake rivers every year, obeying primal instincts honed over millennia. In the space of thirty years, however, the basin's salmon and steelhead populations have been decimated, with some species completely wiped out and others poised on the verge of extinction. Many observers claim that the single greatest reason for this precipitous decline in the number of Columbia salmon—loved by sportfishermen, vital to the economic vitality of Pacific Coast fishing fleets, and sacramental symbols in the worship systems of Northwest Indian tribes—is the network of hydropower dams that now block their migratory routes in the Columbia-Snake River systems. Some studies estimate that these dams now kill up to 95 percent of all migrating young salmon and steelhead in the basin.

The Columbia River system is North America's fourth largest, draining 250,000 square miles in the Pacific Northwest and Canada. Over time, engineers have dramatically reshaped the Columbia and its tributaries with 250 reservoirs and 150 hydroelectric

(continues)

projects, including 18 mainstem dams on the Columbia and Snake rivers. Several of these dams were built in a manner that made allowances for salmon and steelhead runs, but others were not. For instance, the largest of the Columbia dams, the Grand Coulee in northeastern Washington, has no fish ladders. Located almost halfway between the Columbia's headwaters and its delta, this dam (operated by the Bureau of Reclamation) eliminated about 40 percent of the watershed's spawning habitat when it came online.

But despite the Grand Coulee's impact on the regional ecosystem, it is the eight federal dams operated by the Army Corps of Engineers—four on the Columbia, four on the Snake—that have received most of the blame for the loss of salmon in the Pacific Northwest. For years, the federal dams on the Columbia main stem (the Dalles, Bonneville, John Day, and McNary dams) ruined dozens of salmon runs, devastating dozens of local and aboriginal fishing communities in the process. Finally these dams were retrofitted to accommodate the salmon runs, although operations at one of these—John Day Dam—continue to be regarded as problematic by pro-salmon groups.

The modifications made to the Columbia dams, however, were not extended to their four sister dams on the Lower Snake River, which had been more controversial from their very inception because of their potential impact on the Northwest's salmon-oriented economy. Constructed in the 1960s and 1970s, the dams tamed the Snake's surging current and reshaped the river into a massive barge canal—a "working river" that carried barges laden with timber, wheat, and other products from the interior down to the Columbia River and, ultimately, to shipyards on the Oregon coast. The dams even transformed Lewiston, Idaho, a town located more than 300 miles inland from the Pacific Ocean, into a port city.

In the meantime, the Columbia Basin salmon population plummeted. Forced to navigate towering fish ladders, flesh-shredding turbines, and warm and still water that blunts migratory instincts, only to reach tributaries blocked by dams hundreds of feet high, various salmon species declined precipitously. By 1986 all Pacific Northwest coho salmon populations dependent on the Snake River migratory corridor were extinct. In 1998 only 306 wild chinook returned to the system, while during the entire decade of the 1990s, a total of only 20 sockeye salmon were able to claw their way back to their spawning grounds. In 1999 the Idaho spring/summer chinook run—which used to provide tens of thousands of salmon to fisheries off the coast of Japan, the islands of the Aleutian chain, and other distant waters—was reduced to 2,400 returning adults (Duncan, "Salmon's Second Coming," 2000).

These grim figures lead some observers to predict that the Snake's endangered chinook and steelhead are doomed to follow in the footsteps of

(continues)

the extinct Snake River coho, perhaps within the next two decades. If that occurs, biologists warn that the entire Columbia River basin will be hard pressed to recover (according to some estimates, 70 percent of the restoration potential for the system's spring/summer chinook and summer steelhead lies within the Snake River basin).

In light of this deteriorating situation, a coalition of organizations ranging from the Columbia River Intertribal Fish Commission to the Natural Resources Defense Council to the Pacific Coast Federation of Fishermen's Associations joined together during the 1990s to call for the partial or complete removal of the four Lower Snake dams. Proponents of dam removal argue that such a step—taken in conjunction with restoration of spawning habitat, water quality improvements, improved fish hatcheries, and new fishery harvest practices—can save the salmon. "The conservation community and the vast majority of the scientific community believe that if we want to assure survival of the salmon, improvements to habitat, hatcheries, and harvest must be coupled with removal of the four salmon killing dams on the Lower Snake River," stated Charles Gauvin, president of the Trout Unlimited conservation group. "That fact must be understood and accepted if the ultimate goal of this plan is to save the salmon from extinction" (American Rivers Online, "White House Releases Final Salmon Plan," http://www.americanrivers.org [accessed February 7, 2001]).

But dam removal is fiercely opposed by regional business interests and politicians who worry that the loss of the dams would be catastrophic for the economy in the Lewiston area, depriving it of inexpensive electricity and eviscerating its many transportation-oriented businesses. The general manager of the Port of Lewiston, for instance, told *Audubon* that "the economy here is absolutely intertwined with the many benefits those dams provide. It's not just western Idaho's economy. We handle grain shipments from as far away as eastern Montana and the Dakotas" (Reisner, "Coming Undammed," 1998). The Columbia River Alliance—a coalition of local chambers of commerce, agricultural and lumber interests, labor organizations, electric utilities, and port and navigation companies opposed to dam removal—also contends that the collapse of the Pacific salmon population is attributable to warming ocean conditions and compromised habitat elsewhere in the basin. They point out that salmon runs on Northwest rivers with no dams have also declined—sometimes dramatically—because of habitat damage from farming, logging, mining, grazing, road construction, and industrial pollution. "The idea of breaching the four dams on the lower Snake River as an anadromous fish recovery strategy is an attempt to solve a 5,000-mile problem with a 100-mile solution," declared one forest product association (Pulp and Paperworkers

(continues)

Resource Council, "The Other 4900 Miles," 1998). As an alternative to dam removal, the Columbia River Alliance has developed its own $225 million salmon recovery plan that emphasizes upper-river land management and irrigation reforms.

Opponents of the Snake River dams are unmoved by these arguments. They argue that Lewiston has an extensive rail network that could serve as a cost-effective alternative for moving products from Lewiston to the coast. Dam opponents also point out that the structures provide only modest power and agricultural benefits. The four Lower Snake dams produce about 7.2 billion kwh of electric power annually, only 4 percent of the total electricity used in the Pacific Northwest. They are also operated as "run of the river" dams, meaning that they have minimal storage capacity and thus do not provide any meaningful flood control or storage for major irrigation operations. Indeed, proponents of dam removal argue that the structures are economic boondoggles of the highest order. They point out that more than $3 billion has already been spent on salmon recovery efforts (dam bypass systems, trucks and barges to bypass turbines, hatchery construction and operations), with little appreciable benefit. In addition, "fisheries advocates note that in addition to the huge expenses for salmon restoration efforts, taxpayers are subsidizing the dams by paying $18 million each year to pay off the debt for building the locks and $25 million a year to maintain and operate them" (Gleick, *The World's Water 2000–2001*, 2000). One study commissioned by the Oregon Natural Resources Council estimated that total operating costs for the dams amounted to more than $230 million a year, between subsidies, salmon recovery programs, and ongoing maintenance expenses.

Finally, groups seeking to remove the dams have sought to defuse the argument that the region depends on them for economic security and jobs. Critics charge that the Snake River dams and the port in Lewiston have actually hampered economic growth in towns up and down the Columbia and along the Pacific Coast. Independent economic studies have stated that even a modest recovery of Snake River wild salmon populations could generate $2.6 billion in annual income for the region. Moreover, in 2000 the American Rivers conservation organization released a report stating that dam removal would, with proper mitigation, create over 23,000 short-term jobs and more than 3,000 permanent jobs. The Army Corps of Engineers estimated that removal would create between 13,000 and 27,000 new jobs. And a 1993 study indicated that the sport—not commercial—fishery for only one Snake River species—summer steelhead—generated $90 million and 2,700 jobs for the region, even though the run is a small fraction of its former size. That same year, the port of Lewiston directly employed twenty-two people (Whitelaw, "Dam Breaching Myths," 2000).

In December 2000 the U.S. government issued a Columbia basin salmon rescue plan (called the

(continues)

Biological Opinion of the National Marine Fisheries Service) that requires the Army Corps to implement a series of measures to avoid the extinction of remaining wild chinook salmon and steelhead runs, including improvements in salmon habitat, water quality (including flow, temperature, and quantity), hatchery management, and dam operations. If these measures are not fully implemented or fail to rescue the salmon, the plan calls for Congress to authorize removal of the four federal dams on the lower Snake in 2003. Two months later, a federal district court ruled that existing operations at the Lower Snake River dams violated the Clean Water Act by raising water temperatures and dissolving nitrogen above mandatory water quality standards. The court directed the U.S. Army Corps of Engineers to produce a plan that protects threatened and endangered salmon and steelhead.

These developments encouraged the scientists, conservationists, and fishermen working to remove the Snake River dams. But the future of wild salmon in the Columbia-Snake river systems may ultimately be determined by the Bush administration, which has stated its opposition to dam removal. Indeed, pro-salmon activists have expressed concern that the administration will not allocate sufficient funds to pay for the federal salmon rescue plan, setting up a 2003 showdown over the dams' ultimate fate. In the meantime, the prognosis for the long-term viability of Pacific Northwest salmon continues to dim. Columbia Basin hydroelectric facilities operated to full capacity for much of 2001 in order to supply energy-hungry California, further taxing Washington rivers and reservoirs that were already at unusually low levels because of meager winter snowfall. This combination of factors sparked widespread fears that the Pacific Northwest's remnant salmon populations would find insufficient water levels to complete their spawning runs in 2001 and beyond.

Sources:

"Dam Breaching Is Not the Answer." Columbia River Alliance. http://www.teleport.com/~cra (accessed March 7, 2001).

"Dams, Energy and Salmon." 1998. Northwest Energy Coalition and the Columbia and Snake Rivers Campaign.

Duncan, David James. 2000. "Salmon's Second Coming." *Sierra* 85 (March–April).

Gleick, Peter H. 2000. *The World's Water, 2000–2001*. Washington, DC: Island Press.

Harden, Blaine. 1996. *A River Lost: The Life and Death of the Columbia.* New York: W. W. Norton.

Lammers, O. 1998. "Undamming the Snake River to Free Salmon." *World Rivers Review* 13, no. 6.

Lichatowich, Jim. 1999. *Salmon without Rivers: A History of the Pacific Salmon Crisis.* Washington, DC: Island.

McCully, Patrick. 1996. *Silenced Rivers: The Ecology and Politics of Large Dams.* London: Zed.

Pulp and Paperworkers Resource Council. 1998. "The Other 4,000 Miles."

Reisner, Marc. 1998. "Coming Undammed." *Audubon* (September–October).

Whitelaw, Ed. 2000. "Dam Breaching Myths." *Oregon Quarterly* (autumn).

The contiguous United States, meanwhile, has drained, flooded, or otherwise destroyed more than half of the 220 million acres of wetlands that once carpeted the country. California, Missouri, Kentucky, Ohio, Iowa, and Illinois have each lost more than 80 percent of their wetlands to development, primarily of the agricultural variety. This conversion of wetlands to farmland or commercial development reached its peak in the middle of the twentieth century, when agricultural growth, urban expansion, and major hydroelectric projects all put tremendous pressure on previously untouched areas of the countryside.

Federal statistics indicate that annual loss of wetlands in the United States decreased to less than 59,000 acres during the 1990s, an 80 percent reduction compared with yearly losses during the 1980s. In addition, wetlands restoration efforts, spurred on by a blend of private and public initiatives, enjoyed a belated surge of support. For example, the Department of Agriculture launched a Wetland Reserve Program that purchases cropland and restores it to wetland. By 1999 it had set aside 665,000 acres of wetlands and in 2002 the total acreage enrollment cap was raised to 2.275 million acres. "By the 1990s, restoration was an idea whose time had come," explained Ann Vileisis. "With Americans stuck between the vision of preserving wetlands and the tradition of property [rights] that would ultimately consign

Rivers winding through the mangroves of the Everglades U.S. GEOLOGICAL SURVEY

wetlands to oblivion, many people involved in the wetland debate saw alternatives to regulation, such as purchasing easements, buying wetlands, and working cooperatively with landowners, as attractive" (Vileisis, *Discovering the Unknown Landscape,* 1997). In addition, the Florida Everglades—the only real tropical wetland in North America—has received significant, albeit belated, attention from legislators. In 2000 it received approval for a $7.8 billion, twenty-year restoration plan to eliminate chemical contamination from upstream agricultural operations and industries and return some of the natural flow of the wetlands, and in 2002 the federal government announced plans for a major buyback of exploration rights in the Everglades in order to help preserve the fragile region.

Still, the regulatory environment remains a favorable one for developers wishing to drain wetlands for commercial purposes. In 1996 the U.S. Army Corps of Engineers approved 99.7 percent of all applications to develop wetlands areas. The Environmental Protection Agency has veto power in this regard, but during the 1980s and 1990s, it denied only eleven permit applications. In 2001 the U.S. Supreme Court ruled that the nation's Clean Water Act does not give the federal government authority to regulate isolated wetlands not connected to other bodies of water. Conservationists believe that this ruling will make wetlands increasingly vulnerable to development in the future. And in 2002, the Army Corps of Engineers removed "acre-for-acre" requirements for individual development projects. The "acre-for-acre" regulations had stipulated that for every acre of wetland loss, a compensatory acre would be created—an exchange known as wetland mitigation. But the 2002 changes merely required that there be "no net loss" of wetlands in any of the Corps's thirty-eight U.S. districts. This change was adopted without comment by the Department of the Interior, despite complaints from its Fish and Wildlife Service that the Corps had not adequately assessed the potential impact of the changes on wetlands ecosystems.

Debate over Dams and Other "River-Taming" Projects

Over the course of the past century, the United States and Canada used dams to transform the landscape of North America from New England and Quebec to the Pacific Northwest. These structures ranged from small private dams used for logging, mining, and farming efforts to towering, publicly funded structures that became the centerpiece of massive agricultural and municipal operations. An important source of clean and bountiful energy in the form of hydroelectric power, these dams and their affiliated reservoirs of freshwater also became invaluable tools in achieving economic expansion, agricultural

Hoover Dam COREL

growth, navigational improvements, and population dispersement for both nations. The great U.S. dams of the 1930s and 1940s—Grand Coulee, Hoover, Shasta, and Bonneville—are even credited by some historians as being pivotal in deciding the outcome of World War II (the single biggest source of electricity in the world at the time, the Grand Coulee Dam provided the hydroelectric power to build half of the U.S. fighter planes during the war).

Yet despite their unquestioned role in improving the economic fortunes of countless U.S. and Canadian citizens and their continued value in many settings, dams are no longer regarded as an absolute positive in the fabric of either nation's infrastructure. Indeed, the value of many of these monuments to engineering ingenuity is the subject of heated debate, sparking a slowdown in dam construction and increased calls for modification or removal of some dams. "Historically, questions about dams were limited to where to build them and how big they should be," wrote Peter Gleick.

> What we have learned over the past decades, however, is that we should have been asking a far wider range of questions related to their economic and social costs and their environmental and ecological impacts. . . .Some dams are so egregious in their impact on the environment, local communities, or fisheries that their removal must be seen as a clear benefit. Even the possibility that dams can be removed has raised the hope of many communities that have suffered from the oftentimes ignored consequences of dam construction, such as destruction of fisheries, population displacement, land inundation, and more. (Gleick, *The World's Water 2000–2001,* 2000, p. 114)

Significantly, this perspective has gained a measure of acceptance among both U.S. and Canadian governmental agencies. "Viewed in one carefully chosen dimension, many dams have been worthwhile," stated the U.S. Geological Survey, the sole science agency of the Department of the Interior, in a 1998 study called *Dams and Rivers.* "[But] the adverse environmental effects of a dam may extend in circles far wider than had been appreciated in the past." For example, few dambuilders of yesteryear were cognizant of the devastation that such structures would wreak on anadromous salmon populations. But on the heavily dammed Columbia and Snake rivers of the Pacific Northwest, mortality rates for young salmon journeying upriver to spawning grounds now approach 95 percent (see sidebar on page 160), while the hundreds of dams that dot the rivers of New England and Atlantic Canada have been cited as a major—though not the only—factor in the precipitous decline of Atlantic salmon populations (agricultural pollution, increased predation by burgeoning seal populations, depleted food sources, and degraded spawning grounds have also been blamed).

The slowing rate of dam construction in North America is not only due to increased ambivalence about the environmental tradeoffs associated with such projects, however. It can also be attributed to the fact that the United States, in particular, is running out of rivers to dam. By 1995, U.S. Army Corps of Engineers data indicated that there had been more than 35,000 dams completed in the United States over the previous thirty-five years. But whereas more than 9,400 dams were completed in the five-year span from 1966 to 1970, only 1,044 were erected between 1991 and 1995. In addition, the average size of dams built dropped significantly during this same time period. In the 1960s, the average reservoir volume of new U.S. dams averaged 15 to 20 million cubic meters each. By the 1990s, that average had dropped to less than 6 million cubic meters each (ibid.).

In the meantime, members of North America's scientific community have united with grassroots conservation, paddling, and fishing groups to call for modification or removal of dams that take an unacceptable toll on local ecosystems or adversely change the fundamental character of wilderness areas. In many cases, these critics augment their conservation-based arguments with warnings about public safety. For instance, Gleick points out that according to the U.S. National Dams Inventory, more than 30 percent of the nation's dams have a "high" or "significant" downstream hazard potential, a percentage that is likely to rise in the future as they reach the end of their design life. The American Society of Civil Engineers estimates that by 2020, the proportion of U.S. dams exceeding average life expectancy will top 85 percent. Dam opponents also are increasingly using studies purporting to show that dam modifications or removals can bring considerable economic benefits in the form of improved fisheries, heightened tourism associated with free-flowing river recreation, and reallocation of budget resources from dam upkeep.

By 2000, efforts to return U.S. rivers and streams to their natural states had resulted in the decommissioning and removal of nearly 500 dams across the country. The most celebrated of these removals was probably the 1998 removal of the Edwards Dam, which had spanned Maine's Kennebec River since the 1830s. At a ceremony honoring the agreement to remove the antiquated dam, Secretary of the Interior Bruce Babbitt's remarks reflected the country's changing sentiments toward dams: "There are 75,000 large dams in this country, most built a long, long time ago. Many are useful but some are obsolete, expensive, and unsafe. They were built with no consideration of the environmental costs. We must now examine those costs and act accordingly. This is not a call to remove all, most, or even many dams. But this is a challenge to dam owners and operators to defend themselves—to demonstrate by hard facts, not by sentiment or myth—that the continued operation of a dam is in the public interest, economically and environmentally." Momentum to restore free-flowing rivers shows little sign of abating, either. In 2002 alone, 63 dams in 15 states and the District of Columbia were scheduled for removal.

A similar reassessment of dams is taking place in Canada, which currently diverts more water via dams, canals, and locks than any other nation. Canada maintains 600 large dams and 60 major domestic interbasin diversions, from which it draws enough hydroelectric power to meet a significant portion of the nation's power needs. But despite the undeniable benefits that these systems provide in the provision of clean energy, municipal water supplies, and irrigation, criticism of dams and reservoirs has mounted in Canada as well. As a result, a smattering of small dams—most of which have outlived their economic usefulness—have been removed from British Columbia, Ontario, and other provinces, and a number of proposals to expand existing hydroelectric systems have been shelved.

As in the United States, most of the criticism directed against Canadian dams is centered on the issues of drowned ecosystems and decimated fisheries. But several Canadian dam projects have also been denounced for trampling aboriginal rights. The most publicized example of dam-building's negative impact on Native Canadians was Quebec's $35 billion James Bay Hydroelectric Project. This colossal series of dams and reservoirs built during the 1980s now exports huge amounts of power to the United States and is a major source of electricity for eastern Canada. But it also drowned the ancestral hunting grounds of northern Quebec's Cree Indians and destroyed huge swaths of wetlands, forests, and floodplains that had been essential habitat to numerous animal species. In northern Manitoba, Cross Lake Crees complain that hydroelectric dams have displaced aboriginal communities and drowned economically and culturally vital hunting and fishing grounds. Elsewhere in northwestern Canada, the erection of the W.A.C. Bennett Dam on the Peace River made the Peace Valley an agriculturally viable one and provided much-needed power to Vancouver. But it disrupted the livelihoods of the Athabascan Chipewyan First Nation, which makes its home in the Peace-Athabasca freshwater delta region. "It is more than the First Nation's treaty rights to hunt, fish, and trap for food that have been affected," declared Canada's Indian Claims Commission in a 1998 report responding to the tribe's allegations that the dam constituted an egregious violation of their treaty rights. "The First Nation's very way of life and its economic lifeblood were substantially damaged as the government of Canada, armed with full knowledge of the ecological destruction that would follow, did nothing"

("Athabasca Chipewyan First Nation Inquiry: Report on WAC Bennett Dam and Damage to Indian Reserve No. 201 Claim," 1998).

Sources:

Abramovitz, Janet N. 1996. *Imperiled Waters, Impoverished Future: The Decline of Freshwater Ecosystems.* Washington, DC: WorldWatch Institute.

American Rivers. "Dam Removal Success Stories." http:/www.amrivers.localweb.com (accessed January 21, 2001).

"Athabasca Chipewyan First Nation Inquiry: Report on WAC Bennett Dam and Damage to Indian Reserve No. 201 Claim." 1998. *Indian Claims Commission Proceedings* 10.

Commission for Environmental Cooperation. 1999. *On Track? Sustainability and the State of the North American Environment.* Montreal: Commission for Environmental Cooperation.

De Villiers, Marq. 2000. *Water: The Fate of Our Most Precious Resource.* New York: Houghton Mifflin.

———. 2000. "Water Works." *Canadian Geographic* 120 (May–June).

Dewar, Heather, and Tom Horton. 2000. "Cycle of Growth and Devastation." *Baltimore Sun,* September 25.

Doern, G. Bruce, and Thomas Conway. 1994. *The Greening of Canada.* Toronto: University of Toronto Press.

Farid, Claire, John Jackson, and Karen Clark. 1997. *The Fate of the Great Lakes: Sustaining or Draining the Sweetwater Seas?* Buffalo, NY: Canadian Environmental Law Association, United Buffalo State College.

Gleick, Peter H. 2000. *The World's Water, 2000–2001.* Washington, DC: Island.

Government of Canada. 1996. *The State of Canada's Environment, 1996.* Ottawa: Supply and Services Canada.

Graham, Wade. 1998. "A Hundred Rivers Run through It." *Harper's Magazine* 295 (June).

Hinrichsen, Don. 1998. *Coastal Waters of the World: Trends, Threats and Strategies.* Washington, DC: Island.

International Joint Commission. 2000. *Tenth Biennial Report on Great Lakes Water Quality* (July).

Leslie, Jacques. 2000. "Running Dry." *Harper's Magazine* 297 (July).

McCully, Patrick. 1996. *Silenced Rivers: The Ecology and Politics of Large Dams.* London: Zed.

Organization for Economic Co-operation and Development. 1995. *Environmental Performance Reviews, Canada.* Paris: OECD.

———. 1996. *Environmental Performance Reviews, United States.* Paris: OECD.

Postel, Sandra. 1996. *Dividing the Waters: Food Security, Ecosystem Health, and the New Politics of Scarcity.* Washington, DC: WorldWatch Institute.

———. 1997. *Last Oasis: Facing Water Scarcity.* New York: W. W. Norton.

Rawsom Academy of Aquatic Science. 1992. *Ecological Security and Canada's Freshwater Resources.* Ottawa: Rawsom Academy of Aquatic Science.

Reisner, Marc. 1993. *Cadillac Desert: The American West and Its Disappearing Water.* Rev. ed. New York: Penguin.

———. 1998. "Coming Undammed." *Audubon* 100 (September–October).

Schildgen, Bob. 1999. "Unnatural Disasters." *Sierra* 84 (May–June).

Simon, Paul. 1998. *Tapped Out: The Coming World Crisis in Water and What We Can Do About It.* New York: Welcome Rain.

UN Environment Programme. 1999. *Global Environment Outlook 2000.* London: Earthscan.

U.S. Geological Survey. 1997. *Estimated Use of Water in the United States in 1995.* Washington, DC: U.S. Department of the Interior, USGS.

———. 1998. *Dams and Rivers.* Washington, DC: U.S. Department of the Interior, USGS.

Vileisis, Ann. 1997. *Discovering the Unknown Landscape: History of America's Wetlands.* Washington, DC: Island.

Wilkinson, Charles. 1993. *Crossing the Next Meridian: Land, Water and the Future of the West.* Washington, DC: Island.

Young, Gordon J., James C. I. Dooge, and John C. Rodda. 1994. *Global Water Resource Issues.* Cambridge: Cambridge University Press.

7

Oceans and Coastal Areas

North America's oceans and coastal shores are among the most scenic and biologically rich marine areas in the world, but during the past half-century these resources have come under siege from a broad array of threats. Perhaps the most economically significant of these dangers is overfishing, a practice that has taken a heavy toll on many fish species off the Atlantic and Pacific coastlines girding the continent. But other potential threats to the long-term viability of North America's marine ecosystems include pollution, flawed aquaculture practices, and rampant coastal development.

Fishery Resources in Jeopardy

The North American coastline is approximately 248,000 miles (400,000 kilometers) long, including all major and minor islands. Canada alone boasts approximately 25 percent of the world's total seacoast, with 36,000 miles (58,500 kilometers) of mainland coastline and 265,000 total kilometers of seacoast with islands included. The U.S. mainland coastline adds another 12,383 miles (19,936 kilometers) to the continent's total; including islands, its total coastline is estimated to span more than 133,300 kilometers.

The size of the Canadian and U.S. coastlines gives the two nations authority over vast sections of the Atlantic and Pacific oceans. Under the United Nations Law of the Sea, which came into force in 1994, all coastal nations have sovereign control over the waters and seafloor that lie up to 12 miles off their shores, as well as dominion over seas extending 200 miles from inhabitable land. Canada and the United States were among the first countries to claim this 200-mile zone, known as an Exclusive Economic Zone, or EEZ (both nations actually laid claim to their respective 200-mile EEZs in the 1970s, when concerns about global overfishing began to influence public policy). As a result of this international arrangement, Canada has jurisdiction over 1.44 million square miles (3.7 million square kilometers) of ocean, while the size of the U.S. EEZ is even greater, at 3.36 million square nautical miles (8.73 million square kilometers).

Over the centuries, the waters now controlled by the United States and Canada have supported a tremendous array of marine life, from mammals (whales, dolphins, seals, etc.) to fish (salmon, cod, halibut, swordfish, tuna) to shellfish (shrimp, lobster, scallops). Indeed, the marine life harvested from these waters emerged as the economic and cultural cornerstone of hundreds of coastal communities in both the United States and Canada, and they remain an important facet of the regional economies along the Atlantic, Pacific, and Arctic ocean shorelines and in the Gulf of Mexico.

According to Canada's Department of Fisheries and Oceans, the value of Canada's commercial fisheries industry—which numbers approximately 24,000 vessels—reached a record high of C$1.973 billion in 2000, most of it (C$1.689 billion) from Atlantic waters. The quantity of fish caught to achieve these robust figures exceeded 958,000 tons in live weight (Department of Fisheries and Oceans, "Summary of Canadian Commercial Catches and Values," 2001). According to the National Marine Fisheries Service, the dock value of the U.S. commercial haul that same year—an estimated 9.1 billion pounds of edible fish and shellfish—was approximately $3.63 billion.

At first glance, these statistics seem to suggest that the North American fishing fleet's capacity to satisfy prodigious Canadian, U.S., and international appetites for seafood remains intact. After all, U.S. consumers alone spent more

Table 7.1 Summary of Canadian Commercial Catches and Values

	2000	
	Quantities (metric tons, live weight)	*Value (in thousand Canadian dollars)*
Atlantic — Total	*819,361*	*1,689,365*
Nova Scotia	306,473	647,718
New Brunswick	118,509	169,712
PEI	62,922	131,698
Quebec	58,209	158,889
Newfoundland	273,248	581,348
Pacific (British Columbia) — Total	*139,383*	*283,707*
Canada — Total	*958,744*	*1,973,072*

SOURCE: Department of Fisheries and Oceans—Canada.

than $52 billion on seafood in 1999, with $35 billion of those expenditures in restaurants. But these robust levels of consumption are skewed by increased reliance on shellfish, which fetch high prices in the marketplace. For example, shellfish (principally lobster, crab, shrimp, and scallops) now rank as the most important fisheries product of all four of Canada's eastern maritime provinces. The Department of Fisheries and Oceans (DFO) reported that in 2000, lobster alone accounted for C$452 million of the total C$968 million catch of Nova Scotia, New Brunswick, and Prince Edward Island, according to the Canadian government. That same year, shellfish accounted for $488 million of Newfoundland's total $587 million harvest.

This increased dependence on shellfish is attributable in part to the enduring popularity of lobster, crab, and shrimp dinners from Boston to Vancouver and beyond. It also can be traced to the increase in imports of cheap shrimp from farms in developing countries, and increased consumer access to these shrimp with the expansion of seafood restaurant chains. But some observers feel that shellfish are also being pursued by default as other formerly lucrative fisheries have collapsed over the past two decades as a result of unsustainable harvesting practices. Indeed, several of North America's fisheries are in a marked state of decline, with long-term recovery of several important fishing stocks in serious doubt. Many fishing communities have adjusted to these downturns (in cod and salmon stocks, to name two) by shifting their attention to alternative species or aquaculture. But marine experts say that the diminishment of important stocks will still have long-term consequences for North America's ocean ecosystems.

Modern Fishing Fleets Empty the Oceans

Historically, North America's coastal regions have been home to some of the largest and most valuable fisheries in the world. In the northern Atlantic, fishing banks extending from the Gulf of Maine to Newfoundland supported tremendous populations of cod, flounder, pollack, haddock, hake, herring, menhaden, mackerel, swordfish, northern bluefin tuna, and migrating Atlantic salmon, as well as crabs, lobster, and other shellfish. On the other side of the continent, the stormy north Pacific fishing grounds of the Gulf of Alaska and the Bering Sea attracted fleets hunting for crab, pollack, char, flounder, and other species. Farther south, the coastal communities of the Pacific Northwest prospered on the strength of the wild salmon that roamed to and from their spawning rivers in Oregon, Washington, Idaho, and British Columbia.

These fisheries continue to be better managed than those in most other regions of the world, thanks to extensive scientific knowledge of the fisheries and various regulations governing capture of various species. Nonetheless,

A fisherman stands on the pollack-covered deck of the Saga Sea, a factory trawler fishing in the Bering Sea, Alaska. NATALIE FOBES/CORBIS

North America's perennially rich fishing grounds are troubled. Their decline began in the 1950s, when a new generation of fishing vessels bristling with postwar technological innovations began criss-crossing the ocean's surface. Some of these ships were modified whaling vessels that, having hunted many whale populations to near extinction, were forced to shift their attention to cod and other commercial fish. Other ships in this emerging high-tech fleet were vessels of immense size and scale built specifically to trawl the world's seas for weeks on end.

Japan, Spain, West Germany, France, Britain, and other countries—many of them former whaling nations—built large fleets of these floating fish-processing factories. But all paled when compared with the Soviet fleet, which had 400 massive trawlers cruising the world's oceans by the 1970s. "The Soviet fleet fished the world," wrote Michael Berrill. "With their freezer factory trawlers, the Soviet ships hunted for Atlantic cod, Alaskan pollack, and Antarctic fish and krill. They ranged from pole to pole, but they had the greatest destructive impact on the fishing banks off the northeast coast of North America" (Berrill, *The Plundered Seas,* 1997)

With each passing year, the world's fishing nations managed to boost the size and harvesting capacity of their fleets. According to the UN Food and Agriculture Organization (FAO), total fish catches in North America alone rose from 3.9 million tons in 1961 to a peak of 7.56 million tons in 1987 on the strength of this overwhelming technology. "Radar, fish finders, and, later, satellite navigation allow the enormous ships to locate and capture fish schools with lethal accuracy. Today's factory-freezer trawlers haul nets large enough to swallow a formation of twelve Boeing 747 jumbo jets. . . . In an hour they can haul up as much as 200 tons of fish, twice as much as a typical sixteenth-century ship would have caught in an entire season. Recrewed and supplied by oceangoing tenders, the ships could pursue fish anywhere in the world for months on end without ever visiting a port or even sighting land" (Woodard, *Ocean's End,* 2000).

Wasteful industry practices put additional pressure on already stressed fish stocks up and down both North American coastlines. For instance, fishing vessels utilizing driftnet or bottom trawling technology accumulated massive amounts of "bycatch," a term that encompasses both unintended catch of nontarget species and juvenile fish of the target species. This bycatch—which continues to account for roughly one-quarter of the world's total marine fish catch — is discarded, shoveled back into the sea as refuse. Most of this bycatch consists of unwanted fish species, but dolphins, porpoises, sea turtles, and seabirds also drown when they become entangled in nets. In a positive development, the FAO reports that a significant reduction in discards took place between the mid-1980s and mid-1990s because of progressive fishery management, improved harvesting technologies, restrictions and closures of some fishing areas, and an overall decline in the level of fishing. Nonetheless, the FAO admits that "some level of discarding will always be a feature of fisheries, regardless of gear," and in some niches of the fishing world, the amount of bycatch remains tremendously wasteful. Gulf Coast shrimping operations, for example, are notorious for the volumes of bycatch accumulated (UN Food and Agriculture Organization, *A Global Assessment of Fisheries By-catch and Discards,* 1994; ibid., 1996).

The bycatch toll, coupled with the ever-accelerating rate of harvest, eventually took their toll on the health of numerous fish stocks. With their ranks being depleted at unsustainable rates, populations of several major commercial stocks began to drop. For a brief period during the 1970s, it appeared that this decline might be arrested before it became severe, as Canada and the United States began policing their newly implemented 200-mile exclusive fishing zones. But North America's fishing fleet merely filled the gap left by the departing Soviet and Japanese fleets, and overharvesting continued unabated.

The Atlantic Fishing Grounds

For centuries the North Atlantic's Grand Banks, located off Newfoundland's southeastern shores, ranked as one of the globe's premier fishing grounds. Today, however, some of the region's fish populations are in steep decline, with some stocks in such grave shape that recovery may never be possible.

Observers trace the decline of these once-glorious fishing grounds back to the 1950s and 1960s, when the world's commercial fishing fleets dramatically expanded in size and harvesting capacity. But critics contend that the long-term viability of Canadian fishing stocks in the Grand Banks and other areas of the Atlantic was also undermined by a series of domestic policy decisions. During the late 1950s, for example, Canada extended unemployment insurance to seasonal inshore fishermen and fish processing/canning workers, enabling them to work for several weeks, then collect unemployment checks for the remainder of the year. At the same time, the federal government in Ottawa gave out fishing licenses to virtually all applicants. As a result of these policy decisions, the number of inshore fishermen increased 33 percent from 1957 to 1964. In subsequent years, Canada's federal Department of Fisheries and Oceans (DFO) also subsidized boat construction, gear replacement, fuel, and equipment purchases; this generosity sparked a tripling in the number of Canadian inshore fishermen (Harris, *Lament for an Ocean,* 1998).

In 1977, Canada became one of the first nations to unilaterally declare the existence of a 200-mile EEZ along its coastlines. This proclamation delighted Canadian fishing communities all along the Atlantic coastline, for the imposition of the EEZ came at a time when the first expressions of concern about dwindling groundfish stocks were being voiced. But Canada replaced the foreign fleets with its own massive trawlers, and the feverish harvesting of groundfish species continued. Moreover, Canada's EEZ proclamation did not eliminate all foreign vessels from the region. Foreign trawlers still had the legal right to fish sections of the Grand Banks that extended beyond the 200-mile zone (and they did so with unrestrained zeal); in addition, the Canadian government granted generous quotas within the EEZ to some nations. For example, in 1978 the Soviets were given permission to take as much as 266,000 tons of capelin—a keystone species of the Banks ecosystem—from Canadian waters (Warner, *Distant Water*, 1977).

From 1962 to 1992, the estimated biomass of spawning northern cod—the single most important commercial species in the North Atlantic—fell an estimated 99 percent. Other stocks suffered severe drops as well. In July 1992 the Canadian government finally closed the Banks to commercial fishing in hopes that the reprieve would allow populations of cod and other species to recover. This moratorium—which was initially of two years' duration but has since been extended indefinitely—devastated the economies of already staggering coastal fishing communities and triggered wholesale flight of younger generations to Canada's inland provinces. Canada put together a $1.9 billion aid package to provide some relief from the economic repercussions of the collapsed fishery and subsequent moratorium. But despite that assistance, the towns and villages of the maritime provinces continue to grapple with the impact—both economic and emotional—of the loss of the great fish harvests of yesteryear.

In the aftermath of the 1992 cod-fishing moratorium, the search for culprits responsible for the decimation of the cod fishery has ranged far and wide. But as Erin Anderssen and Jasmina Sopova noted:

> [T]he collapse of the North Atlantic cod is a tragedy with few innocents. Fishermen, both offshore and inshore, were guilty of misreporting their catches, of swarming the cod on spawning grounds, of dumping tonnes of unwanted fish overboard to rot on the ocean floor. The days of the radar and high-tech trawlers—both foreign and domestic—meant that entire schools of fish could be easily hunted down and sucked out of the Atlantic. Scientists, meanwhile, consistently overestimated the size of the stocks. Fisheries science, at

> best, is imprecise. Too little is known about the nature of the cod and its relationship to the ocean food chain, predators like seals, and temperature changes. But scientists relied too heavily on offshore catch rates for population estimates, and confused efficient, modern fishing with what was really happening in the ocean. With the scientists guessing too high, fishermen slashed a far larger portion of the cod biomass than the quotas intended. (Anderssen and Sopova, "The Cod Collapse," 1998)

Today, Canada's Atlantic Coast fishing communities hold out hope that cod, flounder, and other commercial species will eventually return in some semblance of their previous size and numbers, enabling the moratorium to be lifted. But some analysts fear that the ecosystem suffered such extensive damage that it may never recover. Certainly, recent trends hold out little hope for a dramatic reversal on the Grand Banks or other battered fishing grounds.

In the meantime, those fishermen still plying their trade in the maritime provinces have shifted their attention to shellfish. The resulting boom in shellfish harvests enabled Canada's Atlantic-based fishing industry to post record-breaking performances in terms of total value of product landed during the 1990s. Observers fear that this shellfish-driven success—it accounted for more than 90 percent of the total value of the catch in some years—may also end soon without the imposition of quotas that will ensure the long-term viability of snow crab and other shellfish stocks. But the federal government's efforts to impose sustainable harvest limits have met with fierce resistance from Indian bands along the Atlantic coast. These First Nation communities argue that their right to a catch is protected by treaty and thus can not be regulated by the Canadian government. As of mid-2001, the two sides remained at loggerheads over a comprehensive fisheries agreement.

During the 1990s, U.S. fishing outfits plying their trade in the Atlantic Ocean have also seen significant declines in important commercial stocks, even though the United States steadily cut fishing allotments to foreign nations throughout the 1980s and ended them altogether in 1992. But as in Canada, the departure of foreign fishing trawlers only cleared the way for expansion of the domestic fleet. Indeed, U.S. trawlers are widely viewed as the primary force responsible for the dwindling fisheries off the Atlantic seaboard. "New England fisheries are in disarray," declared one expert. "Between 1982 and 1991, fishing efforts in New England waters rose 13 percent while the total catch slumped by 43 percent. The total groundfish population—cod, haddock, redfish, hake, pollack, and flounder—fell by 65 percent in the decade between 1977 and 1987. Moreover, chronic overfishing on

Georges Bank altered fish populations; skates and dogfish have replaced cod and haddock as the most dominant species" (Weber, *Net Loss,* 1994). Not surprisingly, this downturn has had a pronounced economic impact on U.S. fishing communities along the Atlantic seaboard. According to a report from the Massachusetts Offshore Groundfish Task Force, the region's collapsing fisheries cost New England's economy $350 million in lost revenue and 14,000 jobs annually from the late 1980s through the mid 1990s (Hinrichsen, *Coastal Waters of the World,* 1998).

Farther south, in the offshore waters of the mid and south Atlantic, persistent efforts to restore striped bass have met with gratifying success. But elsewhere in these waters, important commercial and recreational fisheries declined during the 1990s. Key species in this region include flounder, sea bass, herring, mackerel, scallops, lobster, horseshoe crab, and blue crab. Overfishing is the most frequently cited cause of the dwindling numbers, but the introduction of invasive species, pollution, and destruction of coastal habitat have also played major roles. Indeed, vanishing coastal habitat is particularly problematic along the mid and south Atlantic seaboard, where many species rely on estuaries as nurseries. In the Chesapeake Bay, for example, coastal development is cited—along with overfishing, alien species, and pollution—as a primary factor in the current sorry state of the historically famous fishing ground. Oyster stocks in the bay are at 1 percent of historical levels, while blue crab populations have fallen by an estimated 70 percent over the past twenty years (Woodard, "Saving the Chesapeake," 2000).

In 1993 the United States implemented stricter quotas and shorter fishing seasons in an effort to reverse these unwelcome trends. A year later, the United States and Canada reached agreement to rein in fishing on the Georges Bank—a mainstay of both the New England and Nova Scotia fishing industries—for cod, halibut, and haddock. In 1995 much of Georges Bank and sections of the Gulf of Maine were closed for the year to give native fish stocks a respite from the overcapitalized U.S. and Canadian fishing fleets.

Nonetheless, some observers complain that conservation measures are too often insufficient to meet the severity of the situation. For example, the International Commission for the Conservation of Atlantic Tuna estimated that the adult bluefin population in the western Atlantic plummeted from 300,000 in 1970 to about 33,000 by 1993. Commercial and sport-fishing quotas have been put in place to boost bluefin numbers, but some observers believe that more dramatic reductions in harvest rates will be necessary for the fish to recover.

The Atlantic salmon is another species that faces a cloudy future, even though all seven countries in the North Atlantic Salmon Conservation

Organization (NASCO), including Canada and the United States, agreed to a ban on commercial salmon fishing in 1998. This moratorium was prompted by an alarming downturn in salmon numbers. In early 1998 it was estimated that the salmon population in the North Atlantic had plummeted to 114,000 mature fish, which is only about 50 percent of the population needed to meet minimum spawning targets. Three years later, a World Wildlife Fund study estimated that Atlantic salmon stocks had plummeted by 80 percent since 1973.

The commercial fishing moratorium is seen as a vital element of any plan to preserve and nurture remaining Atlantic salmon populations. But as one observer noted: "[W]hile the ban alleviates one part of the problem, it leaves another critical part unaddressed: some of the most serious pressures on Atlantic salmon come not from fishing, but from pressures on spawning grounds. Rivers from Maine to Quebec have been blocked by hydroelectric dams and contaminated with effluent from pulp and paper mills for decades. The task of rehabilitating wild salmon stocks has been further complicated by the growing presence of salmon netcages for the fish farms that dot coastal waters. Farmed salmon can choke waters with their waste, dilute the genetic diversity of wild salmon through escaped fish, and transmit diseases to wild salmon" (McGinn, "Atlantic Salmon Face Perilous Waters," 1999). Each of these obstacles is formidable; together they may prove insurmountable. In 2001 the World Wildlife Fund bluntly warned that North Atlantic wild salmon were on the verge of extinction.

Still, recent developments do suggest that authorities recognize that the scale of the problem demands decisive action. By 1998 the Canadian government had bought out all commercial fishing nets, spending more than C$72 million. Moreover, efforts by organizations such as the Atlantic Salmon Federation, the North Atlantic Salmon Fund, and the North Atlantic Salmon Conservation Organization (the latter an international treaty organization) have helped bring the commercial catch in neighboring Greenland down from a million salmon a year to a subsistence level of 70,000 (Burke, "On the Brink," 2001). In addition, the Atlantic salmon was listed under the U.S. Endangered Species Act in November 2000. These steps, coupled with increased attention to the destructive effects of dams and clearcuts on spawning rivers, give some observers hope that North Atlantic salmon may some day return in at least some semblance of their former abundance.

The Pacific Fishing Grounds

Some of North America's Pacific Ocean fisheries are also in distress, weakened by years of pollution, overharvesting, and habitat degradation. These factors have also damaged a number of vital links in the Pacific food chain, casting doubt on the fundamental well-being of regional marine ecosystems. For example, the Pacific Ocean's zooplankton population, which directly or indirectly feeds virtually all marine life from the Gulf of Alaska to the warm waters of the southern California coast, has fallen dramatically since the late 1970s. Populations of Pacific herring—an essential food source for a wide range of species, including grey whales, Chinook salmon, harbor seals, and myriad sea birds—have also dropped, their spawning waters sacrificed to coastal development or compromised by chemical contamination.

Not all commercial stocks are in decline, however. Indeed, some Pacific fisheries remained in good health at the turn of the century. But Don Hinrichsen notes that "other fisheries have been depleted so thoroughly that the legal season is measured in days. The entire year's quota for Pacific halibut, once harvested over a six-month season, is now taken in two frantic twenty-four-hour periods. Some 6,000 boats compete to haul in as much as they can get in the time allotted. . . . The halibut season is not even the shortest one. So many boats go after herring that the season in some areas is just twenty minutes" (Hinrichsen, *Coastal Waters of the World,* 1998).

Salmon populations are also in jeopardy. In fact, the salmon fishery, which has been the dominant fishery ever since Pacific halibut were hunted to near extinction in the 1930s, is in crisis throughout the Pacific Northwest. Overharvesting by offshore boats is widely recognized as a factor in the plummeting wild salmon numbers. Destructive logging practices (which ruin spawning beds), marine pollution, and increased predation by mackerel and Pacific hake (both of which surged in numbers as a result of El Nino–induced changes in ocean water temperature) have also been cited as harmful factors.

But the plight of the Pacific's anadromous coho, sockeye, pink, chum, and chinook salmon has also been greatly exacerbated by the many dams that span the spawning rivers of the Pacific Coast. In both the United States and Canada, numerous rivers used by migrating salmon have been strung with hydroelectric dams and slackwater reservoirs. These man-made obstacles have throttled countless salmon runs over the years, and they are seen by conservationists as the single greatest impediment to wild salmon recovery in the Pacific Northwest. But efforts to breach or remove the most controversial of these dams—such as the four federal dams on the Snake River in Washington state—have been complicated by a host of political and economic factors.

With significant segments of the Pacific Northwest fishing grounds in disarray, much of North America's Pacific fleet has turned its attention to the Gulf of Alaska and the Bering Sea, described by one expert as "North America's last great seafood bonanza." These cold and stormy waters are home to an immensely valuable and diverse fisheries resource that includes great populations of valuable bottom-dwelling fish such as cod, flounder, sole, perch, and pollack. By 1993 more than 55 percent of the total U.S. commercial fishery catch was being pulled out of Alaskan waters. Since then, the waters of Alaska have remained the most lucrative fishing grounds in the Northern Hemisphere. But concerns about overharvesting are being raised there as well. In Alaska's Norton Sound, gateway to the vast Yukon and Kuskokwim river drainages, returns of king and chum salmon—the lifeblood of numerous aboriginal communities in the region—plummeted alarmingly in three successive years, from 1998 to 2000. Such trends have made Alaskan fishing policies a particularly sore point in the ongoing debate—waged by fishermen, environmentalists, Native communities, and U.S. and Canadian officials at the federal, state, and provincial levels—over wild Pacific salmon and their future.

The Pacific Salmon Treaty

Disagreements between Canada and the United States over management of Pacific salmon stocks have alternately festered and flared for the better part of two decades. In 1985, Canada and the United States reached agreement on a Pacific Salmon Treaty (PST) that reflected their shared interest in ensuring the continued prosperity of the salmon fishery. This treaty set out a framework for cooperative management of the fishery and included components covering everything from quotas to allocation of research expenses. But large-scale "interceptions"—the capture of migratory fish originating in one nation by the fishing fleets of another country—continued to be carried out by both parties in violation of PST parameters.

In addition, the two nations repeatedly clashed over the appropriate means of meeting the conservation and harvest-sharing goals detailed in the treaty. "Despite the joint commitment embodied in the PST to conserve and protect the shared salmon stocks, the United States and Canada spent many years in a diplomatic stalemate, and the health of the salmon stocks has suffered as a result," admitted one congressional report. "Southern boundary stocks (e.g., Pacific Northwest chinook salmon) have suffered extensively from habitat degradation. Most salmon stocks in the Pacific Northwest (and a few in some areas of southern British Columbia) have been subjected to major habitat damage from dams, irrigation projects, agriculture, logging, ports, and pollution. Such habitat damage can degrade salmon production without bearing any of the related costs of resource conservation. A significant problem with the PST was that the framers did not anticipate the magnitude of harm caused by non-fishing activities on Pacific Northwest stocks (and some isolated Canadian chinook stocks)" (Waldeck and Buck, "The Pacific Salmon Treaty," 1999).

Indeed, environmentalists on both sides of the border have been particularly critical of British Columbia's husbandry of vital salmon habitat. They condemn the province's record on salmon protection and preservation, pointing in particular to the degradation of spawning rivers by B.C.'s powerful timber industry and the province's reluctance to reduce the size of its fleet. Farther south, meanwhile, Washington and Oregon also have been criticized for providing inadequate protection for important salmon habitat.

Another problem with PST implementation was the Canadian conviction that the U.S. fleet was taking an excessive share of the Pacific salmon catch that remained. In fact, Canadians insisted in the late 1990s that since passage of the PST in 1985, the U.S. catch of Canadian-origin salmon exceeded the Canadian catch of U.S.-origin salmon by an annual average of about 9 million fish. For its part, the United States contended that Canadian interceptions were depleting particularly vulnerable coho and chinook salmon stocks.

By the time that the 1985 PST expired in 1992, the two nations were deadlocked over the salmon issue. In the meantime, salmon populations continued to decline across much of the Pacific Northwest. In 1995, for example, British Columbia brought in 48,300 metric tons of salmon, its lowest harvest of wild salmon in twenty years, and its all-important Fraser River sockeye harvest came in at only 20 percent of original projections. A year later, the province's fishermen suffered through another dismal campaign. These consecutive poor salmon harvests cost British Columbia an estimated 5,600 jobs and C$75 million, by one DFO estimate.

The prolonged decline in Pacific salmon harvests did eventually prompt stronger action from both governments. In 1996, for example, Canada closed all commercial fishing for chinook salmon (as well as all sport and aboriginal fishing for chinook off the west coast of Vancouver Island) in an effort to boost the chinook population. Two years later, Canada's federal government reached agreement with the state of Washington to curtail some commercial and sport-fishing of shared salmon stocks in selected areas (for example, Washington agreed to limit its catch of sockeye bound for the Fraser River to 25 percent, while Canada restricted sport-fishing in the Strait of Georgia). And in 1997, Canada passed the Oceans Act, which provides the country with the means to move toward a model of oceans management more heavily based on principles of species and habitat conservation. The United States also listed some distinct salmon units as endangered or threatened species under the Endangered Species Act, and in the mid-1990s the National Marine Fisheries Services temporarily imposed greater federal restrictions on salmon harvests.

Despite such proactive measures, however, efforts to cobble together a long-term resource harvesting and conservation arrangement agreeable to all state, provincial, and federal parties have repeatedly failed. In the mid-1990s, for example, Alaska refused to lower salmon quotas to match those proposed by British Columbia, despite the urging of Washington and Oregon. In 1996, Canada shut down all direct commercial fishing for chinook salmon (as well as all sport and Aboriginal fishing for chinook on the west coast of Vancouver Island) for the express purpose of bolstering the chinook salmon population, but their gesture was not reciprocated by U.S. fleets. In August 1997, anger over perceived inequities in salmon harvesting finally boiled over in British Columbia, where protesting Canadian fishermen blockaded a U.S. ferry for three days.

The 1999 PST

During the late 1990s, the ongoing feud spurred both the United States and Canada to establish aggressive harvesting quotas that paid scant consideration to the long-term viability of the resource. But in 1999, after years of negotiation over salmon conservation and equitable harvesting of shared salmon resources, the two nations agreed on a second Pacific Salmon Treaty that covers everything from management of transboundary rivers to conservation measures for specific salmon species.

The cornerstone of the new treaty is "abundance-based management." Under this operating philosophy, harvest quotas will rise and fall in accordance with salmon populations. But even in years of normal abundance, the new PST calls for ocean harvests to be about 40 percent below past levels. It also places new reductions on tribal and sport-fishing. Most of the PST's specifications are in effect for ten years, beginning in 1999 (a side agreement on Fraser River sockeye is in effect until 2011).

Officials of both nations admit that successful long-term implementation of the agreement will require the parties to negotiate several potential pitfalls. One cloud hovering over the agreement is the failure to get British Columbia to sign on, since cooperation of the province is essential to any long-term strategy of preserving wild Pacific salmon stocks. Critics also express concern about the treaty's shortcomings in the realm of dispute resolution. Finally, the ultimate success of the treaty may hinge on alleviating Canadian skepticism that the new PST is in the nation's best interest.

> Some Canadians feel the United States has been, and continues to be, the principal transgressor in failed salmon management, and always achieves the better outcome in any bilateral dealing. For example, many Canadians perceive that the United States has the ability to force Canada to curtail fisheries to address U.S. conservation concerns . . . but that Canada lacks any mechanism to force Alaska to do the same when Canada is concerned about conservation (e.g., southeast Alaska harvest restrictions are triggered by low U.S. coho abundance, not low Canadian coho abundance). Such attitudes will focus considerable attention on how the United States conducts itself in implementing the new agreement. (ibid.)

Environmental Concerns Dog Growing Aquaculture Sector

Aquaculture—the farming or husbandry of fish, shellfish, and other aquatic animals and plants in controlled environments—has grown steadily in North America over the past two decades. Regarded in many quarters as a viable means of counteracting declines in commercially important wild fish stocks, the industry encompasses a range of operations, including fish farming (utilized for freshwater species such as catfish and trout), netpen culture (salmon), and "ocean ranching" (practiced by the Pacific salmon industry, these operations cultivate juvenile salmon, release them to mature in the open ocean, and harvest them when they return to spawn as adults).

Aquaculture has been embraced with particular enthusiasm in Canada, where many coastal communities suffered severe economic hardship after wild fish stocks crashed in the 1990s. The production value for five main aquaculture species in Canada grew from an estimated C$7 million in 1984 to C$460 million in 1997 (World Resources Institute, *World Resources 2000–2001*, 2000), and the industry's growth shows no signs of slowing. According to Canada's DFO, the nation's aquaculture industry produced approximately 113,000 tons of product in 1999, accounting for 22.5 percent of the total value of Canadian fish and seafood production. New Brunswick is Canada's aquaculture leader on the strength of its many salmon farms, but other provinces are also investing heavily in this area. In British Columbia, for example, the provincial aquaculture industry posted a gross domestic product growth rate of 4,000 percent from 1987 to 2000 ("British Columbia Aquaculture Posts 4,000% Growth Rate," 2001).

The value of U.S. aquaculture has also grown steadily, rising at an annual rate of 5 to 10 percent throughout the 1990s. The nation's annual output of 450,000 tons includes trout and tilapia, but catfish farms account for most (about 270,000 tons) of the industry total. U.S. catfish production is centered in the U.S. South and especially Mississippi, home to more than 60 percent of the nation's total farmed catfish (Brown, "Fish Farming May Soon Take Role as Leading Food Source," 2000).

But while aquaculture has been praised in North America and elsewhere for its promise as a viable dietary alternative to stressed wild fisheries, environmental concerns have cropped up about some aspects of aquaculture production. Some observers worry about reduction of genetic diversity in farmed species and reduced hardiness of wild stocks that breed with escaped cultured fish (farm fish are bred for fast maturation, not survival in the wild). Others raise the specter of escaped cultured species competing with native wild species for habitat and food resources (one study by the Atlantic Salmon Federation stated that the proportion of farmed salmon in local wild salmon runs increased from less than 6 percent in 1983 to 90 percent by 1994). Pollution from aquaculture pens is another problem; fish farms produce prodigious quantities of waste that, if not subject to appropriate treatment and disposal, pollute area waters. And some farmed species actually intensify pressure on wild fisheries. "Salmon, a carnivorous fish, are fed a diet consisting primarily of fish meal that is typically made from anchovies, herring, or the remnants of fish processing. In stark contrast to the production of herbivorous species, such as carp and catfish, which lighten the pressure on oceanic fisheries, salmon production actually intensifies pressure because it requires up to five tons of landed fish for each ton of salmon produced" (ibid.).

Finally, environmentalists, fishermen, and scientists all agree that the threat of disease transfer from cultured to wild stock is a serious one for North American aquaculture operations. In March 1998, for instance, New Brunswick salmon growers were forced to kill more than 1.2 million salmon to halt the spread of infectious salmon anemia (ISA), a deadly virus that causes hemorrhaging of a fish's internal organs and is capable of decimating both wild and domestic stocks. This outbreak, attributed to the breeding grounds of Canadian salmon farms, shut down about one-quarter of the salmon farming industry. Since then, isolated cases have been detected on U.S. salmon farms in Maine, casting a pall over the entire industry.

Marine Mammals and Sea Birds in North America's Seas

The coastlines of North America support a wide range of marine mammals, amphibians, and sea birds. Blessed with ocean floors of great geographical diversity, currents with marked temperature variations, and regions of nutritional plenty, the ocean waters off Canada and the United States are home to myriad species of dolphins, whales, seals, otters, walruses, and sea turtles. The shorelines of the continent also serve as the nesting and breeding grounds for millions of sea birds.

But as with the fish stocks of these waters, the populations of many of these creatures are not what they once were. For example, at one time the "cold, nutrient-rich waters [of the Pacific coast] were filled with probably the greatest concentration and variety of marine mammals the world has ever seen," wrote Hinrichsen. "From Alaska south along the Canadian coast to the Pacific Northwest and California, the waters teemed with life—walruses, fur seals, sea lions, harbor seals, elephant seals, Steller's sea cows, sea otters, dolphins, and whales. Within 150 years (1750–1900), however, the populations of most fur-bearing mammals had been harvested to the brink of extinction" (Hinrichsen, *Coastal Waters of the World,* 1998). Unchecked hunting took a heavy toll over on the Atlantic side of the continent as well.

During the latter half of the twentieth century, many of North America's marine mammal populations have recovered to some extent as a result of increased protection of species and habitat, although data on marine species is limited in both Canada and the United States. Indeed, numerous laws and regulations have been implemented that forbid or severely restrict hunting of most animals, and a number of preserves have been created to protect important breeding and feeding grounds. Still, about two dozen of the eighty-five recognized marine species in U.S. waters (including the Atlantic Coast, the Gulf of Mexico, and the Pacific Coast) are listed as threatened or endangered under the country's Endangered Species Act. Degradation of habitat, extensive coastal development, exposure to chemical contamination, and large-scale commercial fishing—which snares and drowns ocean-faring mammals in the massive nets utilized by trawlers—are usually cited as primary factors in these population downturns.

Both the U.S. and Canadian governments have taken some steps to protect vulnerable coastal populations of mammals. Some marine mammals in U.S. waters are protected by the Endangered Species Act, but the chief piece of U.S. law in this regard is the Marine Mammal Protection Act, which was passed in 1972 after high levels of dolphin mortality were traced to destructive tuna fleet operations. This act established a moratorium on the taking of marine mammals in U.S. waters and also outlawed harvests of marine mammals by U.S. citizens in international waters. The law specifically protects mammals from "clubbing, mutilation, poisoning, capture in nets, and other human actions that lead to extinction," and it has been credited with stabilizing many marine populations. But it does authorize limited taking of marine mammals deemed incidental to commercial fishing operations, and it permits Indian,

Aleut, and Eskimo communities of Alaska, the coastal North Pacific and the Arctic Ocean to harvest selected mammals, provided the takings are for subsistence purposes and not executed in a wasteful fashion.

Canada has no federal legislation in place providing protection specifically to marine mammals. But after years of fragmented, overlapping—and sometimes incompatible—efforts on the part of federal, provincial, and Aboriginal authorities, Canada's Oceans Act came into force in January 1997. This comprehensive law included several elements designed to extend greater environmental protection to marine mammals and the habitats upon which they depend. For instance, the act calls for the creation of a number of National Marine Conservation Areas that would provide substantive environmental protection to coastal and offshore areas of particular significance to marine mammals and fisheries.

The United States has explored the idea of creating special marine preserves as well. In 2000 the Clinton administration directed the departments of Commerce and Interior to develop a scientifically based national system of ecologically significant marine areas that would receive varying levels of protection from fishing, oil and gas exploration, mining, and other activities potentially damaging to the environment (more than 1,000 areas within U.S. waters currently receive some level of protection from federal or state governments, but those areas represent only about 1 percent of ocean waters under U.S. jurisdiction). The implementation of any such system, however, will likely be predicated on the guiding perspectives and philosophies of future policy-makers.

In addition to home-front initiatives, both the United States and Canada have labored in the international arena to shield whales and dolphins and other threatened marine mammals from the excesses of the world fishing fleet. This stand is attributable in part to policy-makers' desire to win approval with environmentally conscious U.S. and Canadian citizens or to genuine concern about the threatened species. But it is also grounded in increased recognition of the economic importance of whale watching and other "ecotourism" activities in many coastal communities. In any case, Canada and the United States have both expressed staunch opposition to calls for the resumption of commercial whaling, even though experts believe that the populations of many whale species have recovered over the past thirty years.

The efforts of U.S. and Canadian officials to protect and nourish marine mammal species are not universally popular, however. Many fishermen contend that burgeoning seal populations are partially responsible for plunging commercial fish stocks, and they claim that government intervention in the behalf of some species too often produces economic hardship for themselves and others. For example, fishing communities expressed outrage when concerns about the dwindling population of the Steller's sea lion prompted temporary closure of several major grounds to the Bering Sea pollack fleet in the late 1990s.

The North American marine mammals that receive the least direct impact from human activity are those of the Canadian Arctic. But even there, where marine mammals such as polar bears, orcas, and seals roam over more than 1 million square kilometers of continental shelf ice and water, habitat degradation is evident. Toxic pollutants such as DDT have found their way into the ecosystem, borne to the Arctic by atmospheric winds and north-flowing rivers. Many predators at the top of the Arctic food chain—including humans in some native villages—now register elevated PCB levels, since PCB contaminants biomagnify at each successive link in the chain (Welch, "Marine Conservation in the Canadian Arctic," 1995).

In addition, scientists believe that conditions in many regions of the Arctic Ocean have been substantively changed by hydroelectric projects in Quebec, Ontario, and Manitoba. According to critics, these massive projects have dramatically recast the seasonal flows of many rivers feeding into the Arctic. These modified flows have in turn altered ocean currents, eroded nearshore ice conditions, and compromised algae and phytoplankton production. Any one of those changes materially affects the habitat of seals, whales, and other Arctic marine mammals; taken together, observers worry that they may permanently weaken the entire ecosystem.

Pollution in North American Seas

North America's ocean regions have been contaminated by significant volumes of industrial, agricultural, and sewage effluents. The impact of this pollution is particularly apparent in biologically rich coastal wetlands and estuaries, where toxic materials carried from inland pollution points (farms, factories, urban centers) often become concentrated. This pollution has poisoned countless marine mammals, fish, and shellfish and fundamentally altered coastal ecosystems from the Gulf of Mexico, where large quantities of shellfish are contaminated with high levels of pesticides and other pathogens, to the Pacific Northwest, where fishermen sometimes haul in fish with tumors and other physical abnormalities.

The marine pollution threat is greatest along the U.S. coastline, since the United States contains a far greater population than Canada, and hence produces much greater quantities of waste. According to the EPA, the overall condition of U.S. coastal waters at the close of the twentieth century ranged from fair to poor, depending on the region, with the Gulf of Mexico, the Great

Lakes, and the Northeast Pacific shores faring the worst. Nationally, 44 percent of all estuarine areas in the country were impaired for use by humans or aquatic life (EPA, *National Coastal Condition Report,* 2002). Each year the United States sends 2.3 trillion gallons of partially treated sewage water into its coastal waters, accompanied by another 2.2 million metric tons of chemical waste. In most cases, municipal sewage treatment plants fail to remove nitrogen, phosphorus, and other chemical pollutants that can wreak havoc on marine ecosystems. Moreover, experts have noted that "older big-city [treatment] plants, which were constructed to handle both storm water and sewage, often have to contend with so much effluent that they are overwhelmed; accidents are common, and during heavy rains storm-water runoff can surge through treatment plants, washing tons of raw sewage into rivers and coastal waters. In New England, municipalities and industrial plants discharge some 575 billion gallons of contaminated wastewater into coastal waters every year; with that goes another 700 billion gallons of polluted storm water from the region's highways and streets, much of it contaminated with heavy metals, oils, and salts" (Hinrichsen, *Coastal Waters of the World,* 1998).

Not surprisingly, pollution runoff has caused widespread beach closings up and down the Pacific and Atlantic coasts and the Gulf of Mexico in recent years. According to a 1997 Natural Resources Defense Council (NRDC) report, the United States issued more than 18,500 beach closures and swimming warnings from 1988 to 1996. Most beach closures were the result of high coliform counts, linked mainly to untreated sewage, storm runoff, and other municipal wastes. In 2001 the NRDC reported more than 11,000 beach closings across America in 2000, double the number of closings in 1999. The organization attributed part of the jump to improved monitoring, but also warned that the results reflected the continued degradation of the country's coastal environment.

In recent decades, pathogens, toxic chemicals, and persistent organic pollutants such as dioxins and pesticides have metastasized in North America's ocean environments into a variety of deadly forms. For example, excess nitrogen levels—created by runoff laced with synthetic fertilizers, animal waste, industrial effluents, municipal sewage, and other forms of nutrient pollution and carried to the sea from upstream watersheds—have become problematic in many coastal areas. According to Robert Howart, chairman of the U.S. National Academy of Science's National Research Council, in the report *Clean Coastal Waters,* "[E]xcess nitrogen in our coastal waters starts a dangerous chain of ecological events that is exacerbating harmful algal blooms such as red tides, contaminating shellfish, killing coastal wildlife, reducing biodiversity, destroying sea grass, and contributing to a host of other environmental problems" (Howart, "Deteriorating Coasts," 2000). Moreover, the report notes that "each of these impacts carries associated costs. A single harmful algal bloom, taking place in a sensitive area during the right season, might cost the region millions of dollars in lost tourism or lost seafood revenues" (National Research Council, *Clean Coastal Waters,* 2000).

Nutrient overloads have even been blamed for increased outbreaks of toxic micro-organisms in recent years. For example, *Pfiesteria piscicda*, which flourishes in nutrient-rich environments, has been implicated as a cause of fish kills involving millions of fish at many sites along the North Carolina coast and in various tributaries of the Chesapeake Bay (World Resources Institute, *World Resources 2000–2001,* 2000). "The [outbreak] cost Chesapeake fishermen $40 million in lost sales," reported David Helvarg. "It scared so many area residents that bordering states have joined together to try to reduce runoff by preserving land and regulating nutrient sources" (Helvarg, "Mississippi Delta Blues," 2001).

Excess nutrient enrichment is also responsible for hypoxic "dead zones" that dot the shoreline of the United States. Hypoxic conditions arise when excessive concentrations of nitrates and phosphates spawn feverish plant growth, a condition known as eutrophication. In some areas, this phenomenon has been so severe that oxygen is depleted and marine life is faced with suffocation or relocation. The most infamous of these zones of depleted oxygen is in the Gulf of Mexico (see sidebar on page 194), but others are also taking hold in Puget Sound, Mobile Bay, Corpus Christi Bay, and various points along the Northeastern seaboard.

The quality of ocean and coastal waters is of growing concern in Canada as well. Currently, industrial and chemical effluents enter Canada's oceans from numerous sources. Rivers carry pollutants from inland watersheds that have been compromised by mining, timber, agricultural, and industrial activity, while coastal cities grapple with ever-increasing amounts of waste and chemical discharges generated by expanding populations and increased business activity. In many cases, the pollution-control programs currently in place are woefully inadequate for protection of fragile marine environments. For example, Halifax Harbor in Nova Scotia receives between 100 and 200 million liters of untreated industrial and urban sewage into its waters every year. Elsewhere, populations of Beluga whales that roam up the St. Lawrence River from the Atlantic have become contaminated by the myriad pollutants that are discharged into that waterway from the region's factories, farms, cities, and towns. Scientists have established that milk generated by nursing mothers and passed on to beluga calves is now laced with toxic chemicals. Over on the Pacific side of the country, meanwhile, the Canadian government closed more than

120,000 hectares of coastal marine habitat to shellfish harvesting in the mid-1990s because of elevated pollution levels. Yet despite such grim warning signs, the capital of British Columbia, Victoria, continues to dump untreated waste directly into the ocean. Discarded trash is a problem on both coasts as well. In 1990, for example, a coastal cleanup campaign found more than 1,000 pieces of debris per kilometer on some British Columbia beaches. The overwhelming majority of this trash consisted of plastic items deposited by tides, winds, and storms onto shorelines, where they kill seabirds and marine animals that mistake the debris for food.

Pollution Turns Gulf of Mexico into Seasonal "Dead Zone"

During the 1980s and 1990s, nutrient pollution emerged as a clear threat to the future of the Gulf of Mexico, North America's most vital marine ecosystem. This region accounts for about 40 percent of the nation's total commercial fish catch and is fringed with wetlands that provide habitat for 75 percent of North America's migratory waterfowl. But it receives 90 percent of its freshwater replenishment from the Mississippi River, a heavily polluted waterway that drains 40 percent of the continental United States. Over time, the river's relentless deposit of nitrogen-laced industrial, agricultural, and municipal pollutants into the Gulf from upstream sources has created a hypoxic "dead zone" in the heart of the bay, a great swath of oxygen-depleted water in which few creatures can survive.

"Before the 1980s, small patches of lifeless water occasionally would turn up like a summer rash near the shoreline, where pollution and fertilizers from the Mississippi River promoted a toxic stew in the gulf's warm, slow-moving currents," wrote journalist Joby Warrick. "It's the same pattern that occurs nearly every year in parts of the Chesapeake Bay, Pamlico Sound in North Carolina, and other spots where pollution from rivers mingles with brackish water. But in the Gulf of Mexico the dead zone has evolved from a curiosity to a colossus, a recurring environmental nightmare that just keeps getting bigger" (Warrick, "Death in the Gulf of Mexico," 1999). Indeed, since 1993, when Midwest floods dramatically boosted the volume of nutrients carried by the Mississippi into the gulf, the size of the dead zone has surpassed 6,000 square miles every year. It seemed to retreat slightly in 1998, but in actuality the total volume of the hypoxic zone remained steady; it covered less surface area but extended deeper into the Gulf's waters.

To date, the hypoxic zone remains a seasonal one, forming every spring and summer and dissipating in the autumn months. But scientists warn that the "dead zone" could someday become a permanent feature of the Gulf of Mexico. That would be disastrous for the region's fishing industry, which has thus

Finally, marine transport safety is a source of anxiety for ocean conservationists, wildlife biologists, fishermen, and other interested parties in Canada and the United States. Oil tankers and other marine traffic carrying toxic or harmful substances are commonplace along both the Pacific and Atlantic coastlines; New England ports alone handle an estimated 15 billion gallons daily. The overwhelming majority of these vessels reach their destinations without incident, but accidents do occur. From 1976 to 1987, for example, the Canadian government reported more than 350 spills of 1,000 tons or more in its ocean waters, most of them involving petroleum loss. Both the United States

far adjusted its operations to cope with the emergence of the hypoxic zone. "[Some fishermen] have learned to turn adversity into advantage, trawling around the edges of the zone to vacuum up clouds of shrimp and fish fleeing to safer waters. Such tactics have helped keep the shrimp harvest high, but they haven't relieved the anxiety many watermen say they feel" (ibid.).

Scientists say that halting and reversing this disquieting phenomenon will require significant reductions of nitrogen generation in upstream states, perhaps in conjunction with installation of new wetlands or wooded buffer zones that can remove nitrogen naturally before it reaches the Gulf. But agricultural interests in the heartland—usually cited as the single greatest source of nutrient pollution carried down the Mississippi—are openly resistant to measures that would restrict their use of synthetic fertilizers and pesticides upon which they have long depended. Moreover, efforts to combat the hypoxic zone at state and federal levels have thus far been anemic. Still, members of the environmental and scientific communities have been heartened by some initiatives that attempt to address the problem. For example, "nutrient-trading," a program in which farmers, industrial facilities, and so forth exchange nutrient credits to reach a total load for the entire Mississippi basin, has taken root in some areas. Border states have also taken steps to preserve undeveloped coastal areas. Finally, grassroots education campaigns have increased public awareness of the problem, a key to any long-term success.

Sources:

Beardsley, Tim. 1997. "Death in the Deep: 'Dead Zone' in the Gulf of Mexico Challenges Regulators." *Scientific American* 277 (November).

Ferber, Dan. 2001. "Keeping the Stygian Waters at Bay." *Science* 291 (February 9).

Hallowell, Christopher. 2001. *Holding Back the Sea: The Struggle for America's Natural Legacy on the Gulf Coast.* New York: HarperCollins.

Warrick, Joby. 1999. "Death in the Gulf of Mexico." *National Wildlife* 199 (June–July).

Woodard, Colin. 2000. *Ocean's End: Travels through Endangered Seas.* New York: Basic Books.

An oil cleanup demonstration on Green Island, Alaska, after the 1989 Exxon Valdez *oil spill.* NATALIE FOBES/CORBIS

and Canada report that the size and number of incidents in which oil or toxic materials spill into the ocean have declined significantly over the past two decades. But environmentalists point out that even small spills can be significant, for they often occur close to shore, where marine life is most abundant.

When large-scale spills do occur, they can wreak severe damage on marine environments, as the communities along Alaska's Prince William Sound will attest. The most infamous oil spill in North American history took place there in March 1989, when an Exxon tanker called the *Exxon Valdez* slammed into a reef and dumped 11 million gallons of North Slope crude oil (about 257,000 barrels) into the sound. Ocean currents soon spread the oil along 1,400 miles of pristine Alaska shoreline and over almost 10,000 square miles of the sound, which was home to a terrific array of fish and wildlife. The spill ultimately killed an estimated 300,000 seabirds, 2,600 sea otters, and literally millions of fish. Commercial fishing in the sound, which had brought in more than $400 million the previous year, was wiped out, and the regional ecosystem was completed disrupted. A decade after the accident, only two of twenty-three devastated species studied after the spill—the bald eagle and river otter—had fully recovered from the event, and the fishery remained a shadow of its former self.

In the aftermath of the *Exxon Valdez* tragedy, the United States passed the Oil Pollution Act of 1990. This legislation established new guidelines for handling future spills and imposed new vessel design and operation requirements on tankers operating in U.S. waters, the most meaningful of which was a regulation specifying that all such vessels have double hulls by 2015. But critics noted that in 1999—fully ten years after the tanker spill in Prince William Sound—only four out of twenty-four supertankers operating in Alaska waters were outfitted with this extra protection. In the meantime, observers such as Greg Kellogg, director of the Environmental Protection Agency's Alaska office at the time of the *Valdez* accident, flatly state that future accidents of Valdez-like proportions are inevitable. "It may not happen in Prince William Sound," he told ABCNews.com. "Maybe in Puget Sound or [along] the East Coast. Oil spills will happen. We will never eliminate this risk as long as we demand oil and consume it in the manner we do" (http://abcnews.go.com/sections/science/DailyNews/chat_990324valdez.html). The oil industry, however, claims that environmental groups overstate the damage caused by spills. Certainly, other human activities are responsible for a considerable portion of oil pollution in marine waters. The U.S. Coast Guard has estimated that U.S. sewage treatment plants discharge twice as much oil into oceans as tanker spills. In addition, a 2002 study released by the National Research Council said that nearly 85 percent of the 29 million gallons of petroleum that enter U.S. coastal waters every year come from land-based run-off, polluted rivers, jet skis, and small boats. "Oil slicks visible from the air and birds painted black by oil get the most public attention, but it is consumers of oil—not the ships that transport it—who are responsible for most of what finds its way into the ocean" (National Research Council, *Oil in the Sea*, 2002)

Offshore Drilling and Mining

Both the United States and Canada maintain limited offshore oil and gas drilling operations in their coastal waters. These activities have steadily marched outward from near coastal areas to regions of deeper water, and have become an important source of oil and natural gas for both nations. In the United States, for example, outer continental shelf oil and gas production currently supplies 10 percent of U.S. oil and 25 of natural gas, according to the National Council for Science and the Environment. The offshore outer continental shelf waters of the Canadian Atlantic, meanwhile, are dotted with more than 300 exploratory wells, all built since 1967, that have discovered an estimated 12 trillion cubic feet of natural gas and 2 billion barrels of oil. These wells produce more than 125,000 barrels of oil and 400 million cubic feet of natural gas a day, according to the American Association of Petroleum Geologists.

The estimated value of some offshore oil fields has prompted both countries to build some truly massive extraction operations in recent years. In Canada, for example, the Jeanne d'Arc Basin in the North Atlantic is reported to contain the largest oil reserve ever discovered in eastern Canada, and the fourth largest in the entire country. Oil resources in the basin—one of five in Canadian Atlantic waters cited as potential bonanzas—are estimated to be equal to about 45 percent of established conventional crude oil reserves in western Canada. In order to tap into this resource, an ambitious operation known as the Hibernia Project was erected above the basin. That rig, located 310 kilometers east of St. Johns on the northeast Grand Banks, is a structure of enormous proportions, designed to absorb collisions with mighty icebergs and withstand fierce North Atlantic storms. Farther south, the United States maintains literally hundreds of oil and gas rigs in the Gulf of Mexico, the nation's primary area of offshore drilling activity.

Pressure to develop offshore drilling operations of similar scale may well increase in the future as land-based supplies of oil and natural gas are exhausted and new deepwater deposits are discovered (a dozen new oil and gas deposits were discovered in the Gulf of Mexico in 1999 alone). But efforts to boost offshore drilling activities are complicated by concerns about alteration or contamination of habitat from exploration, accidental spills, and marine transport safety issues. In 2001, for example, strong opposition from Florida residents and officials who feared oil-stained beaches forced the Bush administration to dramatically scale back its plans to lease 6 million acres of the eastern Gulf of Mexico for oil exploration. Instead, the Department of the Interior reduced the size of the tract to 1.5 million acres and established a buffer zone of between 100 miles (160 kilometers) and 285 miles (459 kilometers) from the state's panhandle region and west coast.

Fears of environmental damage from rig accidents have curtailed drilling activity along U.S. Pacific and Atlantic coastlines as well, although spills from offshore operations account for only a small percentage of total oil pollution. A moratorium on new oil and natural gas drilling off California's coastline has been in effect since 1989, for example, and a partial ban on oil drilling was imposed by the Clinton administration in 1998. Offshore drilling proposals are expected to receive a warmer reception from the Bush administration, but local opposition will remain an obstacle in many regions. In June 2001, for example, five U.S. Republican senators from New England cited "potentially negative environmental impacts of ocean oil and gas drilling" in urging the administration to maintain a joint U.S.–Canada moratorium (in effect until 2012) on offshore oil and drilling in the Georges Bank, a tract that extends across the North Atlantic from Cape Cod to Nova Scotia.

Nonetheless, in some areas of North America, the potential economic benefits of offshore drilling operations may ultimately outweigh environmental concerns. In 2001, for instance, British Columbia's newly installed provincial government vowed to review a ban on oil and gas exploration off Canada's Pacific coast that has been in effect since 1971. This stance was prompted in part by a 1998 Geological Survey of Canada report that estimated recoverable offshore reserves to be ten times larger than those found in the Hibernia field, the primary focus of offshore drilling on Canada's Atlantic coast. Proponents of new drilling claim that annual royalty revenues for the provincial government could reach C$4 billion annually and help counteract employment downturns in B.C.'s timber and fishing industries. They also contend that new technological developments make it possible to tap these reserves in an environmentally sensitive manner. If the moratorium is overturned, vast oil and gas reserves near the Queen Charlotte Islands—a major tourism destination and home to a wide array of fish and wildlife—are expected to be among the first extraction targets.

Deep sea mining is currently not taking place in any ocean waters under the jurisdiction of Canada or the United States, although interest in commercial exploration is slowly growing in both countries. Mineral deposits of manganese, chromite, platinum, titanium, and gold have all been found on the ocean floor within the U.S. and Canadian exclusive economic zones over the past several two decades, prompting intense speculation about the potential scope of the holdings as well as the possible economic and ecological cost of harvesting them.

To this point, however, efforts to initiate deep-sea mining operations have not made meaningful progress. One formidable obstacle was the UN's 1982 Law of the Sea Treaty, which came into force in 1994. This agreement contained several controversial provisions on deep sea mining. The treaty held, among other things, that the deep-ocean floor beyond 200-mile territorial zones should be regarded as "the common heritage of mankind," and it called on industrialized nations such as Canada and the United States to share mining claims and engage in mandatory technology transfers with less developed nations. Finally, the treaty established an International Seabed Authority empowered with the authority to dictate mining processes and enforce environmental protections it deems necessary.

These provisions of the treaty disappointed both Canada and the United States, which in 1983 had discovered potentially valuable mineral deposits just outside its territorial waters off the coast of Oregon. In fact, both nations refused to endorse the treaty because of unhappiness with its deep-sea mining provisions, although they conformed to many other aspects of the agreement. The treaty's technology-transfer stipulations also displeased the membership of North America's mining industry. An engineer with Lockheed's Ocean Minerals Division spoke for many corporations when he said that the agreement's deep-sea mining provisions were "a sure way to kill interest in investing in ocean mining technology" (Russell, "The Lowdown on Deep Sea Mining," 1998).

During the 1990s, some of these provisions were adjusted or removed to satisfy international mining interests. Experts caution, however, that the economic and technological challenges of mounting a successful deep-sea mining operation remain daunting. Even proponents of seabed mining admit that such projects will not be commercially feasible for the foreseeable future because of the enormous costs involved. But some observers feel that as land-based mineral deposits play out and technology marches forward, industrialized nations such as the United States and Canada eventually will turn their attention to the potentially vast resources hidden beneath the ocean surface. Indeed, companies in North America and elsewhere have already invested millions of dollars in new extraction technologies that can operate in deep-water environments.

Any efforts to initiate ocean mining projects off the coastlines of Canada or the United States will face intense public scrutiny, however. Environmentalists claim that such operations will take an unacceptable toll on marine ecosystems. Many marine biologists and geologists, meanwhile, express concern that deep sea mining operations will disturb and alter a complex environment that is not yet fully understood. Supporters of seabed mining, however, continue to maintain that environmentally responsible extraction of mineral resources will be possible in the future.

Coastal Areas Threatened by Rampant Development

Many coastal areas of North America have been transformed by decades of unrestrained commercial and residential development. In Canada, for instance, approximately one out of four Canadians lives within 50 kilometers of the Atlantic or Pacific oceans. The coastline of southern British Columbia bristles with communities that have fundamentally altered their natural landscapes to accommodate residential homes and roads, agricultural enterprises, industrial facilities, piers, breakwaters, and harbors, while over in Atlantic Canada, great expanses of coastal wetlands have been destroyed, degraded, or fragmented by urban, industrial, and recreational development. According to observers, this extensive conversion of coastline for human activity has deprived Canadian waterfowl and other wildlife of much-needed

Condemned houses balance on the eroding cliffs along the Chesapeake Bay at Governor's Run, Maryland.
LOWELL GEORGIA/CORBIS

habitat and increased the nation's economic and ecologic vulnerability to severe weather events.

Modification of coastline is even more extensive in the United States, where approximately half of the population lives in coastal regions (according to some estimates, the percentage of U.S. citizens living in coastal areas could reach 75 percent by 2025). To make room for this expanding population, the United States continues to convert coastal beaches, wetlands, and estuaries to residential and commercial use at a rapid rate. The U.S. Fish and Wildlife Service, for example, has estimated that more than 90 percent of the Californian coastal sage ecosystem has succumbed to development (Chen, "The Science of Smart Growth," 2000). Yet wetlands and estuaries also possess significant economic—not to mention environmental—value. For example, they provide food and habitat critical to 70 percent of U.S. marine commercial and sport fisheries, according to the National Council for Science and the Environment. Given that reality, conservationists and scientists believe that accelerating coastal development is already harming populations of fish and other wildlife. "Salt marshes, mangrove forests, sea-grass meadows, and kelp forests are often called the 'nurseries of the sea' since so many fish, shrimp, lobsters, crabs, and other creatures start their lives in these protective, food-rich environments," explained Colin Woodard. "Without these nurseries, large numbers of marine organisms are doomed, from Gulf shrimp to Florida manatees. They represent the ocean's Achilles' heel, for they are located in coastal areas, where they become casualties of human enterprise" (Woodard, *Ocean's End*, 2000).

Coastal wetlands also stabilize sediments, shield coastal communities from severe weather events, and filter out pollutants washed off the land. In some areas of the southeastern United States, tidal marshes are even used to filter wastewater from sewage treatment plants. According to one study, this function alone makes them worth around $123,000 per hectare based on the cost of replacing them with artificial treatment facilities (Dugan, *Wetlands in Danger*, 1993).

Yet these varied benefits are often undervalued or ignored outright in the rush to convert natural breakwaters and wetlands into the shoreline condominiums, hotels, and recreation areas that are now strung along much of the U.S. Pacific, Atlantic, and Gulf coastlines. As a result, these developments bring problems along with their undeniable economic benefits. The loss of wetlands' filtering properties increases regional vulnerability to algal blooms and other dangerous accumulations of pollutants and nutrients, while the loss of coastal buffering properties makes hurricanes, winter storms, and other severe weather phenomena even more dangerous. Indeed, experts contend that the continued substitution of expensive subdivisions, marinas, and other developments for natural buffer zones has dramatically increased the economic damage wreaked by severe weather. From 1988 to 1999 alone, the United States sustained thirty-eight weather-related disasters causing damage that reached or exceeded $1 billion each, for a total cost in excess of $170 billion. The majority of these events—like Hurricane George, which did $5 billion worth of damage to the Florida Keys and the Mississippi and Alabama gulf coasts in September 1998—did the bulk of their damage to heavily developed coastal areas.

Another problem facing North America—and especially the United States—is coastal erosion. By some estimates, 80 percent of the U.S. shoreline is eroding to some degree, retreating under a steady drumbeat of wind, waves, and building development. But erosion conditions vary dramatically from region to region. On the rugged Pacific coastline, for example, erosion is site-specific and episodic. Along some sections of the Atlantic seaboard and the Gulf of Mexico, however, erosion has reached epidemic proportions. An estimated 90 percent of the barrier islands stretching from Maine to Florida are suffering from erosion, and at Cape Hatteras, North Carolina, the sea's rapid rate of encroachment (12 to 15 feet per year) forced the relocation of a historic lighthouse in

1999. Louisiana, meanwhile, is losing coastal wetlands at the stunning rate of 30 to 60 square miles a year, largely because of a century of misguided tinkering with the Mississippi delta ecosystem. A joint federal–state task force created to save the Louisiana coastline estimated that the network of pumps, dams, canals, bulwarks, and other structures necessary for stabilization of the region would cost approximately $14 billion.

Of course, developers, engineers, and lawmakers have taken steps to address this threat (the U.S. Congress passed several significant coastal protection laws in the 1970s, and it has allocated tens of millions of dollars to subsidize beach replenishment in recent years). But their efforts have not always proven effective. "As the sea continues to devour shoreline, many resort towns have resorted to engineering solutions—building barriers, like seawalls and jetties, or constructing groins—in an attempt to hold the sand in place. Unfortunately, many of those solutions fail outright or backfire in unexpected ways. When Ocean City, Maryland, built groins to hold its beaches in place, shifting currents began eating away at the undeveloped beaches in nearby Assateague Island, a national wildlife refuge, increasing erosion from 2 feet to nearly 40 feet a year" (Hinrichsen, *Coastal Waters of the World,* 1998).

Indeed, many attempts to tame ocean winds and currents deteriorate into increasingly desperate holding actions. "Nowhere is the dynamic nature of beaches more evident than on the miles upon miles of sandy capes, spits, and especially, barrier islands that line the Atlantic Ocean," wrote Chana Stiefel and Michael Cannell. "Left alone, they are among the planet's most kinetic natural systems. Hammered by storms, blasted by winds, they are nature's own morphs, shifting, advancing, receding, reconfiguring themselves. . . .Once houses, or entire towns, spring up on this kind of roving real estate, property owners and governments are faced with an unavoidable choice: Succumb to nature and let the sea swallow expensive buildings, or fight back, seek to control nature—pay whatever it costs to roll the rock back up the hill" (Stiefel and Cannell, "Beaches Going, Going, Gone?" 1999).

Finally, the potential impact of climate change looms over every serious discussion of North America's coastal areas. According to experts, sea-level rise triggered by global warming could have serious implications for Atlantic, Pacific, and Arctic coastlines, altering ocean temperatures, salinity levels, and currents, and inundating coastal communities and habitats that currently support millions of humans and wild creatures. Scientists warn that even modest increases in sea-level would trigger widespread dislocation—especially along the Gulf Coast and the mid and south Atlantic—and have significant economic and environmental repercussions.

Sources:

Anderssen, Erin, and Jasmina Sopova. 1998. "The Cod Collapse." *UNESCO Courier* (July–August).

Beckmann, L. 1996. *Seas the Day: Towards a National Marine Conservation Strategy for Canada.* Ottawa: Canadian Arctic Resources Committee/Canadian Nature Federation.

Berrill, Michael. 1997. *The Plundered Seas: Can the World's Fish Be Saved?* San Francisco: Sierra Club.

"British Columbia Aquaculture Posts 4,000% Growth Rate." 2001. *Feedstuffs* 73 (January 29).

Brown, Lester B. 2000. "Fish Farming May Soon Take Role as Leading Food Source." *Feedstuffs* 72 (November 13).

Burke, Monte. 2001. "On the Brink." *Audubon* 103 (November–December).

Chen, Donald D. T. 2000. "The Science of Smart Growth." *Scientific American* 283 (December).

Dean, Cornelia. 1999. *Against the Tide: The Battle for America's Beaches.* New York: Columbia University Press.

Department of Fisheries and Oceans. 2001. *Summary of Canadian Commercial Catches and Valves.* Ottawa: DFO.

Dugan, Patrick, ed. 1993. *Wetlands in Danger.* London: Mitchell Beazley.

Dunn, Steve, Robert Friedman, and Sarah Baish. 2000. "Coastal Erosion." *Environment* 42 (September).

Hallowell, Christopher. 2001. *Holding Back the Sea: The Struggle for America's Natural Legacy on the Gulf Coast.* New York: HarperCollins.

Harris, Michael. 1998. *Lament for an Ocean.* Toronto: McClelland and Stewart.

Heinz III, H. John, Center for Science, Economics and the Environment. 2000. *Fishing Grounds: Defining a New Era for American Fisheries Management.* Washington, DC: Island.

Helvarg, David. 2001. "Mississippi Delta Blues" *Grist Magazine.* http://www.gristmagazine.com/books/books052401.asp (accessed April 22).

Hinrichsen, Don. 1998. *Coastal Waters of the World: Trends, Threats and Strategies.* Washington, DC: Island.

Holing, Dwight. 1990. *Coastal Alert: Ecosystems, Energy and Offshore Oil Drilling.* Washington, DC: Natural Resources Defense Council.

Howart, Robert. 2000. "Deteriorating Coasts." *Amicus Journal* (July–August).

Iudicello, Suzanne, et al. 1998. *Fish, Markets, and Fishermen: The Economics of Overfishing.* Washington, DC: Island.

Lamson, Cynthia. 1994. *The Sea Has Many Voices: Oceans Policy for a Complex World.* Montreal: McGill Queens University Press.

McGinn, Anne Platt. 1999. "Atlantic Salmon Face Perilous Waters." *World Watch* 12 (January–February).

———. 1999. *Safeguarding the Health of Oceans: Worldwatch Paper 145.* Washington DC: Worldwatch Institute.

McGoodwin, James. 1990. *Crisis in the World's Fisheries: People, Problems, and Policies.* Palo Alto, CA: Stanford University Press.

National Research Council of the U.S. National Academy of Sciences. 2000. *Clean Coastal Waters: Understanding and Reducing the Effects of Nutrient Pollution.* Washington, DC: National Academy Press.

———. 2002. *Oil in the Sea.* Washington, DC: National Academy Press.

Naylor, Rosamond L. et al. 2000. "Effects of Aquaculture on World Fish Supplies." *Nature* 405 (June 29).

Russell, Dick. 1998. "Deep Blues: The Lowdown on Deep Sea Mining." *Amicus Journal* (winter).

Safina, Carl. 1995. "The World's Imperiled Fish." *Scientific American* 278 (November).

Stiefel, Chana, and Michael Cannell. 1999. "Beaches Going, Going, Gone?" *Science World* 55 (May 10).

Thorne-Miller, Boyce. 1998. *The Living Ocean: Understanding and Protecting Marine Biodiversity.* Washington, DC: Island.

Trout Unlimited USA and Trout Unlimited Canada. 1999. *Resolving the Pacific Salmon Treaty Stalemate.* Seattle, WA: Trout Unlimited USA and Trout Unlimited Canada.

UN Environment Programme. 1999. *Global Environment Outlook 2000.* London: Earthscan.

UN Food and Agriculture Organization. 1994. *A Global Assessment of Fisheries Bycatch and Discards.* FAO Fisheries Technical Paper no. 339. Rome: FAO.

———. 1996. "Fisheries Bycatch and Discards." Rome: FAO.

———. 1999. *State of the World's Fisheries and Aquaculture.* Rome: FAO.

U.S. Environmental Protection Agency. 2002. *National Coastal Condition Report.* Washington, DC: EPA.

Waldeck, Daniel A., and Eugene H. Buck. 1999. "The Pacific Salmon Treaty: The 1999 Agreement in Historical Perspective." RL30234. Washington, DC: Congressional Research Service.

Warner, William. 1977. *Distant Water: The Fate of the North Atlantic Fisherman.* Boston: Little, Brown.

Weber, Peter. 1994. *Net Loss: Fish, Jobs, and the Marine Environment.* Worldwatch Paper no. 120. Washington, DC: Worldwatch Institute.

Welch, H. E. 1995. "Marine Conservation in the Canadian Arctic: A Regional Overview." *Northern Perspectives* 25, no. 1.

Woodard, Colin. 2000. *Ocean's End: Travels through Endangered Seas.* New York: Basic Books.

———. 2000. "Saving the Chesapeake." *Christian Science Monitor* (October 19–25).

World Resources Institute. 2000. *World Resources 2000–2001, People and Ecosystems: The Fraying Web of Life.* Washington, DC: World Resources Institute.

Energy and Transportation

—Dan Whipple and Kevin Hillstrom

No environmental issue so clearly sets North America apart from the rest of the world more than energy production and consumption. U.S. and Canadian resource extraction operations produce tremendous volumes of energy to run their nations' vast, heavily industrialized economies. Yet because of the enormous appetite for energy in the United States, the continent consumes even greater quantities of energy than it produces. This high consumption arises from several factors, including relatively low energy prices, cold climate (in Canada and the northern United States), an energy-intensive industrial base, an infrastructure that rewards—indeed mandates—extensive automobile use, and high standards of living.

Energy Production and Consumption in North America

North America uses global energy resources at a rate unmatched anywhere else in the world, accounting for 29 percent of worldwide energy use (International Energy Agency, 1999). The United States and Canada together held 3.5 percent of the world's known oil reserves in 2001 (U.S. share, 2.9 percent; Canadian, 0.6 percent). But in 2001, North America used 28 percent of the global total, at 983 million tons. The United States alone accounted for 25.5 percent of global consumption, and Canada 2.5 percent. The same pattern exists for natural gas. The two nations house 4.3 percent of the planet's proven natural gas reserves, yet they accounted for 28.6 percent of global consumption in 2001, with the United States alone using more than one-quarter of the global total (BP, 2002).

For coal, in 2001 the United States had 25.4 percent of known coal reserves in 2001 and used about 24.6 percent of the world total, Canada held 0.7 percent of

Figure 8.1 Energy Consumption by Sector, United States

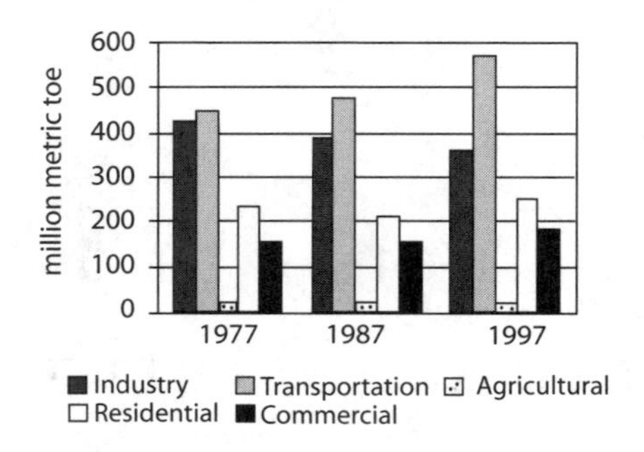

SOURCE: EarthTrends 2001 World Resources Institute.

Figure 8.2 Energy Consumption by Sector, Canada

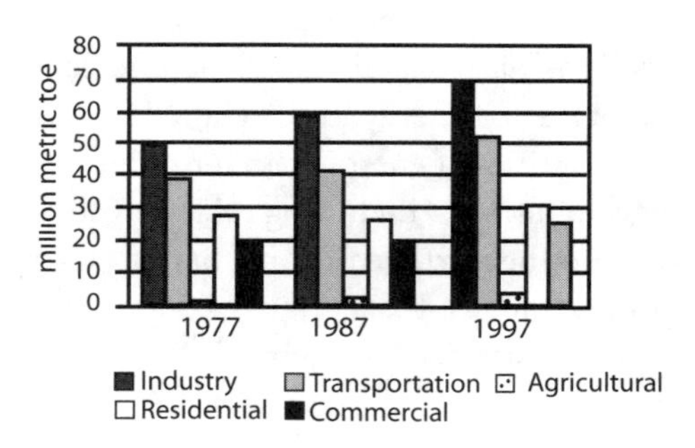

SOURCE: EarthTrends 2001 World Resources Institute.

proven reserves and accounted for 1.3 percent of global consumption. For nuclear power, in 2001 the United States consumed 30.5 percent of the global total and Canada 2.9 percent. Both nations also rely on hydroelectric power. In 2001, Canada generated 12.6 percent of the planet's hydroelectric energy and the United States 8.1 percent (BP, 2002).

Two end-use sectors account for 64 percent of total energy use in the United States: industrial (38 percent) and transportation (26 percent) (Energy Information Administration, *The Americas in a World Context,* 2001). The remainder goes to residential and commercial end-users. In Canada, the patterns of end use are similar. Natural Resources Canada reports that in 1999, industrial production accounted for 39 percent of all energy consumption, followed by transportation (29 percent), residential use (17 percent), commercial use (12 percent), and agriculture (3 percent). Unlike the United States, which consumes more energy than it produces, Canada is a net exporter of energy. In fact, Canada supplies more oil to the United States than any other nation, including those of the Middle East; in 2000 it shipped 1.69 million barrels a day to U.S. destinations.

North America's energy consumption as a percentage of global consumption has actually declined in recent decades because of conservation measures and technological improvements, as well as growing industrialization in developing countries. But actual consumption levels in North America have steadily risen in recent years. Between 1970 and 1998, for instance, energy consumption in North America increased by about 49 percent. All of this energy use has had profound and well-publicized impacts on the environment at the regional, continental, and global levels. Indeed, the environmental repercussions associated with locating, transporting, processing, and consuming domestic and foreign sources of oil, coal, natural gas, and other energy resources continue to be hotly debated throughout the United States and Canada. "Traditional energy sources are facing increasing pressure on a host of environmental fronts, with perhaps the most serious being the looming threat of climate change and a needed reduction in greenhouse gas emissions. It is now clear that efforts to maintain atmospheric CO_2 concentrations below even double the pre-industrial levels cannot be accomplished in an oil- and coal-dominated global economy" (Herzog et al., "Renewable Energy," 2001).

Oil and Automobiles

The single most vital energy resource to the economies of the United States and Canada is oil, the lifeblood of the continent's automobile-dependent culture. According to some estimates, one out of every nine barrels of oil used in the world every day is consumed by the U.S. motorist, much of it pulled from oil fields halfway around the world. Indeed, total North American crude oil and natural gas liquid consumption in 1997 (935 million metric toe) was nearly double the amount of the continent's crude oil and natural gas liquid production (516 million metric toe) that same year (International Energy Agency, *Energy Balances of OECD Countries,* 1999).

Nearly all observers agree that this imbalance needs to be addressed to ensure the continued health and security of the U.S. and Canadian economies, but proposed solutions vary widely. In the United States, which imports more than 50 percent of the petroleum it uses, the environmental community contends that sacrificing undisturbed wilderness areas in exchange for finite supplies of fossil fuels is a foolish, myopic practice. Environmentalists and their allies cite energy conservation and renewable energy as the more sensible pathway to maintaining economic vitality while simultaneously protecting the environment. They point out, for instance, that the U.S. Department of Energy estimates that increasing energy efficiency could cut national energy use by more than 10 percent by 2010 and about 20 percent by 2020. Another recent energy use study estimated that new, cost-effective technologies had the capacity to reduce electricity consumption by about 1,000 billion kilowatt-hours by 2020, which would negate most of the nation's projected growth in electricity use (Interlaboratory Working Group, *Scenarios for a Clean Energy Future,* 2000; Herzog et al., "Renewable Energy," 2001).

Proponents of increased domestic oil exploration and production, however, charge that by opposing extraction activities in undeveloped areas, environmentalists are locking away much-needed oil, gas, and coal deposits. "Environmentalists like to say they're not against energy development, that it's just this *one* precious/wild/irreplaceable/holy piece of 'American Serengeti' that they're trying to 'save,'" wrote one proponent of increased exploration. "But the truth is, it *isn't* just one place. It's here, there, and everywhere" (Zinsmeister, "Beware of Green Fairy Tales," 2001). Advocates claim that the first priority should be to lessen U.S. dependence on foreign oil by expanding fading domestic operations, including extraction and processing capacity. They note that crude oil production in the United States peaked in 1970 at 9.6 million barrels a day and has been declining ever since, to a 1999 level of about 5.9 million barrels, in part because of aging production infrastructure. For example, proponents of increased domestic oil production observe that the last new U.S. oil refinery was built in 1980 (environmentalists are quick to counter, however, that a number of existing refineries have expanded their operations significantly since that time). Advocates of increased domestic drilling also point out that imported oil often comes from nations in politically volatile regions of the world. In 2000, for instance, the United States acquired 46.3 percent of its oil imports from OPEC countries, about half of which came from countries in the volatile region around the Persian Gulf. This level of reliance on other nation-states came under renewed scrutiny in the aftermath of the September 2001 terrorist attacks on New York City and Washington, D.C., which dramatically exposed concerns about religious fundamentalism and political instability in the Middle East and Central Asia (see sidebar on opposite page).

Automobile Use in North America

Any serious discussion of oil consumption in the United States and Canada inevitably pivots on the automobile, a ubiquitous presence in the economies and psyches of both nations. On average, there were 484 cars per thousand people in

North America in 1996. Levels of automobile ownership in the United States and Canada were similar, with 489 cars or trucks per thousand people in the United States and 441 per thousand in Canada—approximately one car for every two people on the continent (International Road Federation, "World Road Statistics," 1999). These automobiles account for 21 percent of all U.S. energy consumption, and about 45 percent of all petroleum used. Indeed, annual gasoline consumption in North America in 1997 was nearly 1,640 liters per person (International Energy Agency, *Energy Balances of OECD Countries,* 1999).

This level of consumption is greatly exacerbated by steadily increasing reliance on the automobile to drive greater and greater distances. In 1980 the average U.S. driver traveled 9,700 miles. In 1998 the U.S. motorist was driving more than 13,000 miles annually, an increase of 34 percent for the nation's 180 million licensed drivers. These statistical trends have prompted environmental

The Debate over Drilling in Alaska's Arctic National Wildlife Refuge

The debate raging around oil and gas drilling in the Arctic National Wildlife Refuge (ANWR) is only the latest in a decades-long conflict between petroleum development and the conservation of wilderness areas. Similar battles have been fought over the trans-Alaska crude oil pipeline, offshore drilling in California and Florida, and oil and gas drilling in Rocky Mountain roadless areas, but perhaps no other fight has become freighted with so much emotion on both sides. "In this debate [over ANWR], Alaska itself has taken on a symbolic heft beyond its value as a wilderness preserve or as a source of oil," observed *Newsweek.* "Once again, the way Americans engage their frontier will reflect, in no small measure, the national character. Are we energy gluttons, or hopeless romantics wedded to a utopian vision of the natural world? ... Which do we value more: greater American oil production or a landscape largely untouched by the hand of man?" (Bartholet, "Alaska: Oil's Ground Zero," 2001).

The contested area of the refuge, which encompasses a total of 19 million acres, including 8 million acres of designated wilderness, is a 1.5-million-acre section of coastal plain known as the "1002 area," located on the Arctic Ocean in northeast Alaska. This area has been vulnerable to oil and gas exploration since ANWR's creation in 1980, when the Alaska National Interest Lands Conservation Act was passed. At that time, lawmakers cognizant of the area's potentially enormous oil and gas reserves included a provision—section 1002—in the act that gave Congress the option of authorizing oil and gas exploration in the so-called 1002 region.

About three-quarters the size of Yellowstone National Park, the 1002 area is a vast expanse of tundra,

(continues)

groups, policy-makers, and other constituencies to call for increased investment in public transportation systems and better development planning. Indeed, they cite "urban sprawl" as one of the key factors in increased automobile use, for it steadily increases the distances that U.S. and Canadian citizens are driving.

marshes, lagoons, and rivers tucked between the northern edge of the Brooks Range and the Beaufort Sea in the Arctic Ocean. Few people visit, but it is important wildlife habitat. About 160 bird species nest or breed in the area. It is the principal calving ground for the 130,000 caribou of the Porcupine herd, the second largest in the United States. It also provides important denning space for polar bears.

But the potential for oil in this inhospitable region is also enormous. No one knows with certainty the size of the reserve, but the U.S. Geological Survey has estimated that the 1002 area contains between 4.3 billion and 11.8 billion barrels (the mean estimate of ANWR's potential yield—5.6 billion barrels—would meet America's oil needs for about 40 weeks). Oil boosters note, however, that the Prudhoe Bay oil field to the west has produced more than 10 billion barrels of oil during its life.

Prodevelopment groups also point out that only 8 percent of the entire ANWR would be affected by extraction—that is, the 1.5 million acre 1002 area. The remainder of the 19 million acres of wilderness and wildlife habitat would be left as is. "If oil is discovered," states Arctic Power, an Anchorage-based industry group, "less than 2,000 acres of the over 1.5 million acres of the Coastal Plain would be affected." Proponents also tout the job creation aspect of drilling in ANWR, claiming that at least 250,000 new jobs would be created, and they note that oil development enjoys support from a majority of Alaskans, who receive hefty annual dividend checks and pay no state income tax because of oil royalties. Advocates of drilling further claim that predictions of the negative impact of such activities on Arctic wildlife are overstated. For example, oil and gas developers are quick to point out that the Central Arctic caribou herd at Prudhoe Bay has grown enormously since that area was developed for oil (Arctic Power, "ANWR Resource Estimates," 2001). Finally, the energy industry and its supporters note that the U.S. Fish and Wildlife Service already permits oil drilling in more than twenty wildlife preserves and refuges around the country.

Opponents of drilling in ANWR are quick to rebut these arguments. Wildlife advocates claim that the caribou herd at Prudhoe Bay increased in size only after a spate of severe winters had ended, and that it moved its calving grounds after development started there. "The Porcupine herd [in ANWR] is almost five times bigger [than the

(continues)

Another commonly cited factor in North America's heavy automobile use is the perennially low price of gasoline, especially in comparison with other regions of the world. Average fuel cost per mile driven has dropped significantly since 1980, when driving cost 17 cents per mile (in 1999 dollars). By 1999 that expense had dropped to approximately 6 cents per mile, with

Central Arctic herd], but it calves in the same amount of acreage. Oil development could push animals to calve closer to the mountains, where there is poorer forage and a higher density of predators such as grizzly bears, wolves, and eagles" (McGrath, "The Last Great Wilderness," 2001).

Conservationists also point out that the United States could save far greater volumes of oil than are available in ANWR and other wilderness areas simply by using current sources of energy more efficiently. And they contend that even if the Arctic National Wildlife Refuge yields oil volumes at the upper end of USGS estimates, the oil will do little to alleviate short-term energy shortages (as it will take several years for the oil to reach the marketplace), and it will not fundamentally relieve America's continued reliance on imported oil. "If energy security and oil independence are national goals, reducing demand for oil in the near term and introducing non-oil energy sources in the longer term will be far more prudent than opening new oil fields," stated one World Resources Institute report (MacKenzie, *Thinking Long Term,* 2001).

Finally, the environmental community charges that even if the energy industry were able to tap oil and gas reserves in ANWR without disturbing the surrounding environment, the activity still contributes to the looming threat of global climate change. "Conservationists ... argue that petroleum geologists miss a larger point: that global warming from the burning of fossil fuel presents an even greater potential danger to [Arctic] ecosystems. Polar bears may or may not be affected by seismic thumping, but they surely will suffer from the rapid melting of their habitat" (Bartholet, "Alaska: Oil's Ground Zero," 2001).

Sources:

Arctic Power. 2001. "ANWR Resource Estimates" http://www.anwr.org (accessed February 15).

Bartholet, Jeffrey. 2001. "Alaska: Oil's Ground Zero." *Newsweek* (August 13).

MacKenzie, James J. 2001. *Thinking Long Term: U.S. Oil Security and the Arctic National Wildlife Refuge.* Washington, DC: World Resources Institute.

McGrath, Susan. 2001. "The Last Great Wilderness." *Audubon* 103 (September–October).

Prendergast, Ben. 2001. "Drill Phobia: Where Will America's Energy Future Come From?" *American Enterprise* (September).

gasoline accounting for only 3.1 percent of household expenditures in the average U.S. household (Cambridge Energy Research Associates, *Gasoline and the American People,* 2000). The modest expense of gasoline has been a balm for the current household budget, but has also provided little incentive for U.S. consumers to curb their rate of consumption.

Still, members of the scientific and environmental communities continue their campaign to rein in automobile use, citing a wide array of negative environmental effects, such as the cumulative impact of carbon emissions on air quality. Automobile emissions are a major contributor to unhealthy smog conditions in metropolitan areas, and they are a major source of the heat-trapping greenhouse gases that are responsible for global climate change. In fact, one-third of the heat-trapping greenhouse gases generated in the United States each year are directly attributed to transportation (Union of Concerned Scientists, *Drilling in Detroit,* 2001). Indeed, greenhouse-gas emissions from the U.S. transportation sector alone exceed the total emissions of many nations.

U.S. and Canadian highways now feature cars that run much cleaner than their predecessors of the 1960s and 1970s. The U.S. auto industry demonstrated enormous innovative ability in the fuel economy sector in subsequent years, doubling passenger car fuel efficiency between 1975 and 1985. But these gains have been neutralized because of the increased popularity of sport utility vehicles (SUVs) and light trucks, which produce more smog-causing pollution because they get fewer miles per gallon. Indeed, by the late 1990s the fuel economy of the U.S. vehicle fleet had sunk to its lowest point since 1980.

Efforts to raise minimum mileage standards of SUVs and light trucks have increased in intensity in recent years. According to advocates of higher fuel economy standards, considerable gains remain available in fuel efficiency through the increased application of improved "conventional" technologies, including vehicle load reductions (aerodynamic improvements and weight reduction); improved transmissions, including five- and six-speed transmissions, optimized shift schedules, and continuously variable transmissions; new engine efficiencies; and integrated starter-generators. The Union of Concerned Scientists contends that a fleet that relies on continuously evolving conventional technologies could reach an average of more than 40 miles per gallon, about 75 percent better than the 2000 average. The typical family car could get 45 miles per gallon (mpg), while the cost of filling up an SUV could be cut in half with a fuel economy of 40 mpg. Compared with the average family car produced in 1970, a car using those technologies to get 45 mpg would save 3,700 gallons of gas over a 170,000-mile auto lifetime, thus generating 30 to 60 fewer tons of greenhouse gas emissions for each vehicle sold, 16 to 34 fewer pounds of toxic emissions, and 35 to 72 fewer pounds of smog-forming emissions. Observers believe that such gains would not only improve air quality but also reduce pressure on wilderness areas that contain untapped oil reserves. "Significant fuel economy improvements would dwarf supplies obtained from proposed expansion into environmentally sensitive areas such as the Arctic National Wildlife Refuge. In 18 years the United States will have saved more than four times the oil available in the Arctic Refuge at today's oil prices. In that same year, we would save more than 10 times what the Arctic would be producing each day if development were begun there today." (ibid.).

Thus far, however, campaigns to mandate meaningful increases in fuel efficiency have repeatedly stalled in the face of resistance from automakers and their political allies. In 2002 the debate took yet another turn when the Bush administration abandoned an eight-year-old government-industry initiative to produce more fuel-efficient cars in favor of a program to develop vehicles powered by hydrogen fuel cells. Environmentalists have long hailed the promise of these fuel cells, which use hydrogen to produce electricity without creating pollution, unlike gasoline-powered engines. But the environmental community declared that increased investments in that technology did not absolve the government or industry from seeking immediate fuel consumption improvements. Other transportation options for the future include ethanol, a product of corn processing, and biodiesel, made from used vegetable oils and animal fats. Both of these fuels burn more completely than gasoline, thus reducing pollution emissions, and they can be blended with traditional petroleum-based fuels.

Demand for Abundant Natural Gas Continues to Grow

North America contains vast underground reservoirs of natural gas, many of which have been tapped to meet the continent's energy needs. In 1997, total natural gas production in North America was nearly 580 million metric toe. Canada accounted for approximately 137 million metric toe of this production. Canada, though, consumes far less natural gas (71 million metric toe in 1997) than it produces, even though natural gas supplanted oil as the leading fossil fuel consumed in the country in the early 1990s. This surplus is due to the nation's aggressive development of abundant natural gas supplies in the 1980s and 1990s (International Energy Agency, *Energy Balances of OECD Countries,* 1999). Alberta, for instance, has an estimated 200 trillion cubic feet of natural gas reserves, enabling it to export 2.4 trillion cubic feet a year to the United States—about one-tenth of total U.S. consumption (Canadian gas exports to the United States more than tripled between 1985 and 1997, when it supplied about 13 percent of the U.S. gas supply). Natural gas exploration is

A natural gas well in a forest south of Fort St. John in British Columbia LOWELL GEORGIA/CORBIS

also on the increase in Atlantic Canada, where large onshore and offshore reserves have been found. "The East Coast's oil and gas potential is considered to be virtually untapped," said one industry executive (Demont, "Dreams of Riches," 2001). And in Arctic Canada, a massive natural gas project designed to tap an estimated 6 trillion cubic feet of gas reserves in the Northwest Territories' Mackenzie Delta region is in the works.

As with oil, the United States is a net importer of natural gas. The United States generated 442 million metric toe of natural gas from domestic fields in 1997, much of it from reserves in Alaska and the Southwest, but it consumed nearly 580 million metric toe (International Energy Agency, *Energy Balances of OECD Countries,* 1999). In the late 1990s, the Department of Energy estimated that 40 percent of the 22 trillion cubic feet of natural gas consumed annually went to industry end-users, with much of the remainder divided among residential users (23 percent), commercial users (15 percent), and electric utilities (14 percent).

Natural gas consumption in the United States has remained fairly stable since the mid-1990s, according to the Department of Energy. But experts believe that demand for natural gas will increase considerably in the coming decades, as the population expands (natural gas heats 56 million households, more than half of all U.S. homes) and as natural gas-dependent power plants come on line (only 16 percent of U.S. power plants are gas-fired, but an estimated 95 percent of new and proposed plants will rely on natural gas to generate electricity). These future demands, coupled with soaring natural gas prices in 1999–2000 attributed to increased demand from Asian markets, have prompted a major push by the gas industry and its allies to boost supplies and update the nation's fossil fuel transportation infrastructure. Some tangible results of this push have already manifested themselves. In early 1999 the Department of Energy (DOE) reported that there were only about 360 rigs drilling for natural gas nationwide. By early 2001 there were 800.

The environmental communities in Canada and the United States are ambivalent about this campaign for increased natural gas drilling. These groups and their allies grant that natural gas does not take the same toll on air quality as coal and heating oil. In 1998, for example, the Ontario Clean Air Alliance issued a report claiming that air pollution from the province's coal-fired electric utilities could be reduced by as much as 90 percent if the plants switched to new power stations fueled by natural gas. But the environmental community also points out that natural gas extraction activities fragment wildlife habitat and can pollute rivers and aquifers alike (see sidebar on page 220). As a result, they have urged the U.S. and Canadian governments to keep some natural gas–rich areas in the Rocky Mountains and elsewhere off limits to development. Pressure to open these areas is strong, however. The Bush administration, for instance, believes that federal lands in the lower forty-eight states hold an estimated 167 trillion cubic feet of natural gas (as well as more than 4 billion barrels of oil), a volume that would enable the United States to meet gas demand at current consumption levels for more than six years. The administration has thus endorsed streamlining of environmental reviews of new natural gas pipelines, additional financial incentives for natural gas drilling, and increased drilling on public land. Indeed, the Department of Interior has already been directed to review management plans for national monuments and other federal lands that have been withdrawn from development and to "consider modifications where appropriate."

"King Coal" Remains a Staple of North American Energy Grid

As recently as the mid-twentieth century, it was considered the fuel of the future for North Americans. In recent decades, the environmental degradation associated with the extraction and use of this energy source has curbed such talk. But in contrast to oil, which it imports in large quantities, North America has abundant coal supplies within its borders. Major coal reserves exist in bands stretching along the flanks of the Rockies from New Mexico to northern Alberta, throughout the U.S. Midwest, and along the western flank of the

Appalachians from Pennsylvania to Alabama. In fact, a 2002 study carried out by the U.S. Geological Survey placed the amount of coal in the Appalachians alone at approximately 66 billion short tons. As a result, "king coal" remains a staple of the continent's—and especially the U.S.—energy diet. "The United States is the Saudi Arabia of coal," said an executive of one of the world's largest coal companies. "There is more energy value in the coal under the state of Illinois than there is in the oil in Saudi Arabia and Kuwait combined" (McMahon, "Cheap, Dirty and Still King," 2001). Indeed, according to some estimates, the United States holds about half of the globe's coal reserves within its borders.

In 1997 the United States produced more than 560 million metric toe of hard coal and lignite, about 20 percent of the global total. Canada added another 43 million metric toe. Both nations typically produce more coal than they consume; in 1997, for instance, the United States used 514 million metric toe and Canada consumed 27 million metric toe of coal (International Energy Agency, *Energy Balances of OECD Countries,* 1999).

The debate over coal is most intense in the United States, where half of the country's electric power is generated by coal consumption. Most regions of the country rely on coal more than any other resource for their power, in part because of increased use of coal by utilities. This dependence has taken a significant toll on the environment, both at the extraction and burning stages.

The most efficient extraction method is surface mining, which removes as much as 95 percent of the coal present in the seam. But concern about this method's impact on human and wildlife welfare resulted in the Surface Mining Act of 1977, which adds $1 to $5 of extra cost per ton to pay for land reclamation. The passage of that law reduced the worst of surface mining abuses, but environmental degradation associated with surface coal mining remains a significant concern.

Indeed, surface mining—also known as strip or open-pit mining—continues to be condemned by environmentalists and wildlife biologists for permanently scarring fragile ecosystems. Nearly all the coal mines in the West are surface strip mines, and while the land that is mined, especially in Wyoming's Powder River Basin—far and away the nation's largest coal-producing region—is fairly level and dry and thus not subject to the kind of catastrophic failures sometimes visited upon the mountainous Appalachians, the land is home to a wide variety of High Plains wildlife. In addition, physical disruption of groundwater aquifers from surface mining remains problematic, especially in arid Western regions, where isolated ranches and small communities often rely on subsurface water wells. Acidic or highly saline runoff from mines—especially long-abandoned facilities—continues to contaminate ground and surface water resources as well. In response to this latter threat, Canada recently announced plans to impose strict regulations on emissions from its ninety-three metal mines, which generate C$11 billion (U.S.$7.2 billion) in annual revenue. Beginning in 2002, the Federal Fisheries Act will impose new limits on metal and cyanide discharges into rivers and streams, and will prevent the discharge of toxins deadly to fish.

Coal has also presented perennial pollution problems at the consumption end. Indeed, the U.S. Environmental Protection Agency has bluntly stated that coal-fired power plants collectively produce more pollution than any other industry in the United States. In 1998 electric power plants across the country were for the first time required to report toxic air emissions to the federal Environmental Protection Agency (EPA). According to these reports, electric utilities discharged more than 1 billion pounds of toxic chemicals into the air. Most of that pollution came from coal, since the other major electric power fuels—nuclear energy, hydropower, and natural gas—release few emissions.

Industries have invested heavily in technology to cut emissions of pollution generated by coal-burning, and sulfur emissions have dropped considerably as a result. Utilities use what is called "best available control technology," and the United States and Canada are cooperating on a clean coal technology program that dates back to the mid-1980s. But acid rain attributed to nitrogen oxides and sulfur dioxides from coal burning remain a lingering problem in numerous regions of the United States and Canada. "High-elevation forests in West Virginia, Tennessee, and Southern California are near saturation level for nitrogen, and high-elevation lakes in the Rocky Mountain, Cascade, and Sierra Nevada mountain ranges are on the verge of chronic acidity. In the Adirondacks, many waterways are becoming more acid even as sulfur deposits drop: by 2040, as many as half the region's 2800 lakes and ponds may be too acid to support much life" (Dunn, "King Coal's Weakening Grip on Power," 1999).

Despite the environmental toll of these pollutants, the Bush administration has approved modifications of air pollution rules for power plants (primarily coal-burning) so that they can meet rising power demand without incurring expensive modification requirements. The administration favors introducing financial incentives for plants to voluntarily reduce their toxic emissions. But environmental groups view this approach as a serious threat to the Clean Air Act, and they contend that these changes will increase problems in the areas of acid rain, smog, and respiratory disease. New England states, which receive airborne pollution from aging power plants in the Midwest, have also vowed to fight any attempts to relax clean air standards.

New Drilling Technologies Used in Sensitive Environments

On the production side of the equation, the oil and gas industry has heeded some of the cries for environmental sensitivity in its activities. By taking advantage of technological advances, it has been able to reduce the adverse impact on land and water from drilling activities. New techniques include the use of satellites, microprocessors, remote sensing, and super computers to generate three- and four-dimensional time-lapse imaging of underground reservoirs. As a result, sharply increased drilling success rates have cut the number of both wells drilled and dry holes.

A major beneficial development has been the increased use of directional and horizontal drilling to reach reservoirs in environmentally sensitive areas and in deep offshore waters. Directional and horizontal drilling allow a single rig to explore and produce in a much wider area from one site, which reduces the overall impact on the land. The industry also now uses durable forged alloys and polycrystalline diamonds to replace cast iron bits, which has improved drilling productivity. The positive results include better worker safety, increased protection of wildlife habitat and open lands, and less toxic waste.

Another major production technology development that has important environmental benefits is enhanced recovery from existing fields. In the early days of oil production, recovery of only 10 percent of the petroleum in place was the norm. Now a new field can expect to yield 50 percent of the oil in place as usable product, thanks to the introduction of sophisticated imaging technologies, including 3-D seismic and 4-D time-lapse systems, which provide oil and gas professionals with detailed pictures of reservoirs and formations. "Since 1990, the vast majority of reserve additions in the United States—89 percent of oil reserve additions and 92 percent of gas reserve additions—have come from finding new reserves in old fields, thus reducing the pressure to explore virgin lands" (U.S. Department of Energy, "Environmental Benefits of Advanced Oil and Gas Exploration and Production Technology," 2000).

(continues)

Nuclear Power Beleaguered by Safety Concerns

The U.S. Nuclear Regulatory Commission regulates 103 nuclear plants in the United States. These facilities generate about 20 percent of total electricity needs in the United States. In Canada, 14 nuclear reactors contribute about 14 percent of the total electricity supply. Combined, the two nations generated

In Bakersfield, California, for example, a previously "played-out" oil field was re-examined using underground imaging technology. This technology confirmed that further reserves existed at the field, and in the ensuing years another million barrels of oil were pulled out of the ground at the site. That "new" oil, noted the U.S. Department of Energy, "is more than half as much oil as the property produced in all of its first 80 years of operation. Project sponsors predict that the advanced technologies ultimately will result in more than 4 billion barrels of oil being produced—all from a 40-acre property once thought to be dead."

Sources:

U.S. Department of Energy, Office of Fossil Energy. 1999. *Environmental Benefits of Advanced Oil and Gas Exploration and Production Technology.* Washington, DC: U.S. Department of Energy, Office of Fossil Energy, October.

Williams, Wendy. 2001. "Good to the Last Drop." *Audubon* 103 (September–October).

and consumed 195 million metric toe of nuclear energy in 1997 (International Energy Agency, *Energy Balances of OECD Countries,* 1999). These facilities, then, are an integral part of the power grid for both nations, but they are immensely unpopular in most environmental circles. In fact, it has been two decades since a new reactor has been commissioned in either country, although the Bush administration has touted new nuclear plants as a partial solution to growing energy needs.

Nuclear power offers many environmental advantages over fossil fuel consumption. This energy source requires no environmentally damaging extraction activity, and nuclear operations do not emit pollutants into the air. Moreover, it is a virtually limitless energy source. For these reasons, many environmental groups endorsed nuclear power as the clean fuel of the future in the industry's early years. But vague concerns over radiation leaks and other safety issues at nuclear facilities crystallized in the 1970s and 1980s, when Pennsylvania's Three Mile Island nuclear plant suffered a partial nuclear meltdown (in 1979) and the Chernobyl nuclear reactor catastrophe in the Soviet Ukraine (in 1986) killed thousands of people and blanketed a large region in harmful radioactive material. Canada has had its difficulties as well, though nothing on the scale of Chernobyl. In 1997, Ontario Hydro—North America's largest electric utility—shut down seven of its nuclear reactors following a damning report that detailed serious operating

Figure 8.3 Location of Existing Nuclear Power Plants, United States

SOURCE: Sierra Club http://www.sierraclub.org/.

In 1997, Pennsylvania's Three Mile Island nuclear power plant suffered a partial nuclear meltdown.
WALLY MCNAMEE/CORBIS

deficiencies and safety problems. Four years later, after the industry had spent billions of dollars on refurbishing, eight of the twenty reactors in the province, home to all but two of Canada's reactors, were not in operation. Construction cost overruns, site decommissioning expenses, and high costs for storage of spent reactor fuels have necessitated extensive subsidization of the industry by the Canadian government as well. Indeed, the federal government estimates that the cost of disposing of the country's nuclear waste over the next century could eventually reach C$11 billion (Wells, "Meltdown," 1997).

The United States is also grappling with the issue of nuclear waste disposal. The battle has raged over this issue for years, but shows little sign of being resolved. Many parts of the nuclear fuel cycle generate radioactive waste. Mine tailings—the rock left over after uranium is processed—are radioactive. Spent fuel wastes, produced at the rate of about 104 metric tons a year in the United States, are highly radioactive and are currently kept in water-filled pools at nuclear power plants. High-level wastes (commercial and defense-related), low-level wastes (about 60 percent from commercial operations), and transuranic waste (nearly all from defense activity) add to the environmental problems.

There have been numerous proposals over the years for disposal of these wastes. In the United States, military wastes are planned for long-term storage in the Waste Isolation Pilot Project (WIPP) in Carlsbad, New Mexico. WIPP, an underground storage facility, was the subject of engineering and public controversy for twenty-four years before the Environmental Protection Agency cleared it to open in 1998. The inevitable lawsuits followed and continue to pile up. As of September 30, 2000, a total of ninety shipments have arrived at WIPP since its opening.

For the time being, commercial nuclear waste from U.S. power plants—waste that can remain dangerously radioactive for 20,000 years—is still stored on site at nuclear generating facilities in water-filled pools. Most experts agree that the safest long-term storage of nuclear waste is underground, but finding a location for such a facility has been very difficult, the result of an understandable "not-in-my-backyard" syndrome among potential sites. At the beginning of the twenty-first century, however, a DOE-endorsed site at Yucca Mountain, Nevada, appears to be the most likely final resting place for most commercial nuclear wastes. According to the DOE, the key advantages of this cite include remote location (it is about 100 miles from Las Vegas, the nearest population center); dry climate, with less than six inches of rainfall a year; and an extremely deep water table (800 to 1,000 feet below the level of the proposed repository). Preventing the intrusion of water is very important, because water can corrode the containers holding the waste and spread radioactive materials underground.

To ensure the long-term isolation of the materials stored at Yucca Mountain, the DOE has said that it would make use of both the natural geologic features of the mountain and man-made barriers. Despite these assurances, though, opposition from local residents, environmental groups, state and regional legislators, and other constituencies has been stiff. Opponents have argued for years that Yucca Mountain is not an acceptable storage site, citing the potential for earthquakes and the risk of intrusion of groundwater.

Hydropower and Other Forms of Renewable Energy

Despite a great deal of discussion about their environmental benefits, most alternative energy sources—solar power, wind, tidal power, hydrogen fuels, and others—have made almost no impact on the North American energy mix since the 1973 OPEC oil crisis. Only hydroelectric power provides a meaningful portion of the juice that keeps the continent's economic engine humming. In 1997, North America's total renewable energy production reached 150 million metric toe. The United States accounted for 109 million metric toe of that total, while Canada's extensive hydroelectric network enabled it to generate almost 41 million metric toe of renewable energy (International Energy Agency, *Energy Balances of OECD Countries,* 1999).

More than half of North America's renewable energy (and three-quarters of Canada's renewable energy) comes from conventional hydroelectric power. Hydropower supplies about 4 percent of the power in the United States, including 70 percent of energy used in the Pacific Northwest. It also accounts for about 10 percent of the energy produced in Canada (ibid.). Hydropower was once widely viewed as an environmentally benign source of energy. But modern conservationists are reluctant to see more large hydropower projects, because dams create problems for fish and wildlife by altering streamflows and flooding habitat, increasing soil salinity, and inducing changes in groundwater patterns and supplies. In addition, Native American and First Nation communities have been disproportionately affected by hydroelectric projects over the years. Manitoba, for instance, has the lowest electric rates in Canada because of its hydroelectric dams, but Cree communities in the province's northern reaches contend that those dams destroyed 1.2 million hectares of tribal hunting and fishing grounds and displaced entire communities.

Analysts also note that the growth of the hydroelectric industry is limited by certain geographical realities. Nearly all of the suitable large hydropower sites in the United States have already been built on, making any substantially larger energy contribution from that source unlikely in the future. Observers point out that power generated from future hydroelectric facilities on currently free-flowing Canadian rivers could be exported to U.S. destinations, but resistance to new hydropower initiatives that would alter the essential character of wild northern rivers is significant.

Of the environmentally friendly energy sources that conservationists usually say they want to see utilized—geothermal energy, biomass, solar energy, and wind—only 3.154 quadrillion BTUs were produced in 1997, about 3 percent of total U.S. energy use. That percentage actually marks a slight decline from the early 1990s. Of those sources, the largest contribution came from biomass. Biomass includes wood burning—not in itself the cleanest fuel, nor a pursuit that much protects forests and wildlife—as well as the burning of municipal solid wastes, landfill gases, and other waste products to produce heat and electricity.

For the most technologically complex and environmentally benign renewables—solar power, geothermal, and wind generation—inroads have been slow. In 1997, renewable energy consumption in the transportation sector—primarily the use of ethanol in motor gasoline—increased by 31 percent. But renewable energy consumption decreased in all other sectors, particularly residential and industrial (ibid.). But encouraging signs of interest in renewable energy can be found. Wind power, for instance, still provides less than 1 percent of the nation's electricity, but the American Wind Energy Association (AWEA)reported that the U.S. wind energy industry doubled its total capacity

Horizontal axis wind turbines in Palm Springs, California CORBIS

in 2001. During that year, a record 1,694 megawatts of generating equipment was installed in sixteen states, enough power to meet the needs of 475,000 U.S. households (the installations boosted the total installed wind power capacity in the United States to 4.258 megawatts). The AWEA noted that more new wind generation was installed in a single state—Texas—than had ever been installed in the entire nation in a single year. The U.S. government has also signaled increased interest in the development of renewable resources, proposing a variety of tax incentives that would encourage further use of renewables. Specific proposals under consideration in 2002 included extension and modification of existing tax credits for producing electricity from renewable sources, as well as introduction of tax credits for residential solar energy systems, purchases of fuel cell vehicles, and energy produced from landfill gas.

None of the principal forms of renewable energy currently in development are without environmental drawbacks. As one official of the Institute for Energy Research noted: "Every major renewable energy source has drawn criticism from leading environmental groups: hydro for river habitat destruction, wind for avian mortality, solar for desert overdevelopment, biomass for air emissions, and geothermal for depletion and toxic discharges." Nonetheless, the potential environmental benefits of renewables are enormous, especially in the area of greenhouse gas emissions, and the environmental community has been united in its campaign to boost investment in and use of these energy generation options. "For many years renewables were seen as energy options that—while environmentally and socially attractive—occupied niche markets at best, due to barriers of cost and available infrastructure. [But] renewable energy technologies have made important and dramatic technical, economic, and operational advances during the past decade. A national energy policy and climate change strategy should be formulated around these advances" (Herzog, et al., "Renewable Energy," 2001).

Sources:

BP. 2002. *BP Statistical Review of World Energy 2002.* London: Group Media and Publications.

Bradley, Robert L., Jr. 1997. *Renewable Energy: Not Cheap, Not Green.* Washington, DC: Cato Institute Policy Analysis no. 280. August.

Cambridge Energy Research Associates. 2000. *Gasoline and the American People.* Cambridge, MA: Cambridge Energy Research Associates.

Caudill, Harry. 1962. *Night Comes to the Cumberlands.* Boston: Little, Brown.

Clean Air Task Force. 2001. *Cradle to Grave: The Environmental Impacts from Coal.* Boston: CATF, June.

Demont, John. 2001. "Dreams of Riches: Onshore Energy Reserves Could Brighten Atlantic Canada's Future." *Maclean's* 114 (February 12).

Dunn, Seth. 1999. "King Coal's Weakening Grip on Power." *World Watch* 12 (September–October).

"Energy and the Environment." 2001. *American Enterprise* (September).

Energy Information Administration. 2001. "Energy Data by Type of Process, 2001." U.S. Department of Energy. http://www.eia.doe.gov/neic/processnj/Process_consumption_ njava.htm.

———. 2001. *The Americas in a World Context.* Washington, DC: U.S. Department of Energy.

Flores, R. M., and D. J. Nichols. *Tertiary Coal Resources in the Northern Rocky Mountains and Great Plains Region—A Clean and Compliant Fossil Fuel beyond 2000.* U.S. Geological Survey Professional Paper 1625-A. Washington, DC: USGS.

Freme, F. L., and B. D. Hong. 1999. *U.S. Coal Supply and Demand: 1999 Review.* Washington, DC: U.S. Department of Energy, Energy Information Administration.

Grubb, M. J., and N. I. Meyer. 1993. *Renewable Energy Sources for Fuels and Electricity.* Washington, DC: Island.

Herzog, Antonia V., et al. 2001. "Renewable Energy: A Viable Choice." *Environment* 43 (December).

Holdren, John P. 2001. "Searching for a National Energy Policy." *Issues in Science and Technology* (spring).

Ih-Fei Liu, Paul. 1993. *Introduction to Energy and the Environment.* New York: Van Nostrand Reinhold.

Intergovernmental Panel on Climate Change. 2001. *Climate Change 2001: The Scientific Basis.* Geneva: World Meteorological Organization–UN Environment Program, January.

Interlaboratory Working Group. 2000. *Scenarios for a Clean Energy Future.* Oak Ridge, TN: Oak Ridge National Laboratory, Lawrence Berkeley National Laboratory, November.

International Energy Agency. 1999. *Energy Balances of Organisation for Economic Cooperation and Development (OECD) Countries, 1960–1997.* Paris: OECD.

International Road Federation. 1999. "World Road Statistics." *World Development Indicators 1999.* Washington, DC: Development Data Group, World Bank.

Kay, Jane Holtz. 1997. *Asphalt Nation: How the Automobile Took over America and How We Can Take it Back.* New York: Crown.

Kenworthy, Tom. 2001. "Wilderness Above, Energy Riches Below." *USA Today,* July 20.

MacKenzie, James J. 1997. *Climate Protection and the National Interest: The Links among Climate Change, Air Pollution, and Energy Security.* Washington, DC: World Resources Institute.

———. 2001. *Thinking Long Term: U.S. Oil Security and the Arctic National Wildlife Refuge.* Washington, DC: World Resources Institute.

McMahon, Patrick. 2001. "Cheap, Dirty and Still King." *USA Today,* January 25.

Motavelli, Jim. 2001. *Breaking Gridlock: Moving toward Transportation That Works.* San Francisco: Sierra Club Books.

Union of Concerned Scientists. 2001. *Drilling in Detroit: Tapping Automaker Ingenuity to Build Safe and Efficient Automobiles.* Cambridge, MA: UCS.

University of Michigan Transportation Research Institute. 2001. "Tenth Biennial U-M Delphi Forecast and Analysis of the North American Automotive Industry." Ann Arbor: UMTRI, December.

U.S. Department of Energy, Office of Fossil Energy. 2000. *Environmental Benefits of Advanced Oil and Gas Exploration and Production Technology.* Washington, DC: U.S. Department of Energy, Office of Fossil Energy, October.

U.S. Geological Survey. 2001. *Arctic National Wildlife Refuge, 1002 Area, Petroleum Assessment, 1998, including Economic Analysis.* Washington, DC: USGS, April.

Weiss, M. A., et al. 2000. "On the Road in 2020: A Lifecycle Analysis of New Automobile Technologies." Cambridge: Massachusetts Institute of Technology, October.

Wells, Jennifer. 1997. "Meltdown: Seven Nuclear Plants Are Shut Down in the Wake of a Stunningly Critical Study." *Maclean's* 110 (August 25).

World Resources Institute. 2000. *Earthtrends 2001.* Washington, DC: World Resources Institute.

Zinsmeister, Karl. 2001. "Beware of Green Fairy Tales." *American Enterprise* (September).

Air Quality and the Atmosphere

—Jody Larson

Although marked reductions in air pollution have been made in the United States and Canada in the past thirty years, the negative health effects of smog and toxic emissions, and the damage to forests and other ecosystems because of acid precipitation, remain major environmental issues in North America. With regard to global warming, the United States remains the leading producer of carbon dioxide emissions in the world, both in terms of per capita production and overall volume (about one quarter of the world's emissions of carbon dioxide). Canada ranks eighth in the world in total carbon dioxide emissions, generating 2.5 percent of the global total. But on a per capita basis, Canada is the third greatest polluter in the realm of carbon dioxide, producing 15 metric tons per capita in 1995 (World Resources Institute, *World Resources 2000–2001,* 2000; Carbon Dioxide Information Analysis Center, *Global, Regional, and National Annual CO_2 Emissions,* 1999).

Both the United States and Canada have acknowledged the importance of addressing climate change issues. Indeed, the Canadian government has characterized climate change as "the ultimate sustainable development issue" (Government of Canada, *A Discussion Paper on Canada's Contribution to Addressing Climate Change,* 2002). But in 2001, concerns over perceived flaws in the Kyoto Protocol led the United States to withdraw from the UN-sponsored agreement, which called on developed nations to reduce their emissions of greenhouse gases (GHGs) to at least 5 percent below 1990 emission levels by 2012. Canada's compliance with Kyoto is also uncertain because of strong provincial opposition, especially in Alberta, where robust economic growth has been attributed to exploitation of vast reservoirs of oil and natural gas.

Table 9.1 Comparison of 1970 and 2000 Emissions

	1981–2000 (%)	*1991–2000 (%)*
NO_X	+4	+3
VOC	-32	-16
SO_2	-31	-24
PM_{10}*	-47	-6
$PM_{2.5}$*	—	-5
CO	-18	-5
Pb	-94	-4

*includes only directly emitted particles
NO_X = nitrogen oxides
VOCs = volatile organic compounds
SO_2 = sulfur dioxide
PM_{10} = particulate matter
CO = carbon monoxide
Pb = lead

SOURCE: U.S. Environmental Protection Agency. *Latest Findings on National Air Quality: 2000 Status and Trends.*

Air Pollution Trends

Emissions in North America

The United States and Canada are among the world's leading producers of major air pollutants. According to the U.S. Environmental Protection Agency (EPA), the United States releases more than 160 million tons of air pollution into the skies every year, and approximately 121 million of its citizens live in areas that have unhealthy levels of one or more of six principal pollutants—carbon monoxide, lead, nitrogen dioxide, ground-level ozone (which is formed by nitrogen oxides and volatile organic compounds: VOCs), fine particulates, and sulfur dioxide. Moreover, millions of other U.S. citizens are subjected to elevated levels of ozone during heavy smog days (Environmental Protection Agency, *Latest Findings on National Air Quality: 2000,* 2001).

These statistics make it clear that the battle for clean air across the continent has not yet been won. But North America has made tremendous progress in cleaning up its air over the past thirty years, a period during which many other regions of the world have experienced staggering downturns in air quality. In the United States, the pivotal event that started the country down the path toward improved air quality was the 1970 passage of the Clean Air Act, a law that has been amended several times since. From the beginning of the twentieth century to 1970, when the Clean Air Act came into force, U.S. emissions of nitrogen oxides increased by an estimated 690 percent, emissions of VOCs increased 260 percent, and emissions of sulfur dioxide increased 210 percent (Environmental Protection Agency, *Latest Findings on National Air Quality: 1999*, 2000). But the pollution controls contained in the Clean Air Act and its amendments dramatically curtailed emissions of these and other contaminants. Indeed, aggregate emissions of the aforementioned six principal pollutants decreased by 29 percent in the United States between 1970 and 2000 (see sidebar on page 239). During the same period, U.S. gross domestic product increased 158 percent, energy consumption increased 45 percent, and vehicle miles traveled jumped 143 percent. Only one of the pollutants—ground-level ozone—recorded an upswing in emissions during that thirty-year period. That increase is attributed to a 20 percent rise in nitrogen oxide emissions, primarily from coal-fired power plants and heavy-duty diesel vehicles (Environmental Protection Agency, *Latest Findings on National Air Quality: 2000*, 2001).

In Canada, emissions in 1995 included 15.68 million tons of particulate matter, 2.65 million tons of sulfur oxides, 2.46 million tons of nitrogen oxides, 3.575 million tons of VOCs, and 17.13 million tons of carbon monoxide (Environment Canada, "CAC Emission Summaries, 1995 National," 2002). Most monitoring and regulation of emissions in Canada takes place at the provincial and territorial level rather than at the national level, with the exception of "transboundary" emissions and ozone-depleting substances. For example, the Ontario Ministry of the Environment has been monitoring, assessing, and reporting on air pollutant trends within Canada's most populated province for the past thirty years. During that time, sulfur dioxide emissions have been reduced by 82 percent, from approximately 28 parts per billion (ppb) in 1971 to about 5 ppb in 2000. Carbon monoxide levels decreased by 81 percent during the same period, and nitrogen dioxide and nitrogen oxide levels decreased 23 percent and 49 percent, respectively, from the mid-1970s to 2000. However, it should be noted that most of these decreases were accomplished in the first ten years of monitoring, and the decrease has been slower or flat since that time (Ontario Ministry of the Environment, *Air Quality in Ontario, 2000 Report*, 2000).

Key Pollution Sources

The most important source of air pollution and atmospheric damage in North America, and indeed in any industrialized nation at present, is the burning of fossil fuels in automobile, airplane, and small gasoline-burning

The Harbor Freeway in Los Angeles, California BILL VARIE/CORBIS

engines, and in coal- and gas-burning power plants. The burning of fossil fuels releases hydrocarbons, carbon monoxide, nitrous oxides, and VOCs such as methane, ethane, ethylene, and terpenes. These substances contribute to an array of air-quality problems.

Technology improvements have produced significant advances in automobile fuel efficiency over the past three decades. But North American consumers use cars more frequently and travel greater distances than ever before. In the late 1990s, annual gasoline consumption in North America reached nearly 1,640 liters per person (International Energy Agency, *Energy Balances of Organisation for Economic Cooperation and Development,* 1999). Moreover, many of these drivers favor sport utility vehicles (SUVs), which consume comparatively larger volumes of gasoline than do fuel-efficient models (SUVs are classified as light trucks in the United States and are thus able to escape the stricter miles-per-gallon regulations that apply to other passenger vehicles). In Canada, for instance, sales of SUVs almost doubled between 1996 and 1997. These purchasing choices—coupled with industry resistance to new fuel efficiency mandates for light trucks—have produced declines in the overall fuel economy of the North American fleet. By the late 1990s, the fuel economy of the U.S. fleet had sunk to its lowest level since 1980.

Other sources of air pollution include industrial processes such as smelting, refining, and manufacturing. Coal-burning power plants, refineries, and smelters emit sulfur dioxide and nitrous oxides, which are the primary components of acid precipitation, as well as dioxin and other toxic substances. Heavily mechanized agriculture, meanwhile, generates particulate matter and often relies upon aerosol pesticides. In addition, naturally occurring events, such as volcanic eruptions and dust storms, may produce acute air pollution episodes that influence human and ecosystem health far beyond the originating country's borders (see sidebar on page 248).

Acid Precipitation in North America

Acid precipitation, also known as acid deposition or acid rain, is created by emissions of nitrous oxides and sulfur dioxide associated with the burning of fossil fuels. These chemicals mix with water and oxygen in air to form sulfuric and nitric acids that return to earth in snow and rain, where they damage buildings and monuments, ruin forests (especially at higher elevations), and acidify lakes, streams, and soil.

By the 1970s biologists knew that air pollution was wreaking considerable damage on the forest ecosystems of Canada and the United States. The forests of the Great Lakes regions and the entire Appalachian range of the Eastern United States were particularly hard hit by acid deposition, although other factors

Trees damaged by acid rain on Mt. Mitchell in western North Carolina. WILL & DENI MCINTYRE/CORBIS

(such as increased ultraviolet radiation caused by stratospheric ozone thinning, increases in other pollutants such as aluminum, opportunistic diseases, and insect infestations) have also been blamed for tree death and forest decline.

Specific examples of species damaged by acid rain include the flowering dogwood, which has been almost completely eliminated from some areas of the southern Appalachians because of infestation of anthracnose fungus, a "black plague" that covers leaves and stems, choking the tree. Anthracnose has been linked to acid deposition. Air pollution is also a suspect in the mysterious oak wilt that threatens the abundance of acorns, which in some areas is the single most important winter food source for wildlife. Crown dieback and decline of the sugar maple in the Northeastern United States and Canada has also been blamed on acid precipitation, although the interactions may be complex. Some researchers believe that the maples are starving to death because of the leaching away of soil nutrients, the result of decades of acid precipitation. Approximately 35 percent of the sugar maples in Vermont have died, and in the Allegheny National Forest some stands have lost 80 percent of their trees (Ayers et al., *An Appalachian Tragedy,* 1998).

In recent years both the United States and Canada have enacted various regulations and programs to reduce acid deposition. The United States, for example, fashioned an emissions trading program specifically designed to reduce the output of sulfur dioxide and nitrogen oxide from electric utility plants that burn fossil fuels (about 64 percent of annual sulfur dioxide emissions and 26 percent of nitrogen oxide emissions in the United States are produced by such facilities). The EPA emissions trading program set a nationwide cap on nationwide power plant emissions of sulfur dioxide that is about half the amount emitted in 1980. There is no nitrogen oxide emissions cap, but other elements of the scheme enabled power plants to reduce emissions in 2000 by 2 million tons from 1980 levels (Environmental Protection Agency, *Latest Findings on National Air Quality: 2000,* 2001).

These efforts have paid visible dividends. In the United States, for example, the volume of acid rain was reduced from an estimated 16 million tons in 1990 to 11.2 million tons in 2000. Lakes in Quebec, Ontario, and Vermont are in varying stages of recovery, and sulfate concentrations have been significantly reduced in the Ohio River Valley and in states immediately downwind. But some areas of the U.S. Midwest, Southeast, and West Coast have shown slight increases in deposition in recent years. Scientists speculate that these heightened concentrations may be partially attributable to a loss of natural buffering capacity in some lakes. Lake soils contain compounds such as calcium and magnesium that can buffer acids. Researchers suspect that prolonged exposure to acid precipitation has leached calcium and magnesium away, and it may take decades or even centuries for the buffers to rebuild, even if further cuts in sulfur and nitrogen oxide emissions are made (Roberts, "Acid Rain," 1999; Environmental Protection Agency, *Latest Findings on National Air Quality: 2000,* 2001).

In recognition of the continued impact of acid rain on ecosystems, the Bush administration in 2002 announced its intention to prosecute coal-fired power plants in the Midwest for violations of the Clean Air Act. It also released a "Clear Skies" initiative that encourages power plants to make further cuts in their emissions of sulfur dioxide, nitrogen oxide, and mercury by

Figure 9.1 Sulfate Deposition in Precipitation

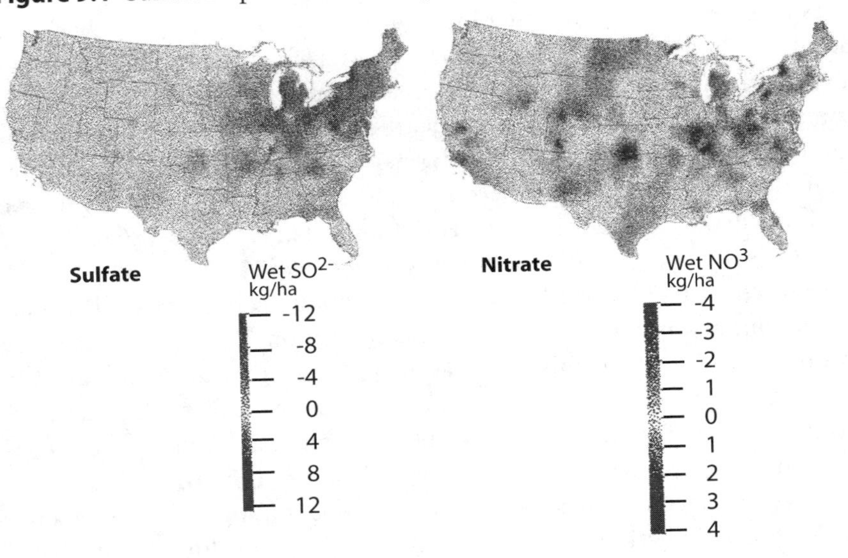

SOURCE: U.S. Environmental Protection Agency. Analysis of National Atmospheric Deposition Program Data.

placing a cap on total national emissions and then allowing companies to trade their emission credits. For sulfur dioxide, the initiative seeks to cut emissions from the current level of 11 million tons per year to a cap of 4.5 million tons by 2010, and 3 million tons by 2018, a reduction of 73 percent. For nitrogen oxide, a 67 percent decrease is planned, from the current level of 5 million tons per year to 2.1 million tons in 2010 and 1.7 million tons by 2018. The mercury cap is the first-ever national cap on mercury emissions; targeted goals for these emissions include a total cut of 69 percent, from 48 tons per year to 26 tons in 2010 and 15 tons by 2018. But some states, skeptical that these requirements will become law (or be effective if implemented), are being proactive in addressing pollution from dirty power plants. States that have instituted or studied regulations to slash emissions from power plants include New York, North Carolina, New Hampshire, and Connecticut.

Reducing Air Toxics

Air toxics, more formally known as "hazardous air pollutants," are pollutants known or suspected to cause cancer or other serious health effects, such as birth defects, or to cause adverse environmental effects. For example, toxic pollutants that enter soils, lakes, and rivers are absorbed in flora and fauna and ultimately magnify up through the food chain, where they can compromise reproductive capacity and other biological functions.

Air Pollution and "Grandfathered" Power Plants

Because of an exemption in the Clean Air Act, 594 older coal-fired electric power plants have been allowed to continue operating in the United States without investing in pollution control technology required in newer facilities. The law exempted these older plants because of an expectation that they would come off line, but instead, many utilities have kept them going, recognizing that since the plants do not have to meet Clean Air Act standards, they enjoy a cost advantage over other facilities. "We created a perverse incentive for the utilities to keep these old dinosaurs running as long as they can," remarked one regional director of the National Parks and Conservation Association. "Rather than replacing the old plants, they're propping them up" (Fordney, "Bad Airdays," 2001). These older plants alone spewed more than 2 billion tons of pollutants in 1999. Moreover, of the nation's 500 largest electricity-generating stations, 51 located in Midwestern states account for about a third of the country's acid rain and nitrogen oxide emissions. These facilities have had a dramatic and sustained impact on air quality in the downwind states of the Northeast. New England has responded with lawsuits aimed at forcing the Environmental Protection Agency to clean up the plants.

The EPA is currently trying to address the issue by imposing "best available retrofit technology" (BART) on "grandfathered" utilities and industrial boilers, pulp mills, refineries, smelters, cement plants, and other sources that contribute to regional haze. The federal government is also weighing various policy responses to the issue. One strategy under review would simply call on the EPA to relax the Clean Air Act's "new source" rule, which exempts antiquated facilities so that they can continue operations without meeting Clean Air Act standards. This option has been widely denounced by the environmental community, public health advocates, and other constituencies, but it enjoys support from the energy industry. Another alternative under consideration would be to employ the same "cap and trade" program that produced meaningful reductions in acid rain during the 1990s. "Industry would be given national 'caps' that rolled all Clean Air Act requirements into a single standard, and then allowed to trade emissions permits in order to achieve the cheapest or fastest means of reduction.... As with the acid rain program, the cap system would require that refinery and power-plant emissions steadily decline. But so long as standards were met, industry would be free to work out the details [themselves]" (Easterbrook, "Air Pressure," 2002).

Sources:

Easterbrook, Gregg. 2002. "Air Pressure." *New Republic* 226 (February 4).

Fordney, Chris. 2001. "Bad Airdays." *National Parks* 75 (May–June).

U.S. Environmental Protection Agency. 2001. *Latest Findings on National Air Quality: 2000 Status and Trends.* Washington, DC: EPA, September

The 1990 Clean Air Act amendments list 188 toxic air pollutants that EPA is required to track and control. Heavily monitored air toxics include benzene (emitted from cars, trucks, oil refineries, and chemical processes), perchloroethylene (used in dry cleaning), methylene chloride (a solvent and paint stripper), dioxin, asbestos, toluene, a variety of pesticides, and metals such as cadmium, mercury, chromium, and lead compounds.

Total air toxic emissions in the United States have dropped by an estimated 48 percent between 1988 and 2000, and chemical releases nationwide decreased by an estimated 700 million pounds from 1999 to 2000 alone (Environmental Protection Agency, *2002 Toxics Release Inventory,* 2002). Output trends for individual air toxics vary considerably from pollutant to pollutant, however. For example, perchloroethylene monitored in sixteen urban sites in California showed a drop of 60 percent from 1989 to 1998, and measurements taken from eighty-four urban monitoring sites around the country showed a 39 percent drop in benzene levels from 1993 to 1998 (Environmental Protection Agency, *Latest Findings on National Air Quality: 1999,* 2000). But releases of other toxic chemicals increased during the 1990s. In fact, in 2002 the EPA released an extremely somber *National-Scale Air Toxics Assessment* based on 1996 emissions data. This report estimated that airborne toxic chemicals posed an elevated cancer risk to two out of three residents of the United States living in every part of the country. The study, which looked at 33 air pollutants (a subset of 32 air toxics from the Clean Air Act's list of 188 air toxics plus diesel particulate matter), concluded that automobile and truck emissions were a major source of the chemicals, along with power plants and various industrial facilities (Environmental Protection Agency, *National-Scale Air Toxics Assessment,* 2002).

According to the EPA's *2000 Toxics Release Inventory* report, the U.S. hardrock mining industry releases more toxins than any other industry in the country. In 1997, for example, the nation's chemical manufacturing industry reported 797.5 million pounds of toxic releases; one year later, mining operations in Nevada alone reported producing approximately 1.3 billion pounds of toxic waste. One mine—the Cyprus Miami copper mine in Arizona—released twice as much toxic waste (123 million pounds) as all of New York state (60 million pounds) in 1998. Smelting and refining operations are another source of highly toxic compounds, including fluorine and aluminum.

Several international initiatives to reduce toxic pollution have also been approved in recent years. The most recent significant pact took shape in 2001, when delegates from 122 countries—including the United States and Canada—agreed to a treaty calling for a worldwide phaseout of the twelve worst persistent organic pollutants (POPs). The pact covers dioxin, PCBs,

DDT, aldrin, chlordane, dieldrin, endrin, heptachlor, mirex, toxaphene, hexachlorobenzene, and furans, and it will go into effect after fifty nations ratify it (Downie, "Global POPs Policy," 2002).

Growing Concern over Fine Particulate Matter

Particulate matter refers to airborne solid particles and liquid droplets, from large and dark particles that are visible as smoke, dust, and soot to smaller particles that can be detected only with an electron microscope. These latter types of particulate matter include "PM10" particles (all particles less than or equal to 10 micrometers in diameter) and "PM2.5" particles (fine particles that are less than or equal to 2.5 micrometers in diameter); for comparison purposes, a human hair has a diameter of 70 micrometers. Particulate matter can be released into the atmosphere either directly (from road dust or as soot from wood burning) or secondarily (from emissions from power plants, automobiles, industrial facilities, and other types of combustion sources) (Environmental Protection Agency, *Latest Findings on National Air Quality: 2000,* 2001).

Environmental problems associated with emissions of particulates include damage to vegetation and reduced air visibility in some North American cities, national parks, and state/provincial parks. Exposure to high levels of particulate matter also can have numerous negative health effects, from aggravation of asthma and other respiratory conditions to heart and lung disease.

The Natural Resources Defense Council calculated in the early 1990s that as many as 60,000 Americans die each year from lung disease, heart conditions, and other health problems brought on by fine particles. In 1999 a study of death rates in the ninety largest U.S. metropolitan areas by Johns Hopkins University School of Public Health found that an increase of 20 micrograms of airborne particulate matter per cubic meter of air brought a 1 percent rise in death rates (Jaret, "Why Tiny Particles Pose Big Problems," 2001).

Between 1991 and 2000 average PM10 concentrations in the United States decreased 19 percent, with direct emissions dropping by about 6 percent. But regional differences in particulate matter concentrations are significant in both the United States and Canada. The eastern side of the continent features significantly higher sulfate concentrations—and hence, higher concentrations of particulate matter—because it is downwind of coal-fired power plants and other fossil-fuel burning activities in Ontario, Michigan, Illinois, Ohio, Pennsylvania, and other Midwest locations (Environmental Protection Agency, *Latest Findings on National Air Quality: 2000,* 2001).

The Pros and Cons of Incineration

Solid waste incineration is a method of disposal that takes some of the burden off landfills. Combustion typically reduces waste volume by up to 90 percent, and the heat can be used for production of electrical energy, lessening the need for fossil-fuel power plants that generate large volumes of greenhouse gases. Environmental groups, however, have been decrying the use of incineration for at least a decade, and have been sharply critical of government agencies that classify incineration as a renewable energy source. These opponents cite the high concentration of heavy metals and other toxic by-products, such as dioxin, that burning trash produces, as well as the difficulty of properly disposing of the toxic ash. They also have noted that many incinerators have been placed in poor urban and rural areas. But proponents of incineration note that the technology has improved dramatically over the past fifty years, and since 1994 the EPA has been monitoring toxic emissions from incinerators and studying possible uses for the ash produced during the incineration process.

Florida leads the United States in trash incineration. It houses 13 of the nation's 102 municipal solid waste incinerators and accounts for 22 percent of all trash disposed of in this manner. Some lawmakers have called for increased reliance on these facilities. "In the real world, if you want to have alternatives to fossil fuel . . . solid waste is by far the largest of those that are available and likely to be available in the foreseeable future," declared Florida senator Bob Graham (Reiss, "Earth Day Finds Heated Debates over Energy," 2002).

Nevertheless, the question of dealing with toxic emissions has not been answered to the satisfaction of many environmental advocates. Fly ash and bottom ash from incinerators may contain 2,000 to 4,000 ppm (parts per million) of lead, which is five to ten times as high as the 1994 EPA "level of concern" for lead in soils (Montague, *Environmental Action,* 1994). Any landfill that accepts incinerator ash must be suitable for toxic heavy metal disposal. In addition, a recent study undertaken by Columbia University and Rensselaer Polytechnic Institute indicated that most of the lead contamination in the New York City metropolitan area in the past 100 years could be traced to the incineration of solid waste ("Incineration," 2000).

Sources:

"Incineration: Cores Absolve Gasoline as Lead Source." 2000. *Waste Treatment Technology News* (April).

Montague, Peter. 1994. "Ash Controversy Smolders." *Environmental Action* (Fall).

Reiss, Cory. 2002. "Earth Day Finds Heated Debates over Energy." *Englewood Herald Tribune,* April 22.

U.S. Environmental Protection Agency. 2001. *Latest Findings on National Air Quality: 2000 Status and Trends.* Washington, DC: EPA, September.

The Battle to Reduce Ground-Level Ozone

Heightened concentrations of ozone in the troposphere—so-called ground-level ozone—kills trees and other vegetation and damages the respiratory systems of humans and other animals. Created when sunlight acts on emissions of nitrogen oxides and volatile organic compounds, ground-level ozone is also a major greenhouse gas that contributes to global climate change.

Excess ozone concentrations can be even more detrimental to natural ecosystems than acid deposition, poisoning entire tracts of forest and other vegetation. Ground-level ozone has been estimated to cause more than $500 million in annual reductions of agricultural and commercial forest yields, and airborne releases of nitrogen oxides are one of the largest sources of nitrogen pollution in Chesapeake Bay and other ecologically and economically significant waterways (Environmental Protection Agency, *Latest Findings on National Air Quality: 1999,* 2000). Researchers in Great Smoky Mountain and Shenandoah national parks alone have found ninety-five plant species that are affected by ozone, many of them important food sources for wildlife and humans (Ayers et al., *An Appalachian Tragedy,* 1998).

Ground-level ozone is also a significant concern in Canada. In fact, it has been cited as "the most pressing factor affecting Atlantic Canada's air quality," because during the summer months, more than half of that region's population is "routinely exposed to unacceptably high ozone concentrations" (Government of Canada, *State of Canada's Environment,* 1996). Much of this accumulation is actually generated hundreds of miles away. In the Bay of Fundy area, southern New Brunswick, and parts of Nova Scotia, 50 to 80 percent of the smog is caused by cross-border pollution from the northeastern United States or by emissions from central Canada (Vincent and Fick, "Blowin' in the Wind," 2000).

Canadians are increasingly aware of health hazards associated with urban smog exacerbated by high ozone levels, and many alter their behavior when high smog level warnings are in effect. But these behavioral changes more often involve staying indoors rather than reducing activities that create smog. The warnings do not, for example, prompt large numbers of Canadians to leave their cars at home and use alternative transportation.

Atmospheric Issues

Fraying of the Ozone Layer

Some man-made air emissions compromise the ozone layer in the stratosphere (which is between 6 and 30 miles above the surface), thinning it to the point that it can no longer protect the earth from the full force of the sun's ultraviolet radiation, a known source of cancer in humans and a suspected threat to plant and aquatic ecosystems. For example, harm associated with increased exposure to ultraviolet radiation includes declines in plankton, a cornerstone of the global marine food chain and an important "sink" or absorber of carbon dioxide, the main greenhouse gas responsible for climate change.

Across much of North America, ozone levels in the upper atmosphere have declined by 5 percent in the summer and 10 percent in the winter (Environmental Protection Agency, *Latest Findings on National Air Quality: 2000,* 2001). But numerous international initiatives to curb ozone loss have been launched in recent years, including the 1987 Montreal Protocol on Substances that Deplete the Ozone Layer and its subsequent extensions. Developing countries concentrated nearer the tropics, where ozone depletion is less severe, were initially skeptical of the plan and its expensive requirements. But once the developed nations created a fund to compensate developing countries, and also threatened trade sanctions against any country that did not participate, the developing nations shifted their position.

The Montreal Protocol committed most of the world, including the United States and Canada, to limit its production of chlorofluorocarbons (CFCs), halons, methyl bromide, and other ozone-depleting chemicals, most of which were generated by air conditioning and refrigeration units, insulating foams, and various industrial processes (under the accord, which now has 157 signatories, all production of CFCs in developed countries was halted on January 1, 1996). International use of hydrochlorofluorocarbons (HCFCs)—a substitute for CFCs that also damages the ozone layer—remains extensive, but current multilateral environmental agreements call for a global phaseout of this class of chemicals by 2020. Finally, both the Canadian and U.S. governments have established their own regulatory programs and laws to deal with the issue.

Scientific evidence suggests that these myriad efforts may be stabilizing ozone levels in the upper atmosphere. But researchers emphasize the importance of continued vigilance in ozone preservation efforts, and they note that full recovery above the Antarctic and Arctic regions, where ozone depletion has been most evident, is still decades away. In 2001, for instance, scientists estimated that the ozone hole above the Antarctic spanned 9.8 million square miles (25.4 million square kilometers).

Greenhouse Gases and Global Warming

Global warming occurs when accumulations of carbon dioxide and other gases trap heat from the sun and hold it close to the surface of the earth instead of letting it escape into space. Under this "greenhouse effect," global temperatures are believed to be increasing. If left unchecked, this climate change could have tremendous repercussions for the earth's ecosystems and its human civilizations. Likely manifestations of global climate change include rising temperatures, increasingly severe and numerous storms, altered rain and snowfall patterns that will bring greater incidence of flooding and drought, inundation of islands and coastal areas by rising seas (created by melting glaciers and polar ice caps), expansion of tropical diseases into previously temperate zones, and possible mass extinctions of species of flora and fauna that are unable to survive in old habitats or migrate to more hospitable areas.

The major compounds contributing to global warming include carbon dioxide, methane, ozone, nitrous oxide, chlorofluorocarbons, and particulate matter. Carbon dioxide generated by the burning of fossil fuels in the transport, energy, and industry sectors is the single greatest contributor to global warming—it accounts for about 81 percent of all greenhouse gases released in the United States—but methane emissions produced by agriculture, landfills, man-made water reservoirs, coal mining, and natural gas systems are the next most significant source. Other contributors include nitrous oxide from agricultural management and transport sources, and fluorinated compounds from aluminum and magnesium production and electrical transmission and distribution systems (Environmental Protection Agency, *Latest Findings on National Air Quality: 2000,* 2001).

The United States is the single greatest source of greenhouse gases in the world. It accounts for about one-third of the industrialized world's total greenhouse gas emissions, including nearly one-quarter of the global output of carbon dioxide, the most important greenhouse gas responsible for global climate change. In 1996 the United States alone produced 5.3 billion metric tons of the compound, 22 percent of the global total of 23.88 billion metric tons (Carbon Dioxide Information Analysis Center, *Global, Regional and National Annual* CO_2 *Emissions from Fossil Fuel Burning,* 1999).

The United States has touted various voluntary climate protection programs as key elements of its efforts to rein in emissions. For example, the EPA contends that in 2000 its voluntary programs reduced greenhouse gas emissions by 58.5 million metric tons of carbon equivalent, the same as taking 40 million cars off the road. Nonetheless, these initiatives have failed to reverse the upward trend in U.S. greenhouse gas output. Indeed, in 1998 total greenhouse gas emissions in the United States increased 11 percent from 1990 baseline levels, and GHG emissions from the U.S. transport sector alone continue to eclipse the total emissions generated by many countries (Environmental Protection Agency, *Latest Findings on National Air Quality: 2000,* 2001). In recognition of these trends, in 2002, California instituted a landmark law regulating vehicle greenhouse gas emission. But the automobile industry has vowed to fight the new law, claiming that it trumps federal laws that reserve for Congress the power to set fuel economy standards.

Canada is also among the world's top ten producers of greenhouse gases, emitting an estimated 410 million tons of carbon dioxide alone in 1996 (Carbon Dioxide Information Analysis Center, *Global, Regional, and National Annual CO2 Emissions,* 1999). In 1999, Canada emitted a total of 699 million tons of emissions, with the energy sector (561 million tons, including 177 million tons attributed to automobiles and other transport), agriculture (61 million tons), and industrial activity (50 million tons) accounting for most of the gases. All told, Canada's output of greenhouse gases by the close of the twentieth century was more than 19 percent higher than in 1990, even though the Kyoto Protocol, to which Canada is a signatory, commits the nation to reducing greenhouse gas emissions by 6 percent from 1990 levels by 2012 (Government of Canada, *Discussion Paper on Canada's Contribution to Addressing Climate Change,* 2002).

Canada's steadily rising emissions of greenhouse gases have been traced to economic growth, increases in coal consumption for electricity and steam generation, and increases in energy consumption by all forms of transport. Indeed, emissions from electricity and heat generation rose 24 percent from 1990 to 1999, as did emissions from the transport sector (Environment Canada, "Canada's Greenhouse Gas Emissions, 1990–1999," 2001).

Canada has managed, however, to find some silver linings among these troubling trends in emission growth. By 1999, for example, the nation's emissions of greenhouse gases were growing by only 1.4 percent annually, while the economy grew at an annual rate of 4.5 percent. "This tells us that the Canadian economy is growing in a more GHG-efficient manner," contended Environment Canada. "In other words, the growth in our GHG emissions has slowed, while our economy has continued to grow, indicating a de-coupling between GHG emissions and economic growth" (ibid.). Nonetheless, this type of positive indicator does not mask the fact that overall emissions in Canada are rising instead of falling.

In fact, some observers contend that in several significant respects, the United States—which has been castigated by environmental groups, scientific bodies, and other governments for its GHG emissions record—actually boasts emission reduction programs that are superior to those in place in Canada. For example, three states (New Hampshire, Oregon, and Massachusetts) require power plants to cut emissions of carbon dioxide, while no similar mandates exist anywhere in Canada. Thirteen states have renewable energy portfolio standards requiring electricity companies to generate a portion of their supply from clean sources such as wind, but only two provinces (British Columbia and Quebec) have similar programs, while Ontario—home to one out of three Canadians—has no such standards. In addition, the United States has twenty times the installed wind energy capacity of Canada, even though it has only nine times the population, and unlike Canada, it requires landfill gas capture from all large landfill sites (only three Canadian provinces have any similar measures on the books). Finally, emissions of greenhouse gases actually grew at a slower rate in the United States than in Canada during the 1990s, even though the former country's economy expanded at a faster rate (Pembina Institute, *Comparison of Current Government Action on Climate Change,* 2002).

In recognition of its failure to reduce emissions during the 1990s, in 2000 the Canadian government announced Action Plan 2000, a five-year, C$500 million initiative that it said would reduce Canada's GHG emissions by about 65 million tons annually during the commitment period of 2008 to 2012. "Action Plan 2000 sets the course for further action in all sectors of the Canadian economy and lays the groundwork for the long-term behavioral, technological, and economic change that is needed to improve the efficiency of our economy" (Environment Canada, "Canada's Greenhouse Gas Emissions, 1990–1999," 2001).

North America and the Kyoto Protocol

The United States has rejected the Kyoto Protocol against global warming, though it signed off on the treaty in 1997. Kyoto was an outgrowth of the 1992 UN Framework Convention for Climate Change (UNFCCC). This accord consisted of voluntary emission targets; however, countries did not in fact reduce emissions under this regime. The next effort was Kyoto, which established "legally binding" reductions in greenhouse gas emissions for all industrialized countries equal to 5.2 percent below 1990 levels by 2008 to 2012. The protocol enters into force when it has been ratified by at least fifty-five parties to the convention, including developed countries accounting for at least 55 percent of carbon dioxide emissions from this group in 1990.

Since its inception, the protocol has been criticized for poor planning and lack of specifics when it comes to implementation and monitoring. The protocol was negotiated in great haste, with the majority of its components assembled in the two months prior to the final session in December 1997. Details of how the emissions trading system would actually work were not included, and the working of such a system is not a simple matter because of the difficulties of international law and of allocation of credits worth trillions of dollars. Enforcement of compliance and monitoring are other unanswered questions. In addition, the treaty called for no participation by developing nations, even though according to some estimates, GHG emissions by China, India, and Brazil, the three largest developing nations, will account for half the world's emissions by later in this century.

From 1997 to 2001, negotiations over the treaty's final form focused on provisions for emissions trading and carbon sink allowances. The European Union, which formally ratified the treaty in mid-2002, opposes both programs, characterizing them as thinly veiled attempts to disguise real failures to meet the emission reduction targets. But the United States and Canada and several other countries voiced strong support for the proposals, arguing that

Human and Natural Disasters Impact Air Quality

Firemen and emergency rescue teams at the site of the attack on the World Trade Center in New York on September 11, 2001 NEVILLE ELDER/CORBIS SYGMA

Unprecedented levels of pollutants were released into the air in New York City following the September 11, 2001, terrorist attacks and subsequent collapse of the World Trade Centers. Fine particulate matter has been of greatest concern, since fine particles may remain afloat for days or even weeks. In addition, emissions from "Ground Zero"

(continues)

emissions trading and credit for carbon sinks (forests and other vegetation that hold carbon dioxide) would be the only way that they could meet reduction commitments without devastating their economies. Negotiations broke down at The Hague in November 2000 when no compromise could be reached, but since that time concessions to Canada and other proponents of carbon sinks have been made (Victor, *The Collapse of the Kyoto Protocol,* 2001; Government of Canada, *A Discussion Paper on Canada's Contribution to Addressing Climate Change,* 2002).

In March 2001, the George W. Bush administration declared that the Kyoto Protocol was "fatally flawed" and announced that it was pulling out of the accord. The administration did not disavow the need to address man-made climate change, but it emphasized that the magnitude and rate of future warming are unknown. It also stated that meeting Kyoto emission

continued for weeks and months as fires in the rubble continued to burn, distributing high concentrations of sulfur, silicon, titanium, vanadium, and nickel into the air. The EPA stated a week after the attack that the air was safe to breathe, but full analysis of the pollutant levels took some months to evaluate. Rescue workers and New Yorkers have complained of what's being called "World Trade Center Cough" as well as asthma and lowered lung capacity.

Volcanic eruptions produce the same gases, in tremendous volume, as are emitted from smelter operations. In both cases, metallic elements and compounds are heated to the melting point and undergo oxidation reactions. In addition, volcanic eruptions throw massive amounts of particulate matter into the atmosphere as superheated clouds rush thousands of feet skyward. This dust mixed with superheated gases can be lethal for miles from a volcano, as was the case during the explosive eruption of Mount St. Helens in Washington state in May 1980. Even after violent activity ceases, volcanoes continue to emit gases, often for years after activity begins. Volcanic smog is an ongoing problem on the island of Hawaii, where the Kilauea volcano has generated 1,000 tons of sulfur dioxide each day since 1986. Levels of sulfur dioxide in the air have been measured at 1,000 parts per billion, a value almost as high as the sulfur dioxide concentrations associated with the deadly London fog of December 1952 that killed an estimated 4,000 people.

Sources:

Monastersky, Richard. 1995. "Attack of the Vog." *Science News* (May 6).

"Study: Pollutant Levels High in NYC." 2002. *New York Times,* February 12 reduction targets would wreck the U.S. economy, and it charged that any multilateral agreement on global warming that did not include China, India, and other developing nations would fail in its ultimate goal of reining in climate change. The United States then outlined its intention to pursue a GHG-reduction course that emphasized voluntary actions and market mechanisms. The Global Climate Change Initiative seeks to reduce greenhouse gas emissions in the United States by 18 percent over the next ten years, a change roughly equivalent to the Kyoto target. Emission credits would be established so that businesses that voluntarily reduce GHG emissions will not be penalized but rather given credit for reductions. The proposal also provides $4.6 billion over the next five years for climate change–related activities and tax credits for renewable energy sources (White House Press Release, February 14, 2002).

Proponents of the Kyoto Protocol point to the need for a global solution to this global problem, however, and they condemned the United States—the nation most responsible for the generation of greenhouse gases—for its stance, claiming that its GHG reduction program would have little impact. Some of the U.S. reasons for rebuffing Kyoto have also been rejected by some researchers over the years. "Under reasonable assumptions about the behavior of the economy and with sensible policy options, reducing emissions would have a negligible impact on U.S. economic growth," stated one analyst. "A climate protection policy based on an explicit strategy of delay—doing little or nothing now and more later—is not credible. Without explicit market and policy signals in the near term, emissions will continue to rise while capital investments and technological developments will continue as before, making it harder, not easier, to implement policies and threatening greater, not less, disruption in the future" (Austin and Repetto, *The Costs of Climate Protection,* 1997).

In addition to the environmental advocacy groups, multinational corporations such as DuPont and Atofina also believe that the United States should reconsider its opposition to the protocol. These corporations support the international emissions trading program because they have already voluntarily cut emissions, and thus would benefit from being able to sell emission credits internationally. The U.S. withdrawal from Kyoto would mean less competition for credits, and the value of the credits would be lower (Franz, "Kyoto Pressure," 2002).

In June 2002 the Bush administration issued a report to the United Nations in which it formally acknowledged that "greenhouse gases are accumulating in the Earth's atmosphere as a result of human activities, causing global mean surface air temperatures and subsurface ocean temperatures to rise." The report, prepared and released by the EPA, forecast that total U.S. greenhouse gas emissions will increase 43 percent between 2000 and 2020, and that average temperatures in the contiguous United States would rise from 5 to 9 degrees Fahrenheit during the twenty-first century. The analysis granted that global warming could increase U.S. production of soybeans, cotton, oranges, and some other crops. But the report also predicted massive disruptions to sensitive ecosystems and drastic shifts in continental precipitation patterns, and it raised the specter of major flooding of coastal population centers. Even after

The EPA and Air Pollution Standards

Although the Environmental Protection Agency has been criticized both by industry groups and environmentalists, EPA regulations under the Clean Air Act have made significant improvements in U.S. air quality over the past thirty or more years. For example, regulation of aluminum smelting facilities has cut the emissions of fluoride, particulate matter, and polycyclic organic compounds by approximately 50 percent. Moreover, these and other regulations have improved Canadian air quality because they have reduced transboundary emissions of pollutants.

With the passage of the Clean Air Act in 1970, the EPA was required by law to establish National Ambient Air Quality Standards (NAAQS) and to reduce levels of pollutants most harmful to human health. Six pollutants were targeted at that time: carbon monoxide, sulfur dioxide, nitrogen oxides, lead, particulate matter, and ozone. In addition, the EPA was mandated to reduce so-called routine emissions of "hazardous air pollutants" (air toxics) known or suspected to cause health problems such as cancer or birth defects (Environmental Protection Agency, *Taking Toxics out of the Air,* August 2000).

Prior to 1990, EPA was mandated to set standards for each toxic air pollutant based on its particular health risk. This "risk-only" approach proved difficult to implement. In twenty years, EPA had regulated only seven pollutants: asbestos, benzene, beryllium, inorganic arsenic, mercury, radioactive compounds, and vinyl chloride. When the Clean Air Act was amended in 1990, the list of air toxics that EPA was required to control grew to 188. One of the chief enforcement tools in the EPA's arsenal is the nonconformance penalty (NCP), which levies financial penalties on companies that fail to meet emission guidelines.

The Clean Air Act amendments in 1990 allowed utilities to trade "emission allowances." One allowance equals the right to emit one ton of sulfur dioxide per year. A facility that goes beyond the standards accumulates credits, which it can then either sell or save to use later. Some environmentalists contend that emissions trading merely rewards power plants for polluting; however, the program has met with some success in

(continues)

that emissions of sulfur dioxide have decreased by 1.7 million tons from 1990 levels. More than 23 million trading allowances have exchanged hands in more than 660 transactions, worth a total of $2 billion (Reese, "Bad Air Days," 1999).

The obvious drawback to emissions trading is that air polluters can essentially buy the "right to pollute"—and because air pollution knows no boundaries, these polluters can affect air quality far from their own locale. For example, New York state set allowable pollution limits for its own power plants well below the federal cap established by the Clean Air Act. But these limits did little good for the air quality of the state; New York and other states in the Northeast are still experiencing acid rain as a result of emissions from "dirty" power plants located upwind, in the South and Midwest. In response, Northeastern states have pursued lawsuits aimed at curbing these emissions, and some states have imposed more stringent operating restrictions on their own power plants. In May of 2000, for example, New York state enacted a law to stop in-state power companies from selling their sulfur dioxide credits to utility companies in fourteen states located upwind from New York. The law imposes a fee equal to the price of the credit, effectively nullifying the gain from the sale (Mitchell, "New York Aims to Halt Sale of Sulfur Dioxide Credits," 2000).

The Environmental Protection Agency announced tighter rules for emissions of ozone and particulate matter in 1997. Implementation of these antismog measures would place many more U.S. cities in violation of federal smog standards. Under the old standard, seventy-three urban areas with 118 million people are in violation. The new rules would add thirty-five more cities with an additional 47 million people to the list, and force them to take active measures to reduce their smog levels. The new standards were delayed by court appeals until February 2001, at which time the U.S. Supreme Court ruled in favor of the agency. But as of mid-2002, these new standards had not yet been implemented. This delay prompted a coalition of environmental and public health groups to announce plans to sue the EPA to force it to enforce its own restrictions. For its part, the EPA insists that it cannot finalize all aspects of its implementation strategy until 2004.

Sources:

Mitchell, Stacy. 2000. "New York Aims to Halt Sale of Sulfur Dioxide Credits." *New Rules Journal* (fall).

Reese, April. 1999. "Bad Air Days." *E Magazine* 10 (November).

U.S. Environmental Protection Agency. 2000. *Taking Toxics out of the Air.* Washington, DC: EPA, August.

———. 2001. *U.S. Latest Findings on National Air Quality: 2000 Status and Trends.* Washington, DC: EPA, September.

the report's release, however, the Bush administration reaffirmed its rejection of Kyoto and reiterated its belief that voluntary measures to control greenhouse gases generated by polluters are the best way to address global warming.

Canada, meanwhile, ratified the Kyoto Protocol in December 2002 after months of heated debate. Canadian energy producers, business groups, and conservative legislators all strongly opposed ratification, citing implementation as prohibitively expensive and damaging to the national economy. Advocates of Kyoto ratification, however, forecast a much more modest economic impact, and they characterized the ratification vote as one that was integral to the country's environmental future. In the end, Prime Minister Jean Chrétien and his Liberal Party majority, bolstered by public opinion polls showing broad support for adoption of the treaty, prevailed over pro-business opposition groups.

The Canadian government has already produced a Kyoto implementation plan that calls for basic changes in energy use, with provisions for introducing more fuel-efficient cars, greater use of ethanol-spiked fuel, and incentives to increase household energy efficiency. In addition, Canada is continuing to seek credit under Kyoto mechanisms for the clean energy (primarily hydroelectric) that it exports to the United States and its vast carbon-holding forests. However, Canada is also grappling with outright defiance from the energy-rich province of Alberta. Provincial officials have indicated that Alberta might opt out of the Kyoto Protocol should Ottawa ratify it without provincial consent, and that it would take the federal government to court if necessary. "We clearly will not implement the Kyoto agreement as it applies to Alberta," said Alberta environment minister Lorne Taylor in May 2002. "We recognize the federal government has every right to sign international agreements, but it's very clear who owns the resource. The people of Alberta own the resources of Alberta" (Jones, "Alberta Won't OK Kyoto," 2002). For its part, Canada's federal government insists that it has the constitutional right to ratify Kyoto and other international agreements over the objections of individual provinces.

Sources:

Adler, Jonathan. 2001. "Better Safe than Sorry?" *Consumers' Research Magazine* 84 (July).

Austin, Duncan, and Robert Repetto. 1997. *The Costs of Climate Protection: A Guide for the Perplexed.* Washington, DC: World Resources Institute.

Ayers, Harvard, Jenny Hager, and Charles E. Little, eds. 1998. *An Appalachian Tragedy: Air Pollution and Tree Death in the Eastern Forests of North America.* San Francisco: Sierra Club.

Baumert, Kevin A., and Nancy Kete. 2002. *The United States, Developing Countries, and Climate Protection: Leadership or Stalemate.* Christian Layke and Wendy Vanasselt, eds. Washington, DC: World Resources Institute.

Carbon Dioxide Information Analysis Center. 1999. *Global, Regional, and National Annual CO_2 Emissions from Fossil-Fuel Burning, Hydraulic Cement Production, and Gas Flaring: 1951–1996.* Oak Ridge, TN: Oak Ridge National Library, DOE.

———. 2000. *Trends: A Compendium of Data on Global Change.* Oak Ridge, TN: Oak Ridge National Library, DOE.

David Suzuki Foundation. 2002. *Keeping Canada in Kyoto.* June. Vancouver: David Suzuki Foundation.

Dietz, Francis. 1998. "Clearing the Way for Emissions Reductions." *Mechanical Engineering-CIME* (February).

Downie, David. 1995. "Road Map or False Trail: Evaluating the Precedence of the Ozone Regime as Model and Strategy for Global Climate Change." *International Environmental Affairs* 7 (fall).

———. 1999. "The Power to Destroy: Understanding Stratospheric Ozone Politics as a Common Pool Resource Problem." In J. Samuel Barkin and George Shambaugh, eds., *Anarchy and the Environment: The International Relations of Common Pool Resources.* Albany: State University of New York Press.

———. 2002. "Global POPs Policy: The 2001 Stockholm Convention on Persistent Organic Pollutants." In David L. Downie and Terry Fenge, eds., *Northern Lights against POPs: Combating Global Toxic Threats at the Top of the World.* Montreal: McGill-Queens.

Environment Canada. 1998. *Canada's Greenhouse Gas Inventory: 1997 Emissions and Removals with Trends.* Ottawa: EC.

———. 2001. "Canada's Greenhouse Gas Emissions, 1990–1999." Ottawa: EC.

———. 2002. "CAC Emission Summaries, 1995 National." http://www.ec.gc.ca/pdb/ape/ape_tables/canada95_e.cfm (accessed May 28).

Fordney, Chris. 2001. "Bad Airdays." *National Parks* 75 (May–June).

Foster, John Bellamy. 2001. "Ecology against Capitalism." *Monthly Review* 53 (October).

Franz, Neil. 2002. "Kyoto Pressure Will Mount for U.S." *Chemical Week* 164 (April 3).

Government of Canada. 1996. *The State of Canada's Environment.* Ottawa: Government of Canada.

———. 2002. *A Discussion Paper on Canada's Contribution to Addressing Climate Change.* Ottawa: Government of Canada.

Haberer, Kym, and Julie Stauffer. 1999. "Small Engine Woes." *Alternatives Journal* 25 (winter).

Harder, James, Jennifer G. Hickey, and Sheila R. Cherry. 2001. "Something Stinks about Sewer-Sludge Fertilizer." *Insight on the News* (January 15).

Intergovernmental Panel on Climate Change. 1998. *The Regional Impacts of Climate Change: An Assessment of Vulnerability.* Geneva: IPCC.

———. 2001. *Climate Change 2001: Mitigation, Impacts, Adaptation, and Vulnerability: Summaries for Policymakers.* Geneva: IPCC.

International Energy Agency. 1999. *Energy Balances of Organisation for Economic Cooperation and Development (OECD) Countries, 1960–1997.* Paris: OECD.

Jaret, Peter. 2001. "Why Tiny Particles Pose Big Problems." *National Wildlife* (February–March).

Jones, Jeffrey. 2002. "Alberta Won't OK Kyoto, May Take Ottawa to Court." Reuters News, May 23. http://www.planetark.org.

Kay, Jane Holtz. 1999. "Car Sick Country." *Sierra* 84 (July).

Legge, Allan H., and Sagar V. Krupa, eds. 1986. *Air Pollutants and Their Effects on the Terrestrial Ecosystem.* Advances in Environmental Science and Technology series, vol. 18. New York: John Wiley.

Lynch, J. A., et al. 2000. *Atmospheric Environment and GAO Report.* Washington, DC: General Accounting Office.

Maloney, Jennifer. 2001. "Grime Be Gone." *Canadian Geographic* 121 (January).

McCormick, John. 1997. *Acid Earth: The Politics of Acid Pollution.* 3d ed. London: Earthscan.

Meek, Chanda. 2001. "Oil, Gas, and Native Rights." *Earth Island Journal* 15 (winter).

Mehlman, Myron A. 1998. "Pollution by Gasoline Containing Hazardous Methyl Tertiary Butyl Ether." *Archives of Environmental Health* 53 (July–August).

Ontario Ministry of the Environment. 2000. *Air Quality in Ontario, 2000 Report.* http:// www.ene.gov.on.ca/air.htm.

Pembina Institute for Appropriate Development. 2002. *A Comparison of Current Government Action on Climate Change in the U.S. and Canada.* Drayton Valley, AB: PIAD.

Ristorph, Elisabeth Barrett. 2000. "Law and Odour." *Alternatives Journal* 26 (summer).

Roberts, Leslie. 1999. "Acid Rain: Forgotten, Not Gone." *U.S. News & World Report* 127 (November 1).

Skolnick, Sharon. 2000. "Airports' Poison Circles." *Earth Island Journal* 14 (winter).

Smith, William H. 1981. *Air Pollution and Forests: Interactions between Air Contaminants and Forest Ecosystems.* New York: Springer-Verlag.

St. Louis, Vincent L., et al. 2000. "Reservoir Surfaces as Sources of Greenhouse Gases to the Atmosphere: A Global Estimate." *BioScience* 50 (September).

UN Environment Programme. 1999. *Global Environment Outlook 2000.* London: Earthscan.

———. 1999. *Synthesis of the Reports of the Scientific, Environmental Effects and Technology and Economic Assessment Panels of the Montreal Protocol.* Geneva: UNEP.

UN Environment Programme, World Meteorological Organization, National Oceanic and Atmospheric Administration, National Aeronautics and Space Administration, and European Commission. 1998. *Scientific Assessment of Ozone Depletion: 1998.* Geneva: UNEP.

U.S. Environmental Protection Agency. 2000. *Air Pollution Emissions Trends 1900–1998.* Washington, DC: EPA, March.

———. 2000. *Latest Findings on National Air Quality: 1999 Status and Trends.* Washington, DC: EPA, August.

———. 2000. *Taking Toxics out of the Air.* Washington, DC: EPA, August.

———. 2000. *2000 Toxics Release Inventory.* Washington, DC: EPA.

———. 2001. *Latest Findings on National Air Quality: 2000 Status and Trends.* Washington, DC: EPA, September.

———. 2001. *Non-Conformance Penalties for Heavy-Duty Diesel Engines.* Washington, DC: EPA, December.

———. 2002. *National-Scale Air Toxics Assessment.* Washington, DC: EPA.

———. 2002. *2002 Toxics Release Inventory.* Washington, DC: EPA.

Victor, David G. 2001. *The Collapse of the Kyoto Protocol and the Struggle to Slow Global Warming.* Princeton: Princeton University Press.

Vincent, Mary, and Steven Fick. 2000. "Blowin' in the Wind." *Canadian Geographic* 120 (May).

World Resources Institute. 2000. *World Resources 2000–2001, People and Ecosystems: The Fraying Web of Life.* Washington, DC: World Resources Institute.

Yunus, Mohammad, and Muhammad Iqbal, eds. 1996. *Plant Response to Air Pollution.* Chichester, UK: John Wiley.

10

Environmental Activism

—Kathryn Miles

Scholars of the environmental movement differ widely in their accounts of the birth of environmentalism in North America. While some believe that the movement came to life in the 1960s along with the civil rights and women's movements, others point back as far as the initial exploration and settlement of the continent. Still others argue that the movement is thoroughly contemporary. One expert contends that, for most environmentalists, "even the committed activist, the Green Movement has no history. Worries about the environmental destruction seem very modern" (Wall, *Green History,* 1994). The history of social movements and political trends in North America, though, suggests a more moderate view of the inception of environmentalism.

Environmental awareness, if not organized political activism, has been present since Colonial times. In what would become the United States, the Plymouth Colony depended upon cutting ordinances as a way of regulating timber harvests, and the Rhode Island and Pennsylvania colonies both regulated land and resource use in an effort to conserve raw materials. Colonial Canada saw similar initiatives with the regulation of fur trapping and the Hudson Bay Company. These actions, while providing clear evidence of environmental awareness, nonetheless pale in comparison to the flurry of environmental activity that began in the nineteenth century. Indeed, a veritable explosion of activist and aesthetic groups, as well as local and federal legislation, appeared in the mid-nineteenth century and continued to gain momentum throughout the twentieth.

Organizing Awareness, 1820–1880

Movement Begins with Appreciation of Nature

The prevailing artistic culture of the mid-nineteenth century was nature-loving. The Hudson River School—a movement of artists including William Cullen Bryant, Henry Inman, Thomas Cole, and Asher Durand—brought the U.S. landscape into a dramatic and arguably Romantic focus by emphasizing the sublimity and beauty of the natural world through large landscape paintings that showed the divine within the natural. The work of these artists was complemented by the world of letters. New England Transcendentalism found the likes of Ralph Waldo Emerson, Henry David Thoreau, and Bronson Alcott singing the praises of wilderness and its connection to spirituality. These writers eschewed Enlightenment's emphasis on rational thinking and empiricism. Instead, they cultivated a doctrine based on the ideals of British Romanticism: pantheism (the idea that the divine can be found within common objects and the natural world) and the idea that the human imagination can "transcend" the physical and achieve a sense of grace through nature. Thoreau's famous dictum that "in Wildness is the preservation of the World" is just one such example of this philosophy (Thoreau, *Walking*, 1994). Through their literature and paintings, these artists sent a powerful message about the need to appreciate and conserve the natural world.

This ideology began to take root in social and political circles as well. Although ideas of the unending expanse of the frontier and manifest destiny were at the heart of early definitions of North America, rapid westward expansion and improved transportation—particularly rail transportation—had proven just how finite the country's resources really were. This rapid growth in technology was coupled with a rural exodus felt throughout North America, as the agrarian culture was replaced by urban development and opportunity—a shift resulting in the further use of resources as well as growing pollution and land use problems. Many embraced these changes in the name of progress. However, a small yet powerful group of individuals were becoming increasingly concerned about the status of North America's wilderness.

In response to this growing unease, nineteenth-century citizens of the United States began to form groups and coalitions designed to halt the rapid consumption of materials and the natural sphere. To this end, the mid-nineteenth century witnessed a rise in environmentally focused organizations, both private and federal. In Washington, lawmakers worked with concerned citizens to create policy and the governing structures necessary to carry out that policy. This trend began with the establishment of the U.S. Department of the Interior in 1849, followed by the U.S. Department of Agriculture in 1862 and U.S. Fish

Commission in 1871. These federal departments and programs bore witness to what was becoming a national concern over the use of natural resources, a concern reflected in the creation of the American Forestry Association in 1875, the U.S. Geological Survey in 1879, and the division of forestry (a branch of the U.S. Department of the Interior) in 1881.

During this era, concern about the environment also gained the scientific backing necessary to legitimize the growing amount of federal money earmarked for its advance. One scientist, George Perkins Marsh, brought soil erosion and nutrient exhaustion to the attention of the nation and highlighted the need to protect what was once considered the limitless potential of the vast American landscape. Through his seminal work *Man in Nature* (1864), Marsh emphasized the need for human responsibility and accountability. In his preface to the work, Marsh explains that the aim of his treatise is not only to illustrate the effect of human civilization on the earth but also "to point out the dangers of imprudence and the necessity of caution in all operations which, on a large scale, interfere with the spontaneous arrangements of the organic and inorganic world" (Marsh, *Man and Nature,* 1994). Pointing to the failed civilizations throughout history, Marsh warned that a failure to regulate resource use would result in the rapid decline of U.S. civilization as well.

Another early voice in the conservation movement was George Catlin, a painter made famous by his advocacy for American Indians, who first proposed the need for a national park. After traveling to the West and witnessing both the magnificence of the American buffalo and its dwindling habitat, Catlin urged protection of the species. Catlin got his wish in 1872, when an act of Congress set aside 2.2 million acres for the creation of the first national park, Yellowstone. Canada soon followed suit with the creation of Banff National Park in 1885.

Individual cities and states responded in kind. Myriad municipal parks and landscaped cemeteries began blossoming in city centers. Formal city parks, such as New York's Central Park and the Boston Common, soon followed. Philadelphia purchased 4,000 acres to ensure that a part of nature would remain within its quickly expanding boundaries. Other cities hired professional landscape artists to create "oases of natural beauty within the cities." Meanwhile, states such as New York set aside reserves of their own (Wilkins, *John Muir,* 1995). This era also saw the inception of Arbor Day in the United States. What began in 1872 as an attempt to inspire Nebraska's settlers to plant trees for shade and fruit quickly became—under the direction of journalist and Nebraskan J. Sterling Morton—a national movement to prevent soil erosion and replenish dwindling timber supplies.

Early Environmental Organizations Form

Similar protection was also soon afforded the feathered occupants of North America. In 1887, Canada created the Last Mountain Lake Migratory Bird Sanctuary, a federally funded sanctuary in Saskatchewan still in existence today. The creation of this sanctuary spoke to a growing concern throughout North America about the plight of migratory birds, particularly the passenger pigeon. Public interest was immense, and powerful lobbying ensured the passage of the Migratory Birds Convention in 1916, an agreement between Canada and the United States regulating the hunting of birds and ensuring the continuation of conservation programs. One year later, the Canadian Parliament passed the Migratory Birds Convention Act, which allowed the government to manage migratory birds.

In the United States, George Bird Grinnell, who had grown up on John James Audubon's estate and was educated by his wife, wrote an editorial for *Field and Stream* in 1886 in which he advocated the creation of a society devoted to the protection and appreciation of birds. The New York Audubon Society was founded the same year, and it became a national organization by 1905. The creation of the Audubon Society points to an interesting trend in early environmentalism. John James Audubon was not just an appreciator of birds. He often killed the specimens he wanted to paint and was an avid sportsman. Such was the tenor of much of the environmental movement at this time. Although appreciation and concern for the environment were quite clearly motivating factors for the creation of such organizations, the driving force behind their inception—and their fight to protect North American wilderness—sprang from their collective interest in sport. To varying degrees, hunting, fishing, and mountain climbing all ranked among the organizations' defining activities.

Indeed, people of the mid- to late–nineteenth century associated the environment with recreation. In Canada, fish and game clubs—also called Fish and Game Protective Associations—combined sport and conservation interests. In the United States, the Appalachian Mountain Club, established in 1876, touted itself as the first conservation group. Its mission statement confirms a belief that "the mountains and rivers have an intrinsic worth," but it also emphasizes that this worth rests not only in "spiritual renewal" but also in "recreational opportunity" and "economic health." Enjoying the natural world meant being in it. Campers, fishers, hikers, and hunters were encouraged by organizations like the Appalachian Mountain Club to spend their leisure time in the wilderness.

A similar ideology was at the heart of another nascent environmental group, the Sierra Club. Founded in 1892 by a fifty-four-year-old naturalist from Wisconsin named John Muir, the Sierra Club represented the culmination of a lifetime of environmental commitment. The club, devoted to the preservation and celebration of the natural world, was formed in response to Muir's dictum to "do something for wilderness and make the mountains glad" (ibid.). Although Muir's upbringing was agrarian, it was not until he suffered a serious eye injury that he became an active advocate for the environment. Something of a wanderer, Muir began walking in 1867 and covered thousands of miles between Indiana and the Gulf of Mexico. He eventually landed in the California Sierras, which became a spiritual home for Muir. A naturalist, environmentalist, and writer, Muir authored articles on glaciation, critiques of animal domestication, and polemical treatises arguing for the preservation of America's last wild spaces.

That Muir emphasized preservation over what we now call conservation is a distinction of great importance. Biocentric instead of anthropocentric in focus, preservation put the value of wilderness ahead of human needs. For preservationists such as Muir, the aesthetic and spiritual dimensions of nature preclude any possible short-term benefit humans might derive from the exploitation or use—however sustainable—of its resources. This is not to say, of course, that preservationists deny any human benefit of nature. To the contrary, they readily tout the metaphysical and artistic benefits of a close relationship with the natural world. But the human benefit is only one—and a relatively small one at that—benefit of leaving nature natural. Wilderness, according to preservationists, has its own intrinsic value independent of any human demand or desire.

Ideas such as these cast Muir into the spotlight, and he quickly became known in environmental circles as one of environmentalism's most devoted and visionary leaders. In 1892, Muir was approached by J. Henry Senger, a German professor at the University of California, about the prospect of creating "an alpine club for mountain lovers." Senger and Muir enlisted the help of William D. Armes, an English professor, and the three quickly created an organization similar to the fledgling Appalachian Mountain Club in the East (ibid.). Preserving the diminishing wilderness of the United States became the most visible mission of the Sierra Club, and they quickly went to work on a project protesting plans to diminish the size of Yellowstone National Park. But while their first task was to fight for the preservation of Yellowstone, their subsequent endeavors emphasized the sporting aspect of the organization as well. In many regards, the Sierra Club served as the perfect embodiment of the growing environmental movement: federal legislation, aesthetic appreciation, and an emphasis on recreation were the cornerstones of the organization's popularity (Turner, *Sierra Club: 100 Years of Protecting Nature*, 1991).

Two giants of the conservation movement, John Muir and President Theodore Roosevelt, on Glacier Point at Yosemite National Park in 1906 LIBRARY OF CONGRESS

By the end of the nineteenth century, environmentalism had gained a solid foothold in the United States. The increase in private environmental organizations—bolstered by state and federal support in the form of laws, funding, bureaus, and departments—provided evidence of interest in the United States in the status of natural places. The economic boom of the antebellum era meant that a large portion of the country had time to enjoy its great spaces, and continued improvements in transportation ensured that people could reach those destinations conveniently. These developments ensured that the dawn of the twentieth century would feature a continued interest in the delicate balance between humans and the natural world.

Progressive Politics and the Birth of Conservation, 1880–1950

The late nineteenth and early twentieth centuries witnessed radical changes in the governmental structures of North America. In Canada, the rise of the party system originated in 1854 with the creation of the Liberal-Conservative party, which advocated active governmental intervention. The Cooperative Commonwealth Federation political party, which was founded in 1932, took an even more extreme position by attempting to transform the capitalist system into a cooperative commonwealth of farmers and socialists that emphasized the collective interest in and responsibility for natural resources.

The dawn of the twentieth century also brought with it radical change in the U.S. government. What historians and political scientists now commonly refer to as the Progressive Era is perhaps best characterized as a climate of profound change and a rapid rise in social programs. The laissez-faire attitudes of the nineteenth century, which emphasized privatization and little governmental interference, had little place in a society in which the gap between rich and poor were steadily growing (Perry, "The Changing Meanings of the Progressive Era," 1999). Although the Progressive Era is best known for its labor reform and social programs, it is also known for the veritable explosion of conservation strategies and organizations that occurred under its watch. The Progressive Era witnessed the birth of resource management, which quickly became focused on the wild waterways of the North American West.

The growth and development of the West, which had begun with gold prospectors and settlers in the nineteenth century, increased dramatically during this time. Western expansion in Canada resulted in the creation of the Dominion of Canada, an area composed of Ontario, Quebec, New Brunswick, and Nova Scotia. In the United States, pioneers from across social strata moved westward, determined to realize the American Dream. This exodus is embodied by writers such as John Steinbeck and Jack London, both of whom brought the movement to light in their literature. London's depictions of the Klondiking culture spoke to North America's continued desire for exploration in the name of progress. Steinbeck, in turn, wrote of a culture disenchanted with the aging East and hungry for the perceived opportunity and fecundity of the West. These stories were lived by thousands of hopeful Americans who arrived in the West only to find the desert landscape a barren and often inhospitable place. The U.S. government responded to this problem by determining to change the Western landscape and make it a sort of second Eden. That decision would create one of the biggest controversies in the environmental movement.

Conservation vs. Preservation

Changing the Western landscape meant that water had to be harnessed and transported to the developing centers of the West. The philosophy behind this idea was based in what had come to be known as the conservation movement, which argued that the success of the United States rested in the deliberate and controlled use of its natural resources. Although that belief informed many of the land use practices prior to the twentieth century, it was not until this time that these ideas became unified under a formal movement. This phenomenon was due in large part to a man by the name of Gifford Pinchot.

The head of the U.S. Forest Service and one of the first professional foresters in the United States, Pinchot had devoted his life to understanding and furthering the use of U.S. forests. Unlike John Muir and other preservationists, who asserted that nature's worth was both intrinsic and spiritual, Pinchot argued that the value of the American wilderness rested in its potential to serve the needs of a quickly developing country. Forestry, he wrote, "is the art of handling the forest so that it will render whatever service is required of it without being impoverished or destroyed.... Forestry is the art of producing from the forest whatever it can yield for the service of man" (Pinchot, *The Training of a Forester,* 1914). Although many contemporary environmentalists are quick to criticize the potentially exploitative tendencies of Pinchot's conservationism, it is important to recognize that, at the time, his policies were both progressive and protective.

Pinchot, who claimed to have coined the term "conservation," became the leading authority on the subject, with the support of President Theodore Roosevelt. In an essay first published in 1910 entitled "The Birth of 'Conservation,'" he wrote that "[c]onservation stands emphatically for the development and use of water-power now, without delay. It stands for the immediate construction of navigable waterways under a broad and comprehensive plan as assistants to the railroads. . . . The development of our national resources and the fullest use of them for the present generation is the first duty of this generation" (Nash, *American Environmentalism,* 1990). Pinchot's conservation was one based in the tradition of utilitarianism, and he assured the American people that "[c]onservation means the greatest good to the greatest number for the longest time" (ibid.). This idea of "utilitarian conservation" not only emphasized the controlled use of resources but also endorsed governmental controls of these uses.

Pinchot was, of course, not alone in his approach to environmentalism. In 1910, W. J. McGee created the "Conservation Bill of Rights," which emphasized ideas of utility and equality: equality of opportunity, equality of access to resources, and equality in our responsibility to ensure the availability of resources for future generations. McGee, like Pinchot, spoke to the need for continued availability of resources, and both men advocated careful use. Indeed, the conservation movement of the early twentieth century emphasized a careful balance between development and preservation.

The 1909 White House Conference on Conservation perfectly embodies that balance. Hosted by Roosevelt but organized largely by Pinchot, the conference sought to bring together some of the leading minds in the burgeoning environmental movement. Although Pinchot succeeded in bringing together a diverse group of environmentalists, the tone of the conference was decidedly one-sided in favor of his brand of conservationism. To that end, Pinchot deliberately did not invite John Muir to the conference, as Muir's preservationism had little place at Pinchot's table.

The Fight over Hetch Hetchy

The growing ideological tension between Pinchot and Muir points to one of the first schisms in the modern environmental movement. The zenith of this conflict can be precisely located in a small area of California known as Hetch Hetchy, a valley in Yosemite National Park and, perhaps most significantly, a proposed dam site. The city and county of San Francisco went before the U.S. Congress in 1908, asking permission to exchange the section of Yosemite National Park that contained the Hetch Hetchy valley for land adjacent to the park. Their intention was to use the valley as a reservoir and thus create a water supply for the municipal area.

This issue would divide the environmental movement and point to the schism between Muir's preservationism and Pinchot's conservationism—the difference between biocentric and anthropocentric ideologies. Historian Char Miller suggests that the debate was one of aesthetics versus utility, though preservationists contended that far more than beauty was at stake in Hetch Hetchy (Miller, *Gifford Pinchot,* 2001). Muir adopted a sort of zero-tolerance policy in terms of resource use and thus opposed the construction of a dam or anything else that might compromise the pristine wilderness of the U.S. West. His motivation for this position was a belief in the intrinsic

Men stand at the aqueduct tunnel that will be used for generating power and supplying water to San Francisco at the construction site of the controversial Hetch Hetchy Dam (completed in 1923)
SAN FRANCISCO HISTORY CENTER, SAN FRANCISCO PUBLIC LIBRARY

worth and spirituality of nature. Pinchot, on the other hand, pointed to development that had already taken place in the area and the benefits of dam construction to that large group of Western settlers desperately in need of dependable water source.

What was undoubtedly an important—though perhaps unexpected—effect of this debate was the very public and decisive polarization of the environmental movement. Although the Hetch Hetchy debate ended in 1913 with the creation of the O'Shaughnessy Dam—and the victory of conservation over preservation—the debate over the nature of environmentalism persevered and strengthened both in fervor and in volume. The epicenter of these debates was the creation and subsequent actions of one of the most controversial governmental offices, the Bureau of Reclamation.

Created by the Reclamation Act of 1902, the U.S. Bureau of Reclamation was a subsidiary of the Department of the Interior. Along with the River and Harbor Act of 1899, which established the first legal precedent for controlling pollution on the nation's waterways, the Reclamation Act dramatically altered Americans' relationship with their waterways. The bureau's aim—to claim the rivers of the West for human use—manifested itself in a movement to dam many U.S. rivers and thus forever alter the landscape of the West. The philosophy behind this movement was that controlling the flow of Western rivers could make the Southwestern desert—the last U.S. frontier—habitable and even profitable. For example, irrigation could allow for more successful agriculture; reservoirs created by the dams could provide dependable water sources for cities; and the dams themselves could generate the electricity necessary to power developing metropolises. But the dam movement was unpopular in environmentalist quarters, and Reclamation activities provided fodder for battles throughout the second half of the twentieth century (Reisner, *Cadillac Desert,* 1986).

Meanwhile, the spirit of recreation continued to define public and private environmental groups. The Canadian fish and game clubs, in association with game wardens employed by various provinces, worked to create the Game Commission, a province-by-province commission that would regulate the management of Canada's natural resources. The United States undertook similar legislation and passed the National Park Service Act in 1916, which not only created the National Park Service but also ensured that thousands of acres would be conserved. This act set aside land for national enjoyment and prevented development, but only to a point. The founding ideology behind the national parks was more than just one privileging wild space. Public access and recreation were also at the forefront of this move, and automobile access as well as comfort stations meant that much of this "protected" land was rendered anything but wild. The spirit of recreation continued to grow in the 1920s, adding muscle and influence to environmental protection efforts in the process. The Izaak Walton League, founded in 1922 as an organization devoted to sport fishing, spearheaded campaigns against water pollution and the development of marsh land. A national conference on outdoor recreation in 1924 formalized the idea that wilderness could also serve as a playground for sport.

North America's relationship with nature changed dramatically during the Great Depression of the 1930s. Recreation was quickly jettisoned as numerous individuals and families found themselves penniless and plagued by one of the worst droughts in U.S. history. That is not to say, however, that the environmental movement disappeared during this era. To the contrary, it was maintained through a smattering of private and public movements. One of the first full-fledged social programs in the United States, the Civilian Conservation Corps, assisted in this effort. Created in 1915 by conservationist George H. Maxwell, the CCC employed men in conservation work such as trail maintenance, fighting forest fires, and planting thousands of trees. The corps provided jobs for 3 million men during the 1930s and 1940s, and it allowed the federal government to carry out its conservation initiative even in the face of economic hardship.

Conservationism, the leading school of environmental thought for much of the first half of the twentieth century, began to lose some of its green shine for many environmentalists in the 1930s. The damming of several of the nation's canyons and the increasing emphasis on resource use led Robert Marshall, Benton McKaye, Aldo Leopold—whose now-famous *Sand County Almanac* was published posthumously in 1949—and five other men to found the Wilderness Society in 1935. "All we desire to save from invasion," they declared, "is that extremely minor fraction of outdoor America which yet remains free from mechanical sights and sounds and smell" (http://www.wilderness.org). This group and its mission were quickly joined by the National Wildlife Federation, founded in 1936, and the Conservation Foundation, founded in 1948.

Environmentalism also flourished in Canada during this era. In 1931, England passed the Statute of Westminster, which recognized Canada as an equal partner of Great Britain and granted it considerably more sovereignty in terms of policy. Canadian policy—both public and private—quickly became characterized by an interest in and commitment to environmentalism. During this era Canada witnessed the creation of several environmental groups. The Canadian Nature Federation, one of the first strictly Canadian environmental groups, was founded in the early 1940s by Reginald Whittemore. The group, which characterizes itself as an organization of naturalists committed to conservation, grew out of Whittemore's desire to create a tribute to his late wife, Mabel Frances Whittemore. Mabel Frances was a dedicated naturalist who, like her successor Rachel Carson, saw that the future of environmentalism depended upon introducing children to the wonders of nature. After her death, Reginald created *Canadian Nature*, a magazine commemorating the environmental commitment of his wife by exploring the splendor of Canada's wild places.

In the following decade, Canada established the Dominion Wildlife Service. This early incarnation of the modern Canadian Wildlife Service brought funding and policy to Canada's birds and animals. Canada established its own chapter of the Audubon Society in 1948, and in 1951 British Columbia established the B.C. Wildlife Federation, which works with the game commission to ensure outdoor recreation and conservation in the province. What differentiated these organizations from their predecessors was their emphasis on education and research as opposed to advocacy and recreation. They also shifted their focus from resource management to quality of life issues.

At the forefront of issues driving many environmental groups was the emerging post–World War II population explosion, now known as the baby boom. Publications such as Fairfield Osborn's *Our Plundered Planet* (1948) warned that the footprint left by humanity was becoming increasingly indelible. As much of North America lolled in the comfort of postwar status quo—the emphasis on convenience that manifested itself environmentally in increased use of fossil fuels and disposable products—a small but growing movement began to criticize those values and their impact on people and the environment. That movement would spark the revitalization of environmentalism in the second half of the twentieth century and allow for the return of many of the preservationist ideals that first informed environmentalism in the United States.

Environmentalist Action and Activism, 1960–2000

The 1960s was a time of great turmoil in North America. The U.S. civil rights movement, led by such figures as Martin Luther King, Jr., was fighting to end segregation and racism in the South. The women's movement, entering its second and arguably its strongest wave, fought to ensure that U.S. women received the same rights as their white male counterparts. These two movements constituted criticism of and a response to the dominant values of postwar United States. The dissent gained a tremendous amount of steam with the dawn of the Vietnam War, arguably the most unpopular and unsuccessful military action in U.S. history. The combination of these movements meant that a substantial portion of North America's young adults were speaking out against the status quo in numbers never before witnessed.

The rising counterculture was a perfect outlet for the blossoming environmental movement, which championed more sustainable lifestyles and thus offered both implicit and explicit critiques of energy and resource use in the United States that reached to the very core of midcentury value systems. Coupled with these values were ideas of nonviolent protest and an emphasis on decentralized, community-based politics and economics, all of which helped bring environmentalism into the spotlight. The energy of this movement intensified in the wake of a series of environmental disasters. Such events as the burning of the Cuyahoga River near Cleveland, Ohio, the result of contamination with kerosene and other chemicals; the oil spill off the coast of Santa Barbara, California, which washed an oil slick and hundreds of dead seabirds onto a heavily populated shore; and the use of napalm and other toxic agents by the military in Vietnam—all these made the message of the green movement seem relevant and pressing to increasing numbers of U.S. citizens.

David Brower:
Archdruid of the American Environmental Movement

Environmentalist David Brower ROGER RESSMEYER/CORBIS

(continues)

David Brower—widely recognized as one of the leading figures of the U.S. environmental movement during the twentieth century—was born on July 1, 1912, in Berkeley, California. He developed a love of nature while roaming the hills around his home with a topographical map, looking for butterflies and other wildlife. He became familiar with the Sierra Nevada, as a boy during summer camping trips with his family, and by the age of seventeen he was guiding other hikers through the rugged mountain range. After dropping out of the University of California at Berkeley during his sophomore year, Brower spent as much time as he could backpacking and climbing in the Sierra Nevada. He became an expert mountaineer and was eventually credited with first ascents of seventy peaks in the region.

Brower joined the Sierra Club in 1933. He was an active member of the fledgling environmental group, acting as a hiking trip leader and as an editor of the *Sierra Club Bulletin.* After a five-year stint working for the National Park Service at Yosemite National Park, Brower took an editorial position at the University of California Press in 1941. It was there that he met Anne Hus, whom he married in 1943. They eventually had four children. Shortly after the wedding, Brower was sent overseas as part of the U.S. Army's Tenth Mountain Division to fight in World War II. Stationed in the rugged Apennine Mountains of Italy, he took part in several battles.

Brower returned home after the war ended and resumed his work with the University of California Press and his activities with the Sierra Club. He became a member of the organization's board of directors and then was named executive director in 1952. Over the next seventeen years, he increased membership in the Sierra Club from 7,000 to 77,000 and transformed the organization into a powerful force for environmental protection. Some of Brower's most heated battles involved proposed dams on western rivers. He and the Sierra Club fought proposed dams in Dinosaur National Monument in Colorado and Grand Canyon National Park in Arizona with such tactics as research studies, full-page newspaper ads, letter-writing campaigns, and congressional testimony.

Although Brower ended up winning those two battles and several others, he also lost several fights. His biggest regret was agreeing to an alternative proposal to build a dam in relatively unknown Glen Canyon in order to preserve the Grand Canyon. Brower visited Glen Canyon after the agreement was reached and was dazzled by its beauty. The dam was built and the canyon flooded in 1963. "Never give up what you haven't seen," Brower wrote of the experience. "And don't expect politicians, even good ones, to do the job for you. Politicians are like weather vanes. Our job [as environmentalists] is to make the wind blow" (Brower, *Let the Mountains Talk, Let the Rivers Run,* 1995).

By 1969, Brower was widely recognized as America's leading environmentalist. In fact he became

(continues)

known as the Archdruid, after the Druids who haunted the woods in Irish mythology. His relationship with other Sierra Club leaders had deteriorated over the years, however, partly because of Brower's opposition to nuclear energy—which some environmentalists then viewed as a nonpolluting alternative to fossil fuels—and partly because he had pushed expensive publishing projects that created financial problems for the organization. As a result, Brower was fired as executive director of the Sierra Club in 1969.

Brower responded by forming three new environmental groups: Friends of the Earth; the League of Conservation Voters; and the John Muir Institute for Environmental Studies. By the mid-1970s he had patched up his relationship with the Sierra Club, and he received the organization's John Muir Award in 1977. Brower later left Friends of the Earth and founded Earth Island Institute, which operated at the cutting edge of the mainstream environmental movement throughout the 1980s and had several notable successes. For example, the group's International Marine Mammal Project led the fight to protect dolphins from unsafe tuna fishing practices.

Brower remained an active and eloquent defender of wilderness until his death on November 6, 2000. He wrote several books and gave speeches around the world. Late in his life, he adopted an environmental philosophy he called CPR: Conservation, Preservation, and Restoration. "It's exciting to change the world," he once wrote. "I've had some big ideas in my life. I've made some things happen. I've stopped some misguided people from trashing the Earth. But the idea I believe I will be checking out on is restoration. . . . I 've grown very fond of this planet. I want to help save a taste of paradise for our children" (ibid.).

Sources:

Brower, David. 1990. *For Earth's Sake: The Life and Times of David Brower.* Salt Lake City: Peregrine Smith.

Brower, David, with Steve Chapple. 1995. *Let the Mountains Talk, Let the Rivers Run.* New York: HarperCollins.

McPhee, John. 1971. *Encounters with the Archdruid.* New York: Farrar, Straus, and Giroux.

Turner, Tom. 1991. *Sierra Club: 100 Years of Protecting Nature.* New York: Harry N. Abrams.

Silent Spring *Launches the Modern Environmental Movement*

Awareness of escalating environmental degradation crystallized with the publication of Rachel Carson's *Silent Spring*, a national bestseller that brought the public face to face with the implications of heedless resource use. A marine biologist, Carson was employed by the U.S. Fish and Wildlife Service, where she wrote pamphlets on conservation before becoming the editor-in-chief of all U.S. Fish and Wildlife Service documents. Carson changed her focus after World War II, however, when she became increasingly concerned about the effects that synthetic chemicals were having on the environment. In *Silent Spring*, which focused on the pervasive environmental damage and health risks caused by the pesticide DDT, Carson warned of a bleak future if residents of the United States did not begin assuming responsibility for the effects of their actions on the natural world. Carson's message was heard by many, and her book remained on the *New York Times* bestseller list for three weeks, indicating a public interest never before witnessed in environmental writing.

The significance of this text is difficult to overstate. Some environmental scholars, such as Ramachandra Guha, cite the 1962 publication of *Silent Spring* as the dawn of the modern environmental movement. "Most accounts of the American movement date its beginnings to Rachel Carson's book," Guha wrote, "variously described as the 'bible' and 'founding event' of modern environmentalism." Pointing to the popularity of the book, Guha explained that the real significance of *Silent Spring* was its part in allowing environmentalism to emerge "as a popular *movement*, successfully influencing public policy through a mixture of protests in the streets and the lobbying of legislators in the corridors of power" (Guha, *Environmentalism*, 2000).

The public face of environmentalism continued to emerge during this era of North American history. Many of the issues were familiar holdovers from the first half of the century, including the water crisis in the U.S. West that had first pitted the Bureau of Reclamation against the Sierra Club and its zealous founder, John Muir. But while these issues may have been familiar ones, the means and fury with which they were debated was unprecedented. A perfect example of this trend was the ongoing battle between the Sierra Club and the Bureau of Reclamation over the damming of rivers in the West.

The Continuing Controversy over Western Dams

In the 1950s and 1960s, the Sierra Club was led by David Brower (see sidebar on page 270), who served as the first executive director of the quickly growing organization. During Brower's reign, the membership and influence of the Sierra Club increased significantly. Brower joined the Sierra Club in 1933 and led multiple crusades to save his beloved wilderness. Brower's accomplishments while serving as the executive director include establishing the Sierra Club Exhibit-Format book series, advancing the Wilderness Act, and helping to develop the federal government's Outdoor Recreation Resources

Review. Although these initiatives did much to strengthen the environmental movement in the United States, Brower is best known for his long-lived war with the Bureau of Reclamation over the damming of Western rivers.

When the federal government announced plans to build a dam that would flood Dinosaur National Park in 1956, Brower worked tirelessly to block its construction—one of several battles he won. When the Bureau of Reclamation announced plans to dam part of the Grand Canyon in order to offer better access to its remotest areas, Brower and the Sierra Club responded with a publicity campaign suggesting that the flooding of Marble Bridge was tantamount to flooding the Sistine Chapel in order to get a better glimpse of its famous ceiling. Although controversial, Brower's campaign was also successful, as the Grand Canyon dam was defeated in 1968. This campaign did not come without a price, however, as Brower was forced to resign from the Sierra Club in 1969 amid concern that his politics were becoming too extreme for the moderate group (Reisner, *Cadillac Desert,* 1986).

Brower responded by creating Friends of the Earth, an international organization dedicated to environmental stewardship and the creation of environmentally sustainable communities. Two years later, in 1971, a group of environmental activists sailed a hired boat into an atomic test site off the coast of Alaska in order to protest nuclear testing. The group called themselves Greenpeace, a name marrying their ecological concerns with their quest for world peace. The group quickly caught on, and their commitment to direct action for the environment gave them an international presence.

Meanwhile, the Sierra Club established roots in Canada, forming the Sierra Club of Canada in 1969. It is devoted to the same issues of environmentalism as the U.S. chapter, but the SCC is also devoted to uniquely Canadian matters, such as Canadian laws concerning nuclear energy or the harvesting of softwood. The same is true for the World Wildlife Federation-Canada. Founded in 1967, the group is composed of more than 50,000 Canadian citizens committed to conserving biodiversity and working toward sustainable use of resources.

The late 1960s was, indeed, a most significant time in terms of Canada's environmentalism. In addition to the aforementioned organizations, this age also witnessed the creation of groups such as the Nature Conservancy of Canada (1962), which has worked to protect more than 1.67 million acres of undeveloped land in Canada (http://www.natureconservancy.ca). Similar work has been undertaken by the Canadian Parks and Wildlife Association, created in 1963, which has worked to protect more than 40 million hectares of Canadian wilderness (http://cpawsbc.org/index.php).

Governments Respond to Growing Activism

While these organizations were gaining a foothold in the private sector, the U.S. national government was also stepping up its commitment to environmental matters. The federal government—responding to lobbying and activist pressure from groups such as the Sierra Club and the Wilderness Society—took a number of steps designed to address growing public concern about the environment. The first of these steps was passage of the Clean Air Act in 1963, which established air quality standards for the first time. The Clean Air Act helped pave the way for the watershed years of 1969 and 1970, when legislative initiatives and environmental activism soared to new heights.

In 1969 the U.S. government passed the National Environmental Policy Act, which forced federal agencies to analyze and disclose the environmental impact of their programs and actions. The act's mandates became the purview of the newly created Environmental Protection Agency, the first governmental agency with the power to establish environmental standards and impose sanctions for those businesses and individuals not in compliance with set standards. The flurry of landmark environmental legislation continued with passage of the Clean Water Act in 1970 and the Endangered Species Act in 1973.

The growing national concern for the environment was made manifest in the first celebration of Earth Day in April 1970. A bipartisan celebration held in both the United States and Canada, Earth Day was organized largely by Gaylord Nelson, a Democratic U.S. congressman from Wisconsin, and Pete McCloskey, a Republican congressman from California. The day was initially conceived as a "teach-in" intended to inform and inspire the nation. It quickly became larger than anyone could have imagined, however, and in its final form it found an estimated 20 million people participating in rallies, protests, and civil disobedience.

Along with the inception of Earth Day, the United States also witnessed the creation of the League of Conservation Voters in 1970. A nonpartisan political group, the League of Conservation Voters was created "to hold Congress and the administration accountable for their decisions" (http://www.lcv.org). The group's most visible commitment to that process became the *National Environmental Scorecard*, published annually since 1970. Each scorecard offers voters an account of the environmental record of elected officials as well as information about pending environmental legislation.

Canada entered an active period of environmental protection during the 1980s. For example, the Western Canada Wilderness Committee was founded in 1980 with the goal of using scientific research and education to ensure the preservation of the North American west. The Northwest Wildlife Preservation Society, organized in 1987, also worked to preserve the wilderness of western North America through education and outreach programs. In 1989 the Canadian Nature Federation worked with the Canadian government to found the Committee on Recovery of Nationally Endangered Wildlife (RENEW).

National accountability also became of greater concern during this decade, particularly through the activities of the Natural Resources Defense Council (NRDC). Divided into seven distinct programs—each committed to an issue such as land, nuclear weapons, or air quality—the council combines scientific and legal expertise to act as an advocate for the environment. Its emphasis on expertise over emotion differentiated the NRDC from many of its contemporaries. "By the 1980s, the NRDC had become a dominant force in the professionalization of the movement," noted one expert. "Over time, the NRDC became the environmental organization most identified with the technical expertise needed to draft legislation, issue reports, and use litigation as a tool in the policy process. By the end of the second Environmental Decade, it had come to symbolize the ascendancy of professionalism among the mainstream groups" (Gottlieb, *Forcing the Spring*, 1993).

By the 1980s, North American environmentalism had come a long way from its humble beginnings. Savvy, flashy, and politically robust, the environmental movement had embraced mainstream—and pop—culture. To that end, many of the leading environmental organizations seemed determined to adopt, rather than reject, much of the prevailing ideology of the decade. Environmental groups used marketing, media campaigns, and glossy mailings as a way of reaching the U.S. public. "The National Wildlife Federation built its own office complex and conference center in downtown Washington, D.C.," wrote one observer. "Almost all groups published slick, multi-color magazines and regularly sent newsletters to their members, the media, and opinion makers" (Shabecoff, *A Fierce Green Fire*, 1993).

The perceived need for a formal political response to environmental issues also led to the creation of third-party political groups known as green parties in Canada and the United States. The Green Party of Canada developed its first constitution in 1988, which outlined such goals as nonviolence, disarmament, a sustainable economy, and the protection of biodiversity and cultural/racial diversity. In the United States, the green movement began in state politics and moved onto the national stage with the formation of the Association of State Green Parties in 1996. Hoping to fill what they viewed as a void in the major-party platforms toward the environment and social justice, the state green parties formed a national confederation and selected consumer advocate Ralph Nader and Native American activist Winona LaDuke as their candidates for president and vice president in the 2000 elections. Although the Green Party failed to reach the 5 percent threshold that would have earned them federal matching funds for future elections, they succeeded in raising the profile of such issues as the environment and the level of corporate influence in U.S. politics.

Deep Ecology, Earth First!, and Other Radical Movements

Even though all these organizations did much to bring environmentalism to mainstream North America, many activists viewed these groups as too mainstream and too moderate to prove effective. A small group of activists responded by turning to the blossoming "deep ecology" movement. First coined by Norwegian Arne Naess in 1972, deep ecology represented a more encompassing and decisive response to the ecological revolution of the late 1960s. According to Naess, environmentalism had become "shallow" as a result of its anthropocentric concerns over pollution, developing nations, and land use in North America (Sessions, *Deep Ecology,* 1995). What the environmental movement needed, Naess concluded, was a return to the ecocentric beliefs of John Muir, Aldo Leopold, and other land ethicists.

Two members of the environmental group Earth First hold a sign in front of the Lincoln Memorial to protest the destruction of the earth's rainforests. BETTMANN/CORBIS

Working with George Sessions, Naess proposed the eight points of the deep ecology platform: all life (human and otherwise) has intrinsic value; richness and diversity of life has value and helps create value; no being has the right to compromise this value; the flourishing of the planet demands a smaller human presence; humans currently interfere excessively with the natural world; policies must be created to correct this interference; changes must be made to appreciate the inherent value of life; anyone subscribing to these ideas has a moral obligation to uphold them (ibid.).

More a philosophical idea than a proactive movement, deep ecology lent itself to myriad interpretations and applications. As one might suspect, some of these applications came in conflict with each other. Earth First!, an organization citing deep ecology as its founding ideology, is one such example. Founded in 1981, Earth First! sought to make manifest ideas of civil disobedience, eco-sabotage, and monkeywrenching (as it is detailed in Edward Abbey's novel *The Monkey Wrench Gang*). The introduction to the organization's online journal asks readers: "Are you tired of namby-pamby environmental groups? . . . Then Earth First! is for you. Earth First! is effective. Our front-line, direct action approach to protecting wilderness gets results. We have succeeded in cases where other environmental groups had given up, and have drawn public attention to the crises facing the natural world" (http://www.earthfirstjournal.org).

This hard-nosed approach to the environmental crisis provided a niche for those activists who felt that "mainstream" environmental groups had lost their edge. Organizations such as Earth First!—which promises to use "confrontation, guerrilla theater, direct action and civil disobedience to fight for wild places and life processes"—provided a certain breed of activists with an immediate outlet for their impassioned commitment to the environment (http://www.earthfirstjournal.org). There were, however, a sizable number of detractors—both from within and without the deep ecology movement. Much of the criticism of organizations like Earth First! stems from two separate, yet equally demonstrative, issues: the destruction of property and endangering of life as a result of eco-sabotage, and the relatively misanthropic views that allow for the sanctioning of these actions (Zakin, *Coyotes and Town Dogs*, 1993).

The end of the twentieth century also saw the continued division of the environmental movement into factions. The idea of preservation was now too broad to encompass the nuanced ideas of many activists and groups. Like feminism and civil rights before it, environmentalism faced the criticism that it had become an exclusive movement of white men interested in preserving wilderness for its own sake. Women, people of color, and representatives of the urban lower class all found little that spoke to their experience in traditional environmentalism. They responded by adopting the original precepts of the movement—appreciation for and protection of the natural world—and interpreting it in such a way that it would speak to their own unique concerns.

One noteworthy instance of the creation of factions is the rise of ecofeminism in the last twenty years of the twentieth century. Coined by Francoise d'Eaubonne in 1974, the term became a movement emphasizing difference of experience and the ways in which gender shapes our relationship with the natural world (Marks and deCourtivron, *New French Feminisms*, 1981). Ecofeminism emerged at the intersection of "the diverse range of women's efforts to save the Earth and the transformations of feminism in the West that have resulted from the new view of women and nature" (Diamond and Orenstein, *Reweaving the World*, 1990).

The core distinction of ecofeminism is its belief that much of the oppression of women and of nature is premised on a culture that views nature not only through anthropomorphic but also androcentric eyes. This idea that nature and our relationship to it are based on "masculine consciousness" has resulted, according to many ecofeminists, in our devaluation of natural processes, including those associated with women, fertility, and natural biological processes.

Similar sorts of distinctions have also been made by environmentalists of color in recent years. Arguing that mainstream environmentalism speaks primarily to white, middle-class Americans—individuals who grew up in a culture that prized summer camp, wilderness trips, and other environmental experiences of privilege—many environmentalists of color argue that this movement overlooks environmental racism in North America. They responded by creating a new movement called environmental justice, to focus on pollution and other quality of life issues that disproportionately affect people of color.

The environmental justice movement has enjoyed great success in Canada. With the help of activists such as Winona LaDuke and David Orton, Canadian environmentalism has become more inclusive and responsive to people of color, particularly indigenous people of color. Groups such as Native Americans for a Clean Environment and CARE (Citizens Against Ruining Our Environment) have brought the concerns of indigenous people to the environmental movement. These organizations received federal recognition in 1996, when the governor general of Canada proclaimed June 21 as National Aboriginal Day.

Although the dawn of the twenty-first century witnessed an environmental movement more divisive than before, it also saw the largest and most vocal commitment to the environment in the history of North America. Colleges such as Warren Wilson, Green Mountain, and Unity College all offer higher education specializing in environmental stewardship. A plethora of organizations offer outlets for environmentalists with widely varying interests and concerns. The federal government, while far from reaching consensus, continues to place environmental matters on its docket. In many ways, this new incarnation of environmentalism bears little resemblance to its forbearer. Upon closer inspection, however, the same commitment to preserving the great spaces of North America, the same interest in nourishing the tenuous relationship between human beings and their environment, continues to emerge as the fundamental tenets of modern environmentalism.

Sources:

Brower, David. 1990. *For Earth's Sake*. Salt Lake City: Peregrine Smith.

Canadian Parks and Wilderness Association Homepage. http://cpawsbc.org/index.php.

Carson, Rachel. 1994. *Silent Spring*. New York: Mariner.

Catlin, George. 1880. *North American Indians: Being Letters and Notes on Their Manners, Customs, and Conditions, Written during Eight Years' Travel amongst the Wildest Tribes in North America*. London: George Catlin.

EarthFirst! *EarthFirst Journal*. http://www.earthfirstjournal.org.

Diamond, Irene, and Gloria Feman Orenstein. 1990. *Reweaving the World: The Emergence of Ecofeminism*. San Francisco: Sierra Club.

Gaffield, Chad, and Pam Gaffield. 1995. *Consuming Canada*. Mississauga, Ontario: Copp Clark.

Gottlieb, Robert. 1993. *Forcing the Spring: The Transformation of the American Environmental Movement*. Washington, DC: Island.

Greenpeace Homepage. http://www.greenpeace.org.

Guha, Ramachandra. 2000. *Environmentalism: A Global History*. New York: Longman.

League of Conservation Voters Homepage. http://www.lcv.org.

Marks, Elaine, and Isabelle deCourtivron. 1981. *New French Feminisms*. New York: Random House.

Marsh, George Perkins. 1994. *Man and Nature*. Cambridge, MA: Harvard University Press.

McPhee, John. 1990. *Encounters with the Archdruid*. New York: Noonday.

Miller, Char. 2001. *Gifford Pinchot and the Making of Modern Environmentalism*. Washington, DC: Island.

Nash, Roderick Frazier, ed. 1990. *American Environmentalism: Readings in Conservation History*. New York: McGraw-Hill.

Nature Conservancy-Canada Homepage. http://www.natureconservancy.ca.

Osborn, Fairfield. 1948. *Our Plundered Planet.* New York: Little, Brown.

Perry, Elisabeth Isreals. 1999. "The Changing Meanings of the Progressive Era." *OAH Magazine of History* 13 (spring).

Pinchot, Gifford. 1914. *The Training of a Forester*. Philadelphia: J. B. Lippincott.

Reisner, Marc. 1986. *Cadillac Desert: The American West and Its Disappearing Water.* New York: Penguin.

Sessions, George. 1995. *Deep Ecology for the 21st Century*. Boston: Shambhala.

Shabecoff, Philip. 1993. *A Fierce Green Fire: The American Environmental Movement.* New York: Hill and Wang.

Sierra Club Homepage. http://www.sierraclub.org.

Thoreau, Henry David. 1994. *Nature: Walking*. San Francisco: Harpers.

Turner, Tom. 1991. *Sierra Club: 100 Years of Protecting Nature.* New York: Harry N. Abrams.

Wall, Derek. 1994. *Green History*. New York: Routledge.

Wilkins, Thurman. 1995. *John Muir: Apostle of Nature.* Norman: University of Oklahoma Press.

Zakin, Susan. 1993. *Coyotes and Town Dogs: Earth First! and the Environmental Movement.* New York: Penguin.

Appendix

International Environmental and Developmental Agencies, Organizations, and Programs on the World Wide Web

African-Eurasian Migratory Waterbird Agreement (AEWA)
http://www.unep-wcmc.org/AEWA/index2.html

Albertine Rift Conservation Society (ARCOS)
http://www.unep-wcmc.org/arcos/

Association of Southeast Asian Nations (ASEAN)
http://www.asean.or.id/

Biodiversity Planning Support Programme (BPSP)
http://www.undp.org/bpsp/

BirdLife International (BI)
http://www.birdlife.net

Botanic Gardens Conservation International (BGCI)
http://www.bgci.org.uk/

CAB International (CABI)
http://www.cabi.org/

Centre for International Forestry Research (CIFOR)
http://www.cifor.org/

Circumpolar Protected Areas Network (CPAN)
http://www.grida.no/caff/cpanstratplan.htm

Commission for Environment Cooperation (CEC) (North American Agreement on Environmental Cooperation)
http://www.cec.org/

Commission on Genetic Resources for Food and Agriculture (CGRFA)
http://www.fao.org/ag/cgrfa/default.htm

Commission for Sustainable Development (CSD)
http://www.un.org/esa/sustdev/csd.htm

Committee on Trade and Environment (CTE), World Trade Organization
http://www.wto.org/english/tratop_e/envir_e/envir_e.htm

Conservation International (CI)
http://www.conservation.org/

Consultative Group on International Agricultural Research (CGIAR)
http://www.cgiar.org/

Convention on Biological Diversity (CBD)
http://www.biodiv.org/

Convention on International Trade in Endangered Species of Wild Fauna and Flora (CITES)
http://www.cites.org/

Convention on Migratory Species of Wild Animals (CMS)
http://www.unep-wcmc.org/cms

European Centre for Nature Conservation (ECNC)
http://www.ecnc.nl/

European Community (EC)
http://europa.eu.int/

European Environment Agency (EEA)
http://www.eea.eu.int/

Forest Stewardship Council (FSC)
http://www.fscoax.org/index.html

Foundation for International Environmental Law and Development (FIELD)
http://www.field.org.uk/

Global Assessment of Soil Degradation (GLASOD)
http://www.gsf.de/UNEP/glasod.html

Global Biodiversity Information Facility (GBIF)
http://www.gbif.org

Global Coral Reef Monitoring Network (GCRMN)
http://coral.aoml.noaa.gov/gcrmn/

Global Forest Resources Assessment 2000 (FRA 2000), UN Food and Agriculture Organization
http://www.fao.org/forestry/fo/fra/index.jsp

Global International Waters Assessment (GIWA), UN Environment Programme
http://www.giwa.net/

Global Invasive Species Programme (GISP)
http://globalecology.stanford.edu/DGE/Gisp/index.html

Global Resource Information Database (GRID), UN Environment Programme
http://www.grid.no

Inter-American Biodiversity Information Network (IABIN)
http://www.iabin.org/

Intergovernmental Oceanographic Commission (IOC), UN Educational, Scientific, and Cultural Organization
http://ioc.unesco.org/iocweb/

Intergovernmental Panel on Climate Change (IPCC)
http://www.ipcc.ch/index.html

International Center for Agricultural Research in the Dry Areas (ICARDA)
http://www.icarda.cgiar.org/

International Centre for Living Aquatic Resources Management (ICLARM)
http://www.cgiar.org/iclarm/

International Centre for Research in Agroforestry (ICRAF)
http://www.icraf.cgiar.org/

International Cooperative Biodiversity Groups (ICBG)
http://www.nih.gov/fic/programs/icbg.html

International Coral Reef Action Network (ICRAN)
http://www.icran.org

International Coral Reef Information Network (ICRIN)
http://www.environnement.gouv.fr/icri/index.html

International Council for the Exploration of the Sea (ICES)
http://www.ices.dk/

International Council for Science (ICSU)
http://www.icsu.org/

International Food Policy Research Institute (IFPRI)
http://www.ifpri.org/

International Forum on Forests (IFF), Commission on Sustainable Developement
http://www.un.org.esa/sustdev/forests.htm

International Fund for Agricultural Development (IFAD)
http://www.ifad.org/

International Geosphere-Biosphere Programme (IGBP)
http://www.igbp.kva.se/

International Institute of Tropical Agriculture (IITA)
http://www.iita.org

International Maritime Organization (IMO)
http://www.imo.org/

International Rivers Network (IRN)
http://www.irn.org/

International Union of Biological Sciences (IUBS)
http://www.iubs.org/

Man and the Biosphere Program (MAB), UN Educational, Scientific, and Cultural Organization
http://www.unesco.org/mab/index.htm

Marine Stewardship Council (MSC)
http://www.msc.org/

Organization of African Unity (OAU)
http://www.oau-oau.org/

Organization for Economic Cooperation and Development (OECD)
http://www.oecd.org/

Ozone Secretariat Homepage
http://www.unep.ch/ozone/

Pan-European Biological and Landscape Diversity Strategy (PEBLDS)
http://www.strategyguide.org/

Program for the Conservation of Arctic Flora and Fauna (CAFF), Arctic Council
http://www.grida.no/caff/

Protocol Concerning Specially Protected Areas and Wildlife (SPAW)
http://www.cep.unep.org/law/cartnut.html

Ramsar Convention on Wetlands of International Importance (RAMSAR)
http://www.ramsar.org/

South African Development Community (SADC)
http://www.sadc.int/

South Pacific Regional Environmental Programme (SPREP)
http://www.sprep.org.ws/

Species Survival Commission (SSC), World Conservation Union
http://iucn.org/themes/ssc/index.htm

TRAFFIC (the joint wildlife trade monitoring programme of World Wide Fund for Nature and World Conservation Union)
http://www.traffic.org

United Nations Centre for Human Settlements (UNCHS)
http://www.unchs.org

United Nations Children's Fund (UNICEF)
http://www.unicef.org

United Nations Conference on Environment and Development (UNCED), Rio de Janeiro, June 1992
http://www.un.org/esa/sustdev/agenda21.htm

United Nations Conference on Trade and Development (UNCTAD)
http://www.unctad.org/

United Nations Convention to Combat Desertification (UNCCD)
http://www.unccd.int/main.php

United Nations Convention on the Law of the Sea (UNCLOS)
http://www.un.org/Depts/los/index.htm

United Nations Development Programme (UNDP)
http://www.undp.org/

United Nations Educational, Scientific, and Cultural Organization (UNESCO)
http://www.unesco.org/

United Nations Environment Programme (UNEP)
http://www.unep.org/

United Nations Food and Agriculture Organization (FAO)
http://www.fao.org/

United Nations Forum on Forests (UNFF)
http://www.un.org/esa/sustdev/forests.htm

United Nations Framework Convention on Climate Change (UNFCCC)
http://www.unfccc.de/index.html

United Nations Industrial Development Organization (UNIDO)
http://www.unido.org/

World Agricultural Information Centre (WAIC), UN Food and Agriculture Organization
http://www.fao.org/waicent/search/default.htm

World Bank (WB)
http://www.worldbank.org

World Commission on Dams (WCD)
http://www.dams.org/

World Commission on Protected Areas (WCPA), World Conservation Union
http://www.wcpa.iucn.org/

World Conservation Monitoring Centre (WCMC)
http://www.unep-wcmc.org

World Conservation Union (IUCN)
http://www.iucn.org/

World Health Organization (WHO)
http://www.who.int

World Heritage Convention (WHC)
http://www.unesco.org/whc/index.htm

World Resources Institute (WRI)
http://www.wri.org/wri/

World Summit on Sustainable Development (WSSD), Johannesburg, South Africa, September 2002
http://www.johannesburgsummit.org/

World Trade Organization (WTO)
http://www.wto.org/

World Water Council (WWC)
http://www.worldwatercouncil.org/

World Wide Fund for Nature (WWF)
http://www.panda.org/

WorldWatch Institute
http://www.worldwatch.org/

Index

(*Note:* page numbers in italic type refer to illustrations)